EDINBURGH BIBLIOGRAPHICAL SOCIETY
OCCASIONAL PUBLICATION

The Botanical and Forestry Library of Hugh Cleghorn of Stravithie

EDINBURGH BIBLIOGRAPHICAL SOCIETY

Founded in 1890, the Edinburgh Bibliographical Society promotes the study of books and manuscripts of any date, particularly Scottish, and prints articles in the annual *Journal* and monographs in *Occasional Publications*.

A programme of six to eight meetings (including visits to private and other libraries) is organized every year, and members receive the *Journal* at no extra cost as well as being eligible to purchase any other publications by the Society at a substantial discount. Enquiries should be directed to the Treasurer, c/o The National Library of Scotland, George IV Bridge, Edinburgh EH1 1EW.

Contributions for the *Journal* are invited in the fields of bibliography (in its widest sense), the book trade, the history of scholarship, libraries, and book collecting. They should be submitted for consideration to the Society, as advertised on the website http://www.edinburghbibliographicalsociety.org.uk.

Frontispiece

Charcoal portrait drawing of Cleghorn by Theodore Blake Wirgman, dated 6 July 1888, presented to Cleghorn by the Royal Scottish Arboricultural Society at a dinner in the Waterloo Hotel, Edinburgh, on 7 August 1888. (Sprot family collection).

The Botanical and Forestry Library of Hugh Cleghorn of Stravithie

H.J. NOLTIE

EDINBURGH
EDINBURGH BIBLIOGRAPHICAL SOCIETY
in association with the
ROYAL BOTANIC GARDEN EDINBURGH
2018

British Library Catalogue-in-Publication Data
A catalogue record for this book is available from the British Library.

ISBN 978-1-910877-24-1

Cover design by Kamillea Aghtan. Front cover: portrait of Cleghorn by John Moffat,
c 1885, from photograph album of the Botanical Society of Edinburgh.

Typeset by Kamillea Aghtan
in Adobe Garamond Pro.

Printed and bound in Scotland by Bell & Bain,
Thornliebank, Glasgow.

Table of contents

Introduction

This library catalogue forms part of a biographical study of the life and work of Hugh Francis Clarke Cleghorn of Stravithie (1820–1895), which began as an account of the collections made by him, largely in India, now held by the Royal Botanic Garden Edinburgh (RBGE). More than a decade ago it was the collection of c. 3,000 illustrations, originally part of his library, that prompted both the realisation of the need for such an investigation, and of Cleghorn's role as a significant, but unrecognised, posthumous institutional benefactor. At this point even the identity of the source and commissioner of the illustrations was unknown – a victim of 'institutional amnesia' – as was the fact that it was intimately connected with two other collections housed in the same building: Cleghorn's books (which, unlike the drawings, were clearly identified – stamped 'Cleghorn Memorial Library'); and thousands of his equally clearly labelled herbarium specimens. This research led, in turn, to the recognition of his generosity to his two *almae matres*, the Universities of St Andrews (StA) and Edinburgh, and an investigation of the 'Cleghorn Bequest' of books in Edinburgh University Library (EUL). The project resulted in a monochrome biography of Cleghorn,[1] and a polychrome volume devoted to his illustrations collection.[2] The work on his library was originally intended as a chapter of the biography, but became too bulky. As presented here it should, however, be seen as a supplement to *Indian Forester, Scottish Laird*, where full references, and a list of archival sources used for the wider project, are given. The fate of Cleghorn's forestry/botanical library after his death is discussed in Chapter 15 of the biography, but a summary is necessary here as a background to the catalogue.

Distribution of cleghorn's collections post-mortem

It was doubtless his intention, by the bequest of his collections to academic establishments in Edinburgh, that his life's work would be an inspiration to future generations, a trust that was not fully lived up to in the later twentieth century. In his will Cleghorn referred to 'lists [of books] on special topics', the sole exclusion from the very substantial estate left to his nephew Alexander Sprot.[3] However, upon the uncle's death in 1895 no such lists could be found among his papers, and in old age Cleghorn had said different things to different bodies about where he wanted his forestry and botanical books to end up. This led to a (fortunately civilised) division of the books and illustrations between three Edinburgh institutions: the Cleghorn Forest Library within the Museum of Science and Art (about 800 volumes and more than 170 unbound pamphlets), the University Library (about 380 volumes), and, to a very much smaller extent, the library of RBGE. The criteria for what went where are now hard to determine, as is the reason for the division in the first place – not least as the buildings housing the Museum and University Library were then physically adjacent to one another in Chambers Street. However, between the establishment of the Forest Library in 1888 and Cleghorn's death seven years later, a significant event had taken place – the founding, in 1889, of a lectureship in Forestry at the University, a post that was assisted financially with a donation of £1,000 by Cleghorn himself. What on his death became the Cleghorn Memorial Library (CML) at the Museum seems to have received the prime material, but although incomplete works, some non-botanical works and government reports went to EUL, some unexpected ones also went there – books not already in the CML and which would certainly have been useful or relevant to it. With the exception of a handful of works on economic botany RBGE at this point failed to get the books it had been promised in 1891 on the occasion of Cleghorn's being made an Honorary British Fellow of the Botanical Society of Edinburgh (when he had offered the Garden any works not already in its library). This was despite the fact that he made his will only shortly after the expression of this promise, which, as the Regius Keeper, Isaac Bayley Balfour reminded the executors, had been recorded in print in the Botanical Society's *Transactions*.[4]

THE UNIVERSITY OF EDINBURGH COLLECTION

The University's share of the books was placed in the attics of the old (Playfair) University Library with shelf marks Att.64 (shelves 4–6), Att.65 (shelves 1, 2, 4, 5), Att.66 (shelves 4, 5), Att.67 (shelves 4, 5) and X.f.1–2, and were listed in a shelf-list in the library's Accession Register.[5] Within these shelf-marks, however, are also undoubtedly at least a few books that did not belong to Cleghorn, so caution is required. In the printed catalogue of the University Library,[6] the majority of the books are identified with the denominator 'Cleghorn Bequest', and to a minority of these a printed EUL armorial bookplate was attached, on which was written in ink 'Cleghorn Bequest' and the shelf mark (Plate 1.i). There is a small group of about 39 works that seem likely to have been his, but which were not so designated in the printed work (perhaps through oversight). Searching in the library stacks has found the great majority of the books (c. 383 volumes + some unbound journal parts), still more or less in their original shelf order. This has confirmed that some of the 39 works were indeed Cleghorn's – others that cannot be so proved (lacking signature or bookplate) were almost certainly so, but are included here in precautionary [square brackets].

THE MUSEUM OF SCIENCE AND ART COLLECTION

The Cleghorn Forest Library was started with superfluous funds from a total of £200 subscribed for a portrait (Frontispiece) presented to the 'Grand Old Forester' at a meeting of the Scottish Arboricultural Society on 7 August 1888.[7] At the dinner in the Waterloo Hotel at which the presentation was made, Cleghorn intimated that this sum was to be used to purchase books for a Forest Library based at the Museum of Science and Art. However, no books are noted in the Museum register as specifically purchased for it until 1893, which may represent the date on which Cleghorn eventually got round to handing over the promised £200. The Library's founding collection must therefore have been 123 volumes donated to the Museum by the Government of India following the 1884 International Forestry Exhibition, which were specially bound in green buckram with scarlet, gilt-stamped, leather labels. These were accessioned by the Museum on 31 December 1884 and would later be transferred to RBGE along with the Cleghorn Memorial Library.

A catalogue of Botany and Forestry books in the Museum Library printed in 1897 includes the CML,[8] but does not distinguish between different provenances. Fortunately the hand-written Museum Register survives,[9] and only those designated Cleghorn Bequest in this are included here. There is a discrepancy over the number of volumes involved, as in a contemporary newspaper report, and in the museum's Annual Report for 1895, the Cleghorn Bequest was said to amount to 907 volumes (excluding pamphlets), whereas totalling up those in register makes about 801 (it could be that some were not kept, or that this total included 149 portfolios of illustrations). There are other works in the printed CML catalogue that seem likely to have been his, but as no later accessions were noted as coming from Cleghorn, and as these could have been acquired later, from other sources, these titles have not been included here (even in square brackets).

The bequest was accessioned by the Museum on 16 November 1895 (a very busy day for a librarian – unless the date was fudged). The books were stamped on their title pages with the Museum stamp, the date and a shelf mark being added by hand in ink, e.g. Ea.6(–7), Eb.1(–8), Ec.4, Dl.5–7, Dm7 (Plate 1.ii). Some of the books were half-bound in green calf (apt for a forest library, but subsequently blackened by age and pollution). At some point, either in the Museum or after its transfer to RBGE in 1940, storage conditions must have been poor as, from the 1960s onwards, a large proportion of the books had to be rebound. Given economic constraints, but regrettably, this was in most cases done in cheap buckram, and with significant loss of information. Although bookplates on front pastedowns seem usually to have been transferred, ruthless trimming (with a mistaken aim of neatness) led to loss, or damage, of many of Cleghorn's marginal annotations. On arrival at RBGE in 1940 the books were stamped on the front pastedown in blue ink 'Royal Botanic Garden Edinburgh, Aug 1940', and the librarian James Todd Johnstone made a typed list of the books.

Unbound pamphlets were not included either in Johnstone's list or in the Museum's printed CML catalogue, and it had been assumed that these had been either lost or not kept. However, it has recently been discovered that 158 pamphlets listed by Johnstone in the RBGE library accessions register in August 1940 (with numbers 35081 to 35239) came with the material from the Museum, and that the majority of these were Cleghorn's.

History of the collection 1940 to the present day

The comment above about twentieth-century failures of custodianship refers not only to the treatment of his books by insensitive rebinding, but also to the destruction of Cleghorn's substantial donations made during his lifetime of ethno-botanical artefacts to the RBGE Museum of Economic Botany, which was deliberately destroyed prior to 1964. At RBGE 567 volumes have so far been found out of a total of 801 (a survival rate of about 70%). The major reason for the diminished number is that some books are known to have been among the 'duplicate' library stock sold c. 1987, under the Regius Keepership of Douglas Henderson (with permission of the Scottish Office), to the firm of Wheldon & Wesley (a well-known firm of antiquarian book-dealers who specialised in Natural History). Unfortunately no account of provenance or annotations appears to have been taken when designating a work's 'duplicate' status.

A substantial recent find, however, provides a more positive note. Up to December 2016 the only pamphlets of Cleghorn's known to have survived were a substantial bound one (Klotzsch, 1851) at RBGE (which, being soft-bound, was included in the CML catalogue), and three miscellaneous bound collections at EUL, which Cleghorn himself must have had bound. The discovery of Johnstone's listing of unbound pamphlets led to a search for individual items in the extensive RBGE collection of loose 'reprints', and all but eleven of these items have now been located, some of them extremely rare and interesting. It appears that the collection may once have been larger, as an unknown number of items already in the RBGE collection were not listed and laid aside, some of which were disposed of in the early 1990s.

Among those disposed of was a series bearing dedications to Robert Brown from some highly significant early nineteenth-century botanists (including Asa Gray, William Hooker, Auguste St Hilaire and Christian Nees von Esenbeck). The present author rescued these and, having now been proved to have once been in Cleghorn's collection, these have now been re-incorporated, giving a total of 171 'pamphlets'. Of those with an inscription to Brown, the Klotzsch work, as noted above, had always been considered part of the CML; some bear additional annotations in Cleghorn's hand; and one is included in the EUL volume bound by Cleghorn himself. These are fascinating items in terms of provenance, but there is no record of how or where Cleghorn acquired them; perhaps in the London second-hand book trade at some point after Brown's death in 1858.

The EUL collection survives almost intact: 383 volumes (+ some unbound journal parts) have been located – representing approximately 242 titles. These have clearly been consulted less frequently than those at RBGE and the need for rebinding has been correspondingly less, though, having been stored in the attics of Old College, at the heart of 'Auld Reekie' from 1896 to 1967 (when the library moved to George Square), the books are extremely dirty.

BOOKPLATES

As a mark of ownership, Cleghorn commonly signed his name 'H Cleghorn' on the title-page of his books, usually in pencil. He also frequently used a book label, a simple rectangle c. 6 x 4 cm bearing the name 'H Cleghorn' in copper-plate script, lithographically reproduced, and probably printed for him in Madras (Plate 2.i).

A second lithographed label bears the name 'HUGH CLEGHORN' in small capitals, but has been found in only four books (three at EUL, one at RBGE) (Plate 2.ii). As these all date before the death, in 1838, of Cleghorn's eponymous grandfather, it seems possible that this might have been his (most of which would therefore have been in non-botanical works). In earlier days the elder Cleghorn had marked his volumes in an altogether grander manner, with the name 'WAKEFIELD' stamped in gilt in the centre of the front board of full calf bindings (Plate 2.iii) – Wakefield being the original name of Stravithie House prior to his purchase and rebuilding of it from 1806.

THE NON-BOTANICAL LIBRARY AT STRAVITHIE

A classified catalogue of the EUL and CML (at RBGE) works (including the pamphlets) has been made, extending to about 860 titles (though many of these works, especially the journals and reports, are multi-volumed). It is important to note, however, that in the following account 'Cleghorn's library' refers to the works presented by Alexander Sprot to the Museum and University, and that his library at Stravithie contained many other works on a wide variety of subjects. Notable among these are the books that were already in the house when he inherited the estate from his father Peter in 1863 – including his father's books and even some of his sisters', but, most importantly, the library of his grandfather (also Hugh Cleghorn), a significant academic of the Scottish Enlightenment. Also remaining at Stravithie after Cleghorn's death were his own non-forestry/botanical books (probably several thousand in number) – on subjects including medicine, religion, travel and some botanical ones apparently left behind by mistake. In 1979 Cleghorn's great grand-nephew Hugh Sprot (1919–2004) and his wife Elizabeth sold the 'big house' of Stravithie, including most of its furniture. However, his bookcases remain in the library to this day and on the fore-edges of the shelves in the cupboards are Cleghorn's hand-written labels, showing the original dwelling-place of some of the journals and pamphlets (Plate 3). The Sprots at this point deposited the Cleghorn family archives in the University of St Andrews, but retained the books and, on moving to the neighbouring farmhouse of Nether Stravithie, added a room to the house in which to accommodate them. The author was shown this collection on a brief visit in 1998, while preparing an exhibition at Inverleith House, RBGE, which included the first ever public showing of some of the Cleghorn drawings and for which the Sprots kindly lent their ancestor's portrait.

Following the death of Elizabeth Sprot in 2006 this 'residual' collection (i.e. the non-botanical part of the Cleghorn family library) was consigned to the auctioneers Bonhams in Edinburgh, where it was sold on 4 December 2007. The auctioneers failed to realise its significance or the meaning of 'Wakefield' stamped in gilt on the front boards of so many of the books that had belonged to Hugh Cleghorn senior. Many works were lotted together, for example: 'Bindings A large quantity of calf and half-calf bindings ... mostly eighteenth and nineteenth century (quantity)'. The cataloguing was perfunctory and the books fetched low prices,[10] but – given auctioneers' privileging of the sanctity of purchasers' privacy over scholarship – it is impossible to know either what was dispersed or to whom it was sold. By good fortune Alan Grant, an antiquarian book-dealer of the old school, did realise what – and whose – the collection was; he purchased some of the Enlightenment-period works and was appropriately rewarded for his acuity. The benefit of this for historians is that he produced a scholarly catalogue of 43 of the choicest works,[11] so that more is known (or can be reconstructed) than from the auctioneer's catalogue, which provides only tantalising hints. Grant's catalogue included four or five works from the younger Hugh Cleghorn's library – two botanical ones that were subsequently purchased by RBGE; one medical work that went to a Canadian library; and a battered, two-volume copy of the presidential addresses of Sir William Jones to the Asiatic Society that was given by Grant to the present author. Among the lost works was, for example, Lot 19, catalogued as 'Photography, albums', which fetched £60 for a dull-sounding album of 100 albumen prints of Yarmouth, Lowestoft, Sandringham (etc.), but which also contained two 'manuscript volumes, one including a description of a visit to Ireland [c. 1850]', from which much more would have been learned about Cleghorn's visit to the island of Rathlin of August/September 1849.

Biblio-biography – a life through books

From contemporary catalogues, the titles received, both by Edinburgh University and by the Museum of Science and Art, are known. The books and pamphlets have been searched for at EUL and RBGE and, excepting only the official reports, a preliminary study made of their signs of provenance and marginalia. This survey has proved revealing in showing how Cleghorn used his books, of which it is possible to provide only a summary here. The most common annotations are in the form of marginal lines against passages of specific interest to him, or, as he put it to his friend John Hutton Balfour, 'points that I say Amen to'.[12] But also included are many notes copied from his wide reading of related literature and sometimes also original observations – of which some (e.g., on evolution and relating to forest conservancy) are highly significant. Cleghorn was also a prolific 'grangeriser' – not with illustrations, but with clippings from newspapers and periodicals. He used many of his books over a prolonged period, so that the interleaved copies of works such as the *Prodromus Florae Peninsulae India Orientalis* of Wight and Arnott, and Heber Drury's *Useful Plants of India*, became as much manuscript or scrapbook as printed book. Provenances, deduced from bookplates, booksellers' and binders' labels, and annotations, have also proved revealing – of family history, of friendships, and the book-trade both new and second-hand in both Britain and India. These have filled biographical gaps and revealed the authorship of hitherto unknown publications by Cleghorn (including several anonymously published book reviews).

A library catalogue need not be seen merely as a dull list – the subjects and titles of books chosen over a scholar's lifetime represent a résumé of his life, work and intellectual development. The annotations and supplementary insertions can give insights into their owner's friendships, networks and travels, his sources of information and motivation. Such, eminently, is the case with the books in Cleghorn's botanical library, which, while undoubtedly containing many rare and choice works, is a scholar's working collection rather than that of an antiquarian or bibliophile in the strict sense. It represents and illuminates the arc of his life from his Fife childhood at Stravithie, his Indian career as a surgeon, botany teacher and pioneering forest conservator, and his 1868 return to Stravithie as laird. The following account describes some of the more interesting books, and the light they shed on Cleghorn's life and work. Cleghorn is, in many ways, best understood as a figure of the late Scottish Enlightenment (imbued in childhood with the spirit of 'useful knowledge' and 'improvement' by his grandfather) who lived into imperial times. He is a figure of major importance in the history of Forest Conservancy in India, and as this part of his library has survived remarkably intact, it is possible to use it to discover more about his motivation, and sources of inspiration and knowledge, over and above the traditional resources available to the biographer – his publications and autograph manuscripts.

CHILDHOOD (1824–37)

As a significant player in the intellectual life of the Scottish Enlightenment through his tenure of the St Andrews chair of Civil History,[13] to say nothing of his close friendship with Adam Ferguson and relatedness (through his wife) to Adam Smith, Cleghorn's eponymous grandfather (Hugh Cleghorn senior, 1752–1837) inevitably possessed a significant library, with which his grandson would have become familiar from the age of 3½, on his arrival at Stravithie from Madras. Although this library must have been strongest in the arts and humanities, it certainly also included some scientific works,[14] and as Cleghorn had attended John Hope's botanical lectures in Edinburgh in 1770 it is likely that these included botany. Several works in the grandson's botanical library may have come from this source, and one can imagine the curious schoolboy being encouraged to study the local flora by his grandfather and doting maiden aunts. The fourth London edition of the Linnaean *Introduction to Botany* (1788) by the London nurseryman James Lee is one such work, in writing the first edition of which (1760) Lee had been helped by the intriguing figure of Lady Anne Monson.[15] The late eighteenth and early nineteenth century was the era of compilation of the first reasonably comprehensive British Floras. Two of these were written by pupils of Hope, and Cleghorn's copies could have come from his grandfather – the first five volumes of *English Botany* (1795–1804) written by James Edward Smith, for which every species was illustrated by James Sowerby, and William Withering's *Arrangement of British Plants*, though the latter in an admittedly rather late (seventh) edition of 1830. Two of the few Scottish Local Floras available in the early nineteenth century were Thomas Hopkirk's slim volume on the plants of the Clyde valley, *Flora Glottiana*

(1813), and Robert Greville's more substantial *Flora Edinensis* (1824). With its generally similar lowland flora, Hopkirk's work would have been of some relevance to Fife and Cleghorn's copy, no longer extant at RBGE, could have been his grandfather's as might his copy of Greville. A volume seen by the author at Stravithie in 1998, which has since disappeared, would have opened the eyes of the young Hugh to oriental botany – a copy of David Don's 1825 *Prodromus Florae Nepalensis* inscribed by the author to Hugh Cleghorn senior. A presentation copy to the grandfather of a non-botanical, Indian-related work that has survived is Francis (Buchanan-)Hamilton's *Genealogies of the Hindus* (1819) inscribed 'from the author'. The last of the botanical books that may already have been at Stravithie raises a tantalising possibility, if no more – an odd French volume, the first part of a *Dictionnaire Botanique et Pharmaceutique* published by a 'Société de Médicins' in Paris in 1802. Unfortunately, as with many of the books, it has been rebound, so its provenance is uncertain, but the annotations are revealing. A child has added some English names in the margins, and, as one of these is 'Blae-Berry', the child was certainly Scottish – and may have been the young Cleghorn.

One other volume, although it cannot be proved, seems likely to have belonged to another family member and to have slipped accidentally into the botanical books left by Cleghorn to Edinburgh University where it remains, an incongruous shelf companion to the botanical books on either side. Labelled 'German Tales' on the spine it contains two paperback novels by Christoph von Schmid, *Genouvefa* and *Rosa von Tannenberg*, in editions published in Augsburg in 1853 – might these be the sole surviving relics of his invalid sister Isabella Cleghorn, purchased for reading whilst wiling away the hours in a mid-nineteenth century German spa?

Edinburgh undergraduate (1837–42)

As throughout this analysis of Cleghorn's library, caution must be exercised, since the date of publication of a book is by no means certainly the date at which he acquired it. So, for example, of the botanical textbooks in the collection it is conceivable that some might have been acquired to assist or inspire him when he came to teach botany himself in Madras in the 1850s. Despite this caveat there is, nonetheless, a group that he seems likely to have used as an Edinburgh undergraduate under Professor Robert Graham in the late 1830s. First among these is the textbook *Elements of the Philosophy of Plants* (1821), translated anonymously from Kurt Sprengel's *Grundzüge der Wissenschaftlichen Pflanzenkunde zu Vorlesungen* (Leipzig, 1820, itself based partly on A.P. de Candolle's 1819 *Théorie elementaire de la botanique*). This was an Edinburgh publication, dedicated to Robert Jameson, Professor of Natural History, and of interest for its section on natural classification. Cleghorn has marked several passages of this with marginal lines, including comments on the difference between natural and artificial genera. Four other books, which would have been very outdated by the 1850s, were probably also used by him as undergraduate texts – a rather quaint folding *Botanical Chart*, with text and illustrations, by James Rattray published in various undated editions in Glasgow in the 1830s; two London publications, an *Alphabet of Botany* (1834) by James Rennie, an *Outlines of Botany* (1841) by an undergraduate called Thomas Graham; and a work with the same unimaginative title published in Aberdeen in 1828 by William Knight.[16] A further book that Cleghorn might have owned as a student is the set of *Botanical Illustrations* (1837), which William Jackson Hooker had first published for his Glasgow students in 1822.[17] Of Floras that could have been used for identifying plants found on student excursions around Edinburgh and further afield, in addition to 'Sowerby' and Withering, Cleghorn owned the fourth edition of W.J. Hooker's (Linnaean) *British Flora* (1838), purchased from Henry Ormston's bookshop in South College Street, Edinburgh in 1840 (Plate 4.i), and a lesser known *Manual of British Botany* (1837) by Daniel Macreight. The religious and philosophical slant to his botanical interests is demonstrated even at this early stage of his life by two works – John Shute Duncan's self-explanatory *Botanical Theology: Evidences of the Existence and Attributes of the Deity, Collected from the Appearances of Nature* (Oxford, 1826) and Edwin Lees's *The Affinities of Plants with Man and Animals* (London, 1834).

The strictly medical books from Cleghorn's library have not survived – not even a copy of his own MD thesis. A single exception, however, which stayed at Stravithie until 2007 (and has ended up in a medical library in Toronto),[18] is a bound compilation of a dozen pamphlets containing works by older contemporaries (including Robert Knox, and William Cullen, the great-nephew of the eponymous Enlightenment-period medic) and by his own teachers, James Syme and Peter Handyside. Revealing of student friendships are theses with hand-written dedications to Cleghorn by three undergraduate contemporaries – William Robertson (1839), James Mercer (1840) and James Dunsmure (1841). The explanation for the presence of one of only two zoological works in Cleghorn's library, *Prodromus Faunae Zeylanicae* (1852), almost certainly also lies with a fellow student – its author, Edward Kelaart, though born in Ceylon (to which he later returned) studied medicine at Edinburgh, graduating in the same year as Cleghorn, 1841.

When on St Valentine's Day 1839 his colleagues might have been thinking of non-bibliographic matters, Cleghorn made a present, not to a mistress, but to the Botanical Society of Edinburgh. Suggestive not only of his studious nature, the work also provides the earliest sign of his interest in applied botany – William Salisbury's *The Botanist's Companion, or an Introduction to the Knowledge of Practical Botany and the Uses of Plants* (two volumes, 1816), inscribed 'Presented by Hugh Cleghorn Esq 14 February 1839'.

Cleghorn's position as heir to a Fife estate may be represented by two antiquarian books, apparently gifts from neighbouring lairds, as testified to by their original owners' armorial bookplates (Plate 5.i, ii). The copy of Paul Hermann's 1687 catalogue of the Leiden botanic garden (*Horti Academici Lugduno-Batavi Catalogus*) given to Cleghorn as an undergraduate in 1840, bears the bookplate of Sir John Anstruther of Anstruther. And it was probably also around this time that he was given a copy of J.E. Smith's 1792 edition of Linnaeus's *Flora Lapponica*, with the bookplate of James Heriot of Ramornie.[19] Remarkably, this is the *only* work by Linnaeus in the library.

Mysore and madras (1842–48)

Cleghorn's first professional Indian period, as an Assistant Surgeon with the East India Company (EIC), included three years of travelling around Southern India with various army regiments before being posted for two years in the town of Shimoga in the Kingdom of Mysore. For practical reasons, acquisition of books at this period was probably fairly minimal, though in a letter of 1850 there is a reference to his taking J.S. Henslow's *Descriptive and Physiological Botany* (1836, which he must have had as a student, but the copy does not survive) 'twice round the Cape & placed it in the top of my Bullock trunk during many a long Indian March'.[20] Not least through the encouragement of Sir William Hooker, Cleghorn had set his mind on serious botanical study in India, for which books to aid identification were essential. On arrival in Madras in 1842 Robert Wight gave the young surgeon a copy of the first and only volume of the *Prodromus Florae Peninsulae Indiae Orientalis* that he had published with George Walker-Arnott in 1834. This volume, interleaved, copiously annotated and grangerised, is one of the most important in Cleghorn's library: it was to be his botanical bible, and, like many other books, continued to be annotated and added to throughout the whole of his Indian sojourn and beyond (Plate 6.i, ii). With him in Shimoga Cleghorn also had a copy of Wight's *Contributions to the Botany of India* (1834), which may have been acquired from the author before going to India as it bears an inscription 'RW 13th Aug 1839'. Wight most probably also gave the botanical tyro the early parts of his own *Icones*, of which the whole of the first volume (in 16 parts), and three out of four of the second, had been published by the date of Cleghorn's arrival.[21] Beyond these works very little recent literature was available to help an aspiring botanist in India – he could already at this stage have owned his copy of John Graham's *Catalogue of Bombay Plants* (1839), and of earlier works he had Wallich's two-volume, incomplete, edition of Roxburgh's *Flora Indica* (1820, 1824) though, surprisingly, this is completely unannotated, suggesting that Cleghorn used it only for occasional reference. Of greater local relevance was A.W. Roth's *Novae Plantarum Species* (1821), describing collections made by Benjamin Heyne, the botanist on Colin Mackenzie's survey of Mysore (Cleghorn's copy has an attractive bookplate of a previous owner, Dr J.M.W. Baumann – Plate 13.i). During this period of extensive travel and low pay, Cleghorn had yet to acquire any antiquarian Indian botanical works, though, had a copy been available, Rheede's *Hortus Malabaricus* would have been useful in the parts of the Western Ghats that he explored from Shimoga. Although he certainly read Buchanan's *Journey ... through ... Mysore, Canara and Malabar* (1807) at this point – as it was from this that he deduced his observations on the decline in teak – he may not have owned his own copy as, in contrast to Buchanan's other works, it was not among the books left either to the Museum or to the University.

Although Cleghorn's official job was as a surgeon the same ignorance of his medical books applies to this period as for his student days. There are, however, in the extant collection, three works on *materia medica*, one of which he certainly did use in Shimoga in the 1840s. Whitelaw Ainslie's *Materia Medica of Hindustan* was first published by the Madras Government in 1813, but Cleghorn had a copy of the greatly expanded, two-volume, 1826 London edition. His set is a mixed one and of exceptional interest for its annotations. The second volume, which treats 'native' medicines, is inscribed: 'George Ballingall from the author'. The copy could have been given to Cleghorn by Ballingall, a family friend who taught him medical surgery at Edinburgh University, though Cleghorn added no notes to it. By contrast, and significantly as it treats European medicines as used in India, the first volume is interleaved and bears long additional manuscript notes on medicines such as castor oil, sarsaparilla and 'salep misree' written by Cleghorn in Shimoga. He had been presented with the volume in 1846 by an older Madras surgeon, George Beane MacDonell, who had himself used it at Rajahmundry in 1829.[22] This provenance demonstrates how knowledge in book-form was passed around within the medical fraternity in India, both chronologically and geographically. It is not known where or when Cleghorn acquired William Brooke O'Shaugnessey's *Memoranda on Indian Materia Medica* (1838), as it is unannotated; but the third work, another classic written (like Ainslie's work) by a pupil of John Hope, has a fascinating provenance and must have been acquired by Cleghorn in Madras (though probably more likely in the 1850s). John Fleming's *Catalogue of Indian Medicinal Plants* was first published in 1810 in Calcutta, in the journal *Asiatic Researches*, of which the author sent an offprint to the EIC surgeon Andrew Berry in Madras with the inscription 'Dr Berry with Dr Fleming's best compliments'. Berry must have given this copy away as it bears the bookplate of the 'Vepery Mission Library' (Plate 5.iii) and has numerous inscriptions of local plant names added by the missionary Johan Peter Rottler in both Tamil and Roman script (Plate 7.i).[23]

FIRST FURLOUGH (1848–51)

'Mysore fever' (probably malaria) forced Cleghorn's withdrawal from Shimoga and a three-year sick leave spent in Britain – surviving a shipwreck on the *Sutlej*, and a period at the Cape of Good Hope, as dramatic incidents *en route*. While at the Cape he did some botanising, and William Henry Harvey's *Genera of South African Plants*, published in Cape Town in 1838, might, perhaps, be a memento of this time.[24] On an altogether different scale of magnificence, one of the greatest treasures in Cleghorn's library must also be a result of interests developed during this enforced visit. The Cape was a favoured resort for EIC employees attempting to recover shattered health. For this purpose, from 1843, the Madras Civil Servant Thomas Boone Roupell and his wife Arabella had spent two years there, where she made a series of large paintings of the spectacular Cape flora. These included a *Dierama*, proteas, and a member of a genus that for a time commemorated her husband's family name, *Roupellia grata*,[25] a plant that Cleghorn would later grow and have painted in Madras. It so happened that Nathaniel Wallich, on sick leave from Calcutta, was at the Cape at the same time as the Roupells. He saw Arabella's drawings and recommended them for publication in London as *Specimens of the Flora of South Africa, by A Lady*. Eight of the plant portraits, together with an end piece of *Roupellia* and a striking floral title-page, were lithographed by Paul Gauci, son of the lithographer who, 20 years earlier, had produced the exceptional plates for Wallich's own *Plantae Asiaticae Rariores*; the text was written by W.H. Harvey. The elephant-folio volume of 1849 is not only – physically – the largest in Cleghorn's collection, but perhaps the most sumptuous and one of the rarest. Miraculously (given the subsequent fate of many of his books) it is still more or less in its original binding. The 'less' is because the binding was an innovative one, by Joseph Rowbotham of 70 Castle Street East, Oxford Street, London, whereby the pages were attached to the spine by India rubber, furnishing:

> a flexible hinge to every leaf of the Book, causes it to
> lie flat, and open freely without strain or breaking, as
> in the old binding. No paste, glue, or stitching. The
> Caoutchouc resists all insects, and is unaffected by
> mildew or tropical heat.[26]

Rubber, however, perishes, so the volume has been skilfully rebacked, retaining the original boards, which are covered with tan-coloured calf, the front one gold-tooled with borders and a central floral wreath around a version of the title – 'Cape Flowers by a Lady' (Plate 8.i, ii). It is not known when or where Cleghorn acquired this treasure, and his name is not on the list of 100 original subscribers. In 1855 Thomas Roupell sat on the Coimbatore local committee for the Madras Exhibition, and Cleghorn must certainly have had dealings with him at this time, if not earlier.

After eventually reaching Britain in July 1848, and regaining his health, Cleghorn worked on his Indian collections and notes, with a particular emphasis on economic botany. Two works in his library relate to this and may have been acquired at this time: E.A. Duchesne's *Répertoires des plantes utiles et des plantes vénéneuses du globe* (Paris, 1836), in which many of the species entries are marked by him with marginal dots or lines, and the little-known *Plantae Utiliores* (two volumes, London, 1842–5), a work started by Gilbert Thomas Burnett, but completed and published after the author's death by his sister Mary Ann who made the fine, hand-coloured plates. After some relatively minor scientific papers, the botanical achievements of Cleghorn's first furlough culminated in 1851 with his report on tropical deforestation for the British Association for the Advancement of Science, and his work for John Forbes Royle on Indian natural products at the Great Exhibition. Most of the research for the first of these projects, and probably much of that for the second, was undertaken in the library of East India House in Leadenhall Street, London, with the result that little in Cleghorn's own library can be linked to this pivotal period in his career. The works that he consulted in the library included reports, books and Indian periodicals, and among the most important of the last, in which three seminal papers on the forest and climate question were published, was the *Madras Journal of Literature and Science*. Cleghorn did own his own set of this periodical, which for a time he helped to edit, but this was not among the works left either to the Edinburgh Museum or University; rather, at some unknown date, it found its way to St Andrews University library where it remains. One work referred to in the 1851 Report is, however, to be found in his library – the three-volume *Journal of the Indian Archipelago* (Singapore, 1847–9), which includes a paper by James Richardson Logan on climate and deforestation in Penang (Malaysia). This copy is now in EUL, but bears no annotations to show Cleghorn's use of it.

There are also a few items related to Cleghorn's connection with Royle. At this point Robert Wight had been working on cotton in Coimbatore for several years, and Cleghorn had seen experiments using Wight's seed at Kadur near Shimoga (which he reported to the Botanical Society of Edinburgh), so it is not surprising to find that he owned a copy of Royle's *Culture and Commerce of Cotton in India* (1851). But although there are books relating to several later international exhibitions (Paris 1855 and 1878, and Vienna 1873) only a single work in the library can be linked to the Great Exhibition, though this exception does neatly link Cleghorn's developing interest in woods and forests with that of economic botany and public exhibitions. Furthermore, he would cite the work in his own report on timber for the 1855 Madras Exhibition.[27] This is Charles Holtzapffell's *Descriptive Catalogue of Woods*, edited and published by Royle the year following the Great Exhibition. By the time of its publication Cleghorn had returned to India and he was sent the book by William Pamplin. The meeting with this sympathetic and well-informed bookseller and specimen-dealer was one of the most useful contacts made by Cleghorn while he was in London.

While in London Cleghorn had visited the Royal Botanic Gardens at Kew, where he may well have made use of Hooker's *Kew Gardens: a Popular Guide* (1847). The copy that has survived in his library bears perhaps the most interesting of the inscriptions in any of Cleghorn's books (Plate 9.i, ii, iii), but leaves an unanswered question as to how and when he acquired it, though it must certainly have been at a somewhat later date. On the flyleaf the great Yarmouth banker and bibliophile Dawson Turner has written:

> one of a very few copies printed on large & thick paper. That presented to the Queen was precisely like this, except in having the Royal arms on the cover.– A present from Sir W.J. Hooker, whose Autograph see on the following leaf.

This refers to an inscription on the half-title by Turner's son-in-law, the book's author, Sir William Hooker: 'Dawson Turner Esqr. July 14 1847'.

Cleghorn is known to have been sent a copy of the *Popular Guide* by Pamplin in 1856,[28] but this inscribed copy cannot have 'escaped' from Turner's renowned collection until after his death in 1858. Perhaps at this point it was returned to Hooker, who could then have passed it on to Cleghorn as an historically and emotionally weighted gift? Tipped into the copy, though whether by Turner or Cleghorn ('grangerisers' both) is unknown, are several newspaper cuttings (including one concerning the new gates to the garden from Kew Green, designed by Decimus Burton in 1846, with sculpture by John Henning junior).

On returning to Madras following his first furlough, Cleghorn entered the most varied period of his life: teaching botany at the Medical College, as secretary of the Agri-Horticultural Society, and involvement with the 1855 and 1857 Madras Exhibitions. This culminated in his appointment as Conservator of Forests in 1856. It was a time of major book-buying, not least as the period had started in 1852 with the destruction of his library in a fire. The extant books cover and illuminate all of these varied activities though, as with earlier periods, the strictly medical field is unrepresented, and only a single work has survived that relates to the evangelical-religious and spiritual one, which, being of great importance to Cleghorn, must originally have had a significant presence in his library. The exception is a set of *The Works* [mainly sermons] … *with the Life* … (1811) of the anti-slavery Bishop of London, Beilby Porteus, purchased, second-hand, by Cleghorn from the bookseller J.R. Hogg in Madras (Plate 4.ii).[29]

Teaching botany (and *materia medica*) at the Medical College is one of the most likely reasons for the assembly not only of Cleghorn's large botanical library but of his illustrations collection, achieved with the help not only of Pamplin, but of local Madras booksellers especially Abel Joshua Higginbotham and John Browning Pharoah (Plate 4.iv, v). Although no copy survives in his library, it is known that the primary textbook he used for teaching was the *Classbook of Botany* by his Edinburgh friend John Hutton Balfour (Regius Keeper of RBGE). Cleghorn, however, drew his information from a much wider range of sources than a single book – not only published works, but field observations of native vegetation close to Madras and exotics in its gardens, but also drawings made by his artists. This material consisted of notes, drawings and printed illustrations that were sewn together to form a fasciculus for each species, which could be used for teaching, answering enquiries, or his own private study, though these were never to be turned into the textbook on South Indian botany that he contemplated writing at this period. These collections of plates ended up in the Cleghorn Memorial Library (135 octavo and 14 quarto folios), but on reaching RBGE were split up for taxonomic filing. The reference works that Cleghorn scanned for information included great encyclopaedic works, of which the chief contemporary one was De Candolle's *Prodromus Systematis Naturalis Regni Vegetabilis*, a complete world Flora that he purchased as it was issued, the last part not until 1873 after his retirement. One of the subjects covered in his lecture course was botanical geography, for which one of his texts was the Ray Society's English translation of Franz Meyen's *Outlines of the Geography of Plants* (1846). Cleghorn's copy had previously belonged to Adam White, an Edinburgh zoologist who worked at the British Museum (one of the proposers for Cleghorn's fellowship of the Linnean Society). On the title-page White added the information that the translator, Margaret Johnston (daughter of George Johnston, founder of the Ray Society), was now Mrs Philip Maclagan – and therefore mother of the distinguished brood of Maclagans that included three of Cleghorn's particular friends: Douglas (Edinburgh medic), Robert (Indian engineer) and John (his own forest assistant in Madras). Copies of the textbooks that Cleghorn used for teaching *materia medica* (by Royle, and by Ballard and Garrod), as with Balfour's *Classbook*, have not survived, though a related work which has is John Lindley's *Medical and Oeconomic Botany* (1849), to which he must also have referred.

By the mid-1850s more Indian-published botanical works were available than had been the case in the previous decade: Robert Wight's copiously illustrated life's work was by now complete and was all in Cleghorn's library, both in bound form and dismembered in his illustrations collection. Also finished, tragically so, its author cut down by hepatitis in Malacca at the age of 35, was the work of William Griffith whose posthumous works, in an act that combined scientific hero-worship and nationalistic piety, were published in Calcutta and owned by Cleghorn – the *Journals*, *Itinerary Notes*, and three folio volumes of *Icones* of which one was devoted to palms. Of Indian local Floras he had the unillustrated one for Bombay by Dalzell and Gibson (1861), and in folio format Joseph Hooker's splendid *Illustrations of Himalayan Plants* (1855). The latter contains a series of dramatic, hand-coloured lithographs, reworked by Walter Hood Fitch after drawings made by Indian artists for J.F. Cathcart that Hooker had acquired in Darjeeling – an expensive work, for which Cleghorn paid Pamplin £5 11 shillings,[30] and for which he was one of the original subscribers. It may also have been at this period that Cleghorn purchased his copy of Wallich's *Plantae Asiaticae Rariores*.[31] Hooker's most significant taxonomic work of this period was the first, and regrettably last, volume of his and Thomas Thomson's *Flora Indica* (1855). Despite its curtailment this, together with the similarly incomplete *Prodromus* of Wight and Arnott, was Cleghorn's standard reference for identifying the plants encountered in the field and pressed for his herbarium. Although not interleaved, he would annotate his copy of *Flora Indica* for the rest of his time in India (including the Himalayan period), some of the annotations apparently made while reviewing the work for the *Calcutta Review*.[32] These marginalia give unique insights into his scientific beliefs – for example, agreeing with Hooker's view (as expressed at this stage in his life) that mutability was not an innate characteristic of species.

Plants are no respecters of national boundaries, and to study and identify Indian plants a well-equipped library requires works describing plants from much further afield, so it is unsurprising to find that Cleghorn owned Floras devoted to other parts of Asia. He had the unillustrated ones by Linnaeus's pupil and successor C.P. Thunberg on Japan (*Flora Japonica*, 1784) and Manuel Blanco's *Flora de Filipinas* (1837), and also the two, illustrated, folio volumes of *Plantae Javanicae Rariores*. This last was the despair of Thomas Horsfield, on whose extensive Javanese collections, made between 1801 and 1818, the work was based. Horsfield's collections were given to Robert Brown who was less than enthusiastic about floristic work and could not resist the temptation to make a monograph of each family treated. The inevitable result was massive delay, drawn to a conclusion only with the help of Brown's assistant John Bennett in 1840, by which time Horsfield was 67 and only a tiny fraction of his material had been dealt with.[33] With a major interest in the introduction of exotic plants to the fields and gardens of India, Cleghorn also owned floristic works relating to South Africa, North America, New Zealand and Australia. Even Patrick Browne's classic folio *The Civil and Natural History of Jamaica* (1756) was consulted for information about tropical fruit trees such as the 'Sapodilla Tree' (now *Manilkara zapota*) and of the 'Anchovee Pear Tree', which Cleghorn annotated with the binomial *Grias cauliflora*; he also annotated the book's plates, many of which are by G.D. Ehret, with their Linnaean names. That Cleghorn was more of a botanical generalist and economic botanist than a taxonomist explains the very small number of monographs (other than pamphlets) in the collection, the exceptions being Henri Baillon's one on the large and difficult family Euphorbiaceae (1858), and George Bentham's on Labiatae (1832–6).

Cleghorn had serious interests in the history of botany, and in this period acquired some of the jewels of his collection, some by purchase, others by gift. This may have been when he obtained his second oldest book, the palm-sized volume by Carolus Clusius titled *Aliquot Notae in Garciae Aromatum Historiam*, printed in 1582 by the great Antwerp firm of Christophe Plantin (Plate 7.iv). In this work are described some of the strange fruits found on Sir Francis Drake's voyage of circumnavigation; but it also forms a supplement to the work that Garcia da Orta had undertaken in Bombay and Goa in the first half of the sixteenth century, explaining why the book comes to include some of the earliest published woodcuts of Indian plants – including the banyan, betel and black pepper.

In July 1851 the Edinburgh botanist Robert Kaye Greville presented Cleghorn with a handsome gift: the first six volumes of Hendrik van Rheede's *Hortus Malabaricus* (1678–86), commenting that they were 'of no use whatsoever' to himself (Plate 10.i, ii, iii). The following year Cleghorn chose to save these volumes from a fire that consumed the building in Madras in which he was lodging – in preference to the pet dog whose barking had saved his life! Although Cleghorn never did manage to acquire the other six volumes, he did own a copy of the rare first (and only) volume of Sir John Hill's smaller-format, English edition of the work (1774). Also in his library were three related works: Caspar Commelin's *Flora Malabarica* (1696), a contemporary digest of the *Hortus*, and two later commentaries in which Rheede's plants were identified using Linnaean nomenclature. The first of these was Lewis Weston Dillwyn's *A Review of the References to the Hortus Malabaricus of H. van Rheede van Draakenstein* (1839), a gift from the author to Pamplin who had no use for it and passed it on inscribing it 'Dr H Cleghorn Madras from W.P.' (Plate 4.iii). Cleghorn had this volume interleaved at the American Mission Press bindery, and annotated it with updated binomials and numerous notes (Plate 8.iii, 10.iv); slipped into the copy (now at EUL), on two loose folios, is Cleghorn's own manuscript 'Index to Hortus Malabaricus arranged according to De Candolle's Prodromus'. The second commentary, a work of profound botanical scholarship, is that of Francis (Buchanan-)Hamilton, written in his retirement at Leny near Callendar, and infamously read as 'fillers' at 31 threadbare meetings of the Linnean Society between 1821 and 1852. Only four parts of the manuscript were printed in the Society's *Transactions* and in 1875 Cleghorn wrote to Richard Kippist, the Society's secretary, to see if there was any intention to publish the later parts. The reply was that:

> We have still a deal of the MS. in store. It used to be our standing dish, whenever there was nothing else to read; but it is many a year since we ceased to inflict it upon the Fellows, and (Dr H. having omitted to bequeath us the means), it is very unlikely that we shall ever bring out [i.e. publish] any more of it.

This being the case, Cleghorn had the four published parts bound, including Kippist's letter, and the volume is at EUL,[34] though the commentaries are unannotated by Cleghorn.

From Robert Wight (sent via Pamplin) came another handsome gift of valuable antiquarian books (Plate 10.v, vi): four volumes of the collected botanical works of Leonard Plukenet (a set of mixed editions, 1691–1769), which are of importance to Indian botany for the etchings of many plants sent to London from Fort St George at the turn of the seventeenth and eighteenth centuries. To Rheede and Plukenet, as to N.L. Burmann's *Flora Indica* of 1768, Cleghorn added Linnaean binomials in pencil to the plates in his copies. Other great historical works that he owned, and from which he made notes and had illustrations copied by artists for his illustrations collection, include Joseph Gaertner's pioneering work on the fruits and seeds of plants (*De Fructibus et Seminibus de Plantarum*, 1788–91, with the 1805 supplement by the author's son), and the three encyclopaedic works, amounting to a total of 18 substantial quarto tomes, of Jean-Baptiste Lamarck. One of the rarest books in the library is Willdenow's incomplete *Phytographia* (Erlangen, 1794), a particularly interesting copy as it contains an annotation by J.P. Rottler, the last of the Tranquebar missionaries (Plate 7.ii, iii). The work includes species based on collections by his colleagues Klein and König, but is also of interest because it suggests that, like many bibliophiles, Cleghorn seems occasionally to have forgotten to return a borrowed book – it bears the stamp of the Madras Medical College. Information about plants is not to be found only in purely botanical works and, especially with his interest in economic plants, Cleghorn read widely, including travel books, marking incidental botanical references with marginal lines or annotations. Of this genre, relating to South India, are W.H. Smoult's second edition of Robert Baikie's *The Neilgherries* (1857), Gordon Forbes's *Wild Life in Canara and Ganjam* (1855) and his friend the engineer Frederick Cotton's *Tour of Inspection of the Northern Littoral Districts of the Madras Presidency* (1856).

One other travel book in the library calls for notice, not only because it has a direct link with Cleghorn, but because the expedition it concerns deserves to be better known in the non-German-speaking world. This is the general introduction to the Austro-Hungarian voyage of scientific exploration undertaken between 1857 and 1859 on the frigate *Novara* under the command of Bernhard Aloys von Wüllerstorf-Ubair, of which the three profusely illustrated volumes, a great contemporary publishing success, were edited anonymously by Karl von Scherzer. At every port at which the ship put in the dashing young officers turned heads, and probably not only of young ladies, but in no other expedition report ever written can the score of a musical work inspired by expedition members have been printed. In an appendix is to be found a suite of waltzes composed for a ball in Sydney by the *emigrée* concert pianist Frau Amalie Rawack-Mauthner, which are by no means a betrayal of her Viennese musical heritage.[35] In the text is found no mention of Cleghorn, nor of the excursion to Pulicat Lake on which he took the Austrian scientists, but his name does appear in the lengthy list of people who assisted the expedition. Presumably he was sent a free copy of the volumes by the organisers of the lavishly funded expedition, as, even if he had been able to read German easily (which he wasn't), the blackletter typeface would have provided a further stumbling block.

In the 1850s Pamplin was sending a stream of printed treasures from London to Madras – not only books but hand-coloured botanical plates – and in the St Andrews archive are invoices for more than 3500 such prints.[36] The latter included two major sets depicting medicinal plants: folio engravings from the *Icones Plantarum Medicinalum* of Joseph Jacob Plenck (Vienna, 1788–1803) and lithographs from the *Plantae Officinalis* of Theodor Nees von Esenbeck (Düsseldorf, 1821–33), which must have been useful to Cleghorn in his teaching of *materia medica*. There were also plates from the horticultural periodicals the *Botanical Register* and the *Botanical Magazine* (from which Pamplin selected species of Indian interest); much rarer were engravings from the works of Nicolas von Jacquin, and a single fascicle of what are commonly considered to be the finest botanical plates ever made – those by Franz Bauer for Sibthorp's and Smith's *Flora Graeca*. That Cleghorn took a serious interest in the bibliography of botanical illustration is shown by his ownership of the learned and pioneering catalogue of such works, the *Iconum Botanicarum Index Locupletissimus* by George Augustus Pritzel, the first volume of which came out in 1855 (later he would acquire the second part, and the same author's *Thesaurus Literaturae Botanicae Omnium Gentium*). The printed botanical illustrations Cleghorn was acquiring were not, however, only European: one of the most beautiful folios in his library was printed locally, in Madras. Henry Smith, the Fort St George Government Printer, devised a technique for inking dried specimens and passing them through a printing press to obtain Nature Prints. Cleghorn himself experimented successfully with the technique, making many beautifully rich, sooty impressions, but he also owned a copy of the handsome volume that Smith produced in 1857 *Specimens of Nature Printing from Unprepared Plants*, dedicated to the Madras Governor Lord Harris, which ends dramatically with a sinuous double-image of a snake – in which the arch of every rib pair is exquisitely revealed (Plate 11.i, ii, iii).

MADRAS HORTICULTURIST

As Secretary of the Madras Agri-Horticultural Society, Cleghorn took a keen interest in gardening and horticultural literature. This interest fed not only into his teaching (the opportunity to show plants from a wider range of families than was available locally) but into his commitment to economic botany – the search for potentially exploitable natural resources – whether exotics that could be imported into India, or vice versa, by means of trials in the Society's garden. A book embodying such interests (and also his ability to read French, strong since childhood, and which led him to acquire many books in the language) is Casimir Barjavel's *Traité complet de la culture de l'olivier* (1830); Cleghorn commissioned a painting of the olive when it fruited at the Lal Bagh in Bangalore in 1857. The Madras Agri-Horticultural Society was linked to similar bodies in Calcutta and Bombay, but the publications produced by all three are rare, so that Cleghorn's copies of those of the Madras (the *Proceedings* issued by Robert Wight in 1839), and Bombay (*Proceedings* of 1838, 1843 and 1852) societies are particularly valuable. Only a few unbound parts of his own copies of the journal of the national, Calcutta-based, society survive in EUL, as he gave his main set to the Kew library in 1894.[37] More surprising is the absence of a copy of *Hortus Madraspatensis*, the catalogue of the Madras Society's garden written by Cleghorn himself.[38]

Illustrated botanical periodicals contained a wealth of information about the more attractive horticultural introductions, many of which reached

Madras surprisingly soon after their discovery in the wild – by way of Kew, from London nurseries or owners of private gardens. Cleghorn had substantial runs of the *Botanical Register* (1815–47), the *Botanical Magazine* (1793–1832), the *Botanic Garden* (1825–35), the *Florist's Journal* (1840–42) and the *Floral Cabinet* by Knowles and Westcott (1837–38), from all of which he selected plates for copying by his artists for his illustrations collection. Of gardening books, as with more strictly botanical ones, he was supplied from London with works by authors including John Lindley, and with Jane Loudon's attractively illustrated *Ladies' Flower Garden* (*of Ornamental Perennials* in two volumes, 1843–44; *of Annuals* in three, 1844–54). Cleghorn's set of her husband John Claudius Loudon's encyclopaedic, eight-volume *Arboretum et Fruticetum Britannicum* demonstrates another acquisition route as the volumes bear the stamp of the Madras civil servant John Rohde. Several books in Cleghorn's library come from similar sources, doubtless given to him by friends or colleagues on their leaving India, or circulating in the second-hand book trade in Madras. Antiquarian gardening books are also represented in the library (acquired at unkown dates) and include John Evelyn's *Kalendarium Hortense* (third edition, 1669), Richard Bradley's *New Improvements of Planting and Gardening* (1717), and the two-volume, folio *Hortus Elthamensis* (1732) in which J.J. Dillenius described the plants in the garden at Eltham of his patron William Sherard's brother James. A classic botanical monograph, treating several popular horticultural genera, was the Spaniard A.J. Cavanilles's ten dissertations on the Linnaean class Monadelphia (1790), of which Cleghorn owned two parts,[39] including the one devoted to the genus *Passiflora*, with 32 beautiful engravings which he asked one of his Madras artists to copy.

Of particular interest are four horticultural works published in India. Joachim Otto Voigt was a surgeon at the Danish colony of Fredriksnagore (later Serampore), upstream and on the opposite bank of the Hooghly from Calcutta. His posthumous *Hortus Suburbanus Calcuttensis* (1845) listed all the plants in cultivation in the Calcutta Botanic Garden and in the garden of the Rev. William Carey at Serampore (which Cleghorn would visit with Dietrich Brandis in its latter days in the 1860s). Voigt died while on sick-leave in London in 1843 and his widow Rachel asked William Griffith to complete the work. Rachel Voigt was a daughter of Carey's colleague Joshua Marshman and later became the forester Dietrich Brandis's (first) wife. However, its author's premature death was not the only one connected with Cleghorn's copy of the book, which had previously belonged to Charles Drew, a young Madras medical colleague of enormous botanical promise who had died at Vellore in 1857, aged only 31. A real rarity is a work published in Madras in 1837 by the surgeon William Ingledew – entitled *Treatise on the Culture of the Red Rose, Strawberry, Brazil Gooseberry, Peach, Mango, and Grape Vine*, with a preface and notes by Robert Wight who at this point was involved with the Agri-Horticultural Society.[40] Cleghorn owned two practical guides to gardening in

India – the second edition of George T.F. Speede's *Indian Handbook of Gardening* (Calcutta, 1842), notable for its 248-page glossary of Hindustani horticultural and agricultural terms (given in Persian script), and for five lithographed plates by the Calcutta artist Colesworthy Grant. Its southern equivalent, the *Manual of Gardening for Western and Southern India* by Dr Robert Riddell,[41] also ran to several editions, and Cleghorn's copy was of the third (1856), illustrated with exquisite etchings of garden tools, summerhouses and designs for parterres by pupils of Alexander Hunter's Madras School of Art (Plate 11.iv, v).

THE MADRAS EXHIBITIONS

With his experience of working on Indian natural products for John Forbes Royle at the Great Exhibition in London in 1851, Cleghorn was, not surprisingly, closely involved with the exhibition held in the Madras Banqueting Hall in 1855 (and to a much lesser extent with its successor in 1857). His concern was largely with the sections devoted to the products of the Vegetable Kingdom, and although none of his own copies of the Jury Reports or other literature relating to these exhibitions was in the material bequeathed to the Museum or University, there are several works on economic botany relevant to his interest in this field, and dating from this period. For example: Royle's *Fibrous Plants of India* (1855), a collection of *Papers Regarding the Cultivation of Hemp in India* published in Agra (1855), *Cotton and Commerce of India* by John Chapman (1851) and the *Popular Economic Botany* by Thomas Croxen Archer (1853). At this point Archer worked in the Liverpool Customs House, but in 1860 he would move to Edinburgh as Superintendent of the Edinburgh Museum of Science and Art, the institution where so much of Cleghorn's botanical library would end up. Archer held this post until 1885, and in 1862 acted as President of the Botanical Society, a position later held by Cleghorn. In the collection are scarce pamphlets on two of the most economically important palms of South India. That on the coconut palm (*Cocos nucifera*) is by Henry Marshall (1836), a surgeon at one time based in Ceylon, and reprinted in Edinburgh from the *Memoirs of the Wernerian Natural History Society*. The one on the palmyra (*Borassus flabellifer*) is by William Ferguson, who also worked in Ceylon, but as a surveyor, and whose pamphlet (of 1850) was printed in Colombo. It includes fascinating illustrations and, bound into it, is a strip of palm leaf with the name of the plant inscribed in Tamil and Roman scripts.

The volume in the library that reveals most clearly Cleghorn's deep interest in economic botany is his copy of Heber Drury's *Useful Plants of India* (1858). Drury (originally a colonel in the Madras Light Infantry, with interests in sport and natural history) became Assistant Resident at the courts of Cochin and Travancore, where Cleghorn visited him in 1858. This same year Drury asked for help with the proofs of his book, and Cleghorn had this proof copy interleaved and bound. As with his copy of Wight and Arnott's *Prodromus*, he annotated it profusely (with original observations and quotations from a wide range of literature) over a long period, and stuffed it with additional material including newspaper cuttings (for example, on tea, coffee, bamboo and flax), the printed summaries of his own papers, and slips with manuscript notes from other authors. The most notable of these insertions is a manuscript Memorandum on the sal tree (*Shorea robusta*) in the hand of Dietrich Brandis, with additions by Cleghorn, that must date from the 1860s.

Madras conservator of forests (1856–60)

Following discussions with Lord Harris, the Governor of Madras, about the setting up of a Forest Department for the Madras Presidency in 1855, and his appointment as Conservator the following year, Cleghorn realised that he would have to acquaint himself with forestry literature in which he had taken little, if any, interest since writing his British Association report four years earlier. There is little evidence for when he acquired particular books, other than a few from William Pamplin, and the 'Government Records on Forest management, and Timber correspondence' he intended to acquire during a visit to Thomas Thomson in Calcutta in January 1857. But he was acquiring literature from other sources and considered Balfour in Edinburgh to be his 'Chief Patron' in the matter of books and pamphlets.[42] It has already been pointed out that a date of publication is no guarantee as to when a book entered Cleghorn's collection and that all one can say, with few exceptions, is what – from a pre-1860 date – it is *possible* that Cleghorn could have had available for reading at this time. Caution is especially important as Cleghorn's historical interests would continue for the rest of his life and some of the pre-1860 works were certainly purchased at a later date. The books sent by Pamplin in 1856 and 1857 were Loudon's *Arboretum et Fruticetum Britannicum*,[43] 'various Forest Parliamentary papers [on] Teak Forest ... Timber Duties ... Woods and Forests', G.B. Emerson's *Report on the ... Forests of Massachusetts* (Boston, 1846), and, most interestingly (because it includes a pre-Darwinian expression of the theory of evolution by natural selection), though no longer present in the collection, *On Naval Timber and Arboriculture* (Edinburgh, 1831) by the Carse of Gowrie laird and orchard-owner Patrick Matthew.

Given that by this date forest conservancy work had already been started in both Burma and the Bombay Presidency, and given his fact-finding trip to Calcutta, it seems beyond question that the new Conservator would at this point have had the handful of relevant, contemporary Indian publications on forest matters – two compilations of papers on the teak forests of Burma, and Alexander Gibson's *Handbook to the Forests of the Bombay Presidency* (1857) (of which his copy has marginal marks against some of the forest rules and the section on timber agents' salaries). The Burmese works are Hugh Falconer's *Report on the Teak Forests of the Tenasserim Forests* (Calcutta, 1852), and the *Papers on Teak Forests of Pegu* (Calcutta, 1855) which contains papers by Arthur Phayre and John McClelland. Both of these are annotated and 'grangerised', especially the former, which has a newspaper cutting about McClelland's teak report and a revealing note by Cleghorn on the short-term financial advantage, but long-term disadvantage, of the 'unrestrained liberty' of selling off timber rights too cheaply. Given that the steps that had led to conservancy in Bombay were driven by the need for teak for shipbuilding, Cleghorn, at this point, may also have had his copy of a compilation of three rare works published in London that include William Money's *Observations on the Expediency of Shipbuilding at Bombay* (1811), and Captain William Laymen's *Precursor to an Exposé on Forest Trees and Timber*. In the latter the use of Malabar teak was recommended by the author to the Royal Navy.

Cleghorn's previous experience of practical forestry was limited to what he had observed in early life on his grandfather's estate at Stravithie in Fife, and the whole system of British forestry was based on plantations and clear-felling – the treatment of trees as a long-lived crop. There was an extensive literature on such matters, of which the most recent and substantial was James Brown's *The Forester*, of which Cleghorn recommended the 1860 edition as 'perhaps the best manual for the [Madras Forest] department'.[44] It therefore seems likely that Cleghorn's copy of the second edition of this work (Edinburgh, 1851) was already in his possession at this time. There are many other works in the library of a similar nature, on planting and management, both English and Scottish, that he could well have owned and read as a budding forester in Madras in the late 1850s – an example of the former is Francis Blaikie's *Treatise on the Planting and Management of Forest Timber Trees adapted to the System of Farm Clump Planting* (Burton-upon-Trent, 1814). Among the latter are the *Miscellaneous Observations on Planting and Training Timber-Trees; particularly calculated for the Climate of Scotland* by James Anderson (as 'Agricola') published in Edinburgh in 1777, and the pioneering *Treatise on the Manner of Raising Forest Trees* by Thomas Hamilton, 6th Earl of Haddington (Edinburgh, 1761) (Plate 9.iv, v). Cleghorn's copy of the last has an interesting provenance: tipped into it is a manuscript letter from a 'Mr Ainslie' dated 'Dunse July 30 1768'. This is from Robert Ainslie of Darnchester, father of Whitelaw and Robert – the former the Madras surgeon and author of the *Materia Medica of Hindoostan*; the latter a close friend of Robert Burns. The letter records the gift of the book to Ainslie by a 'Mr Ker' (probably one of the Ancram family) recommending its use towards 'Beautifying part of the wast ground of Teviotdale'. Of somewhat more recent date was Robert Monteath's *The Forester's Guide*, in two different editions (Stirling, 1820 and Edinburgh, 1824).

Long before this, as a result of timber shortages felt by the Royal Navy in the seventeenth century, John Evelyn had attempted to encourage tree planting with the publication of his *Sylva*, of which Cleghorn owned copies both of the second edition (1670), and of a later, expanded, one edited by Alexander Hunter (York, 1812). Due to the individualistic attitudes of British landowners, in marked contrast to their *confrères* in France and Germany, and their objections to state intervention, this had not led to any form of legal regulation. In England there was a body of what was called 'Forest Law', dating back to Mediaeval times, but given the self-serving interests of the British aristocracy and royalty, this had little to do with tree-planting, rather with the preservation of habitat, with a greater or lesser numbers of trees, as cover for game for hunting. Cleghorn owned a copy of the third edition (1665) of John Manwood's collection of this corpus of antiquated common law, printed (self-consciously for the date) in blackletter, as *A Treatise of the Laws of the Forest*. Another reason for reforestation beyond the merely economic, and one that, given his religious outlook, is likely to have been shared by Cleghorn, is embodied in a pamphlet by William Hanbury. Its title, *An Essay on Planting and a Scheme for Making it Conducive to the Glory of God* (1758), is self-explanatory, and in it the author urged the planting of trees as a means of 'reviving that too much decayed Sense of the Almighty, which must necessarily arise in the Heart of Man from Contemplation of his Works'.

What would, perhaps, have been slightly more useful in an Indian context, are the large number of French works in Cleghorn's library. More relevant because the French had (at least up to the time of the Revolution) not only attempted to manage forests on a sustainable basis without extensive replanting (though plantations were also made), but, because, in order to ensure the preservation of forests, the French Crown had introduced legislation, which was clearly also going to be necessary in India. Cleghorn owned a copy of Chaussepierre's and Rousselet's 1776 edition of Colbert's famous *Ordonnance* 'relative to waters and forests' originally issued in the name of Louis XIV at St Germain en Laye in the month of August 1669 (Plate 7.v). It is not certain that he had this in his early days as a Madras forester, but it is certainly a possibility; the same applies to other French works including a more up-to-date work on French legislation, Edouard Meaume's *Introduction à l'étude de la législation et de la jusiprudence forestières* (Nancy, 1857). Also in his library were classic French manuals on forestry, arboriculture and plantations by the authors J.-J. Baudrillart (1808), Etienne Calvel (1825) and Alphonse de Breuil (1857) and works on the relation between forests and the navy by P.-E. Herbin de Halle (1815) and Bonard (1826). Of greater interest is Antoine Cesar Becquerel's

Des climats et de l'influence qui exercent les sols boisés et non boisés (Paris, 1853). Given the controversial question of Cleghorn's motivation for promoting forest conservancy (primarily economic, or primarily environmental?) it would be particularly interesting to know where and when he acquired this volume but of this, though in its original binding, it betrays no hint; but neither does it bear any annotations that might suggest that Cleghorn read or was particularly interested in it. His copy of another early French work on forest management and conservation, the *Traité de l'aménagement et de la restauration des bois et forêts de la France* by L. de Perthuis de Laillevault (Paris, 1803), has an interesting provenance, as it is signed by Gilbert Laing Meason. Before going bankrupt, Meason (originator of the concept of landscape architecture) had laid out a fine estate at Lindertis near Kirriemuir, Angus, which was later acquired by the son of Sir Thomas Munro, ironically the Madras Governor who in the 1820s had stopped an early forest conservancy in Kerala.

Strikingly, given the history of the 'science' of forest management, and the influence it was shortly to have in India, there are no German works in the library from this period (and very few from later), but this is doubtless because Cleghorn struggled with the language. There are, however, several interesting earlier Italian works – by Jacopo Ricci (1821), Antonio Fornaini (1825) and Giuseppe del Noce (1849) – but it is probable that these were not acquired until much later, on a visit to Florence in 1868 (possibly given to him by G.P. Marsh), or on a visit to Rome and Vallombrosa in 1875.

What turned out to be the climax of Cleghorn's forestry career in Madras was achieved with the publication, while on furlough in Britain in 1861, of his reports for the period 1856–60 as the *Forests and Gardens of South India*.[45] He must surely have kept an interleaved and annotated working-copy of this book but, if so, this has not survived. The only surviving copy that he owned (in EUL) has only a few minor annotations and inserted newspaper clippings. Of the former the most significant is one placed against a comment about coffee planters: 'applicants should be liberally responded to'. As plantations (along with railway construction) were one of the major causes of deforestation in the Western Ghats, this shows that one should not have too rose-coloured a view of Cleghorn's ideas on forest conservancy and that, true to his Enlightenment upbringing, he always favoured 'improvement', with conservation limited to the minimum required for watershed protection and, up to a point, climatic amelioration. Further interest in coffee plantations is shown by ownership of a pamphlet by Guérin-Méneville and Perrottet (1842) on diseases that were ravaging the crop in the Antilles.

Although the Conservator's job left Cleghorn with no time to practise medicine, his interest cannot entirely have left him and in the pamphlet collection are reprints of two interesting papers written by James Irving (1859, 1860), the civil surgeon at Allahabad, with whom he must have overlapped during medical studies in Edinburgh. The topic is lathyrism, a condition that causes paralysis of the legs in humans, caused by a neurotoxin in the plant *Lathyrus sativa*, a legume whose small seeds were eaten by the poor, despite its adverse effects having been known about for many centuries.

MARRIAGE

Cleghorn came late to marriage, remaining a bachelor until the age of 41 in 1861; through his wife Mabel Cowan he became connected with a wealthy, but enlightened, family of Penicuik paper-makers. Mabel brought with her a handsome financial dowry, but a single volume in her husband's library suggests at least the possibility that she might also have brought some books. This is a work by the English-based, Pomeranian paper-maker Matthias Koops, with the cumbersome title *An Historical Account of the Substances which have been used to Describe Events, and to Convey Ideas, from the Earliest Date to the Invention of Paper* (1801). This is a history of writing materials, of which parts (the engraved frontispiece of papyrus plants and an appendix) of the second edition, which Cleghorn owned, were printed on Koops's own patented recycled paper made from straw. Cleghorn could, of course, have bought the book himself – as part of his interest in economic botany, or after his visit to Sicily where he took an interest in the papyrus plant – but while there are no annotations to prove it, it also seems possible that the volume might have a Cowan origin; and even if it did not, it certainly makes a fascinating link with their business interests.

INDIAN FORESTER (1861–68)

The Punjab and Himalayan fieldwork

After returning with Mabel to India from his second furlough, Cleghorn's life changed in other ways. Rather than resuming his post in Madras he was summoned by the Viceroy, Lord Canning, to undertake forest work in the Punjab and the Himalaya that would lead, in due course, to his taking on a national role in partnership with Dietrich Brandis. The initial period, exploring the forests of the watersheds between four of the great rivers of the Punjab, was the most intrepid of his life, one that is richly represented in his library with accounts by earlier Himalayan travellers – from surveyors to, rather more unexpectedly, a vet and a homoeopath. Today these seem among the most interesting books in the library, but for him they were working tools – as demonstrated by inserted newspaper cuttings and marked passages. Of the latter the most common are marginal lines, but sometimes he added observations or corrections – usually of small extent, but occasionally more substantial quotations from other works. Given the nature of his employment these annotations, unsurprisingly, largely concern vegetation and forests, and there is a satisfaction in being able to view, 150 years later, the creative process at work by which Cleghorn assembled information from his extensive researches into earlier literature that would inform and feed into his own surveys and reports.

Four such works owned and used by Cleghorn will be discussed here (and there are half a dozen others). Of these the designation 'travelogue' will do only for one; the other three belonging firmly to the Scottish statistical tradition of detailed, wide-ranging surveys – from physical geography to ethnology and natural history. The travelogue is contemporary with Cleghorn's own excursions, Torrens's *Travels in Ladâk, Tartary and Kashmir* (London, 1862), jauntily written, with the sort of anecdotal and colourful local detail so signally absent from any of Cleghorn's own publications. It is the work of Lieutenant Colonel Henry D'Oyly Torrens of the 23rd Royal Welsh Fusiliers,[46] whose grandmother Sarah Patton was born at Kinaldy, the next-door estate to Stravithie, and ended her days with her daughter-in-law Lady Anstruther at nearby Balcaskie. Describing a journey up the Sutlej and into Lahul, including a visit to the Moravian missionaries at Keylong, the book is profusely illustrated with woodcuts and chromolithographs, which must be based on Torrens's own evidently more than usually competent sketches. With the loss of Cleghorn's photographic collection, this is the only means to glimpse some of the sights he saw – of buildings, scenery and people. Among the woodcut vignettes are ones of the two types of alarming West Himalayan river-crossing mentioned in Cleghorn's notebooks: the *twig bridge* (a suspension bridge, over which pedestrians walked) and the *jhula* (a rope, across which the passenger slid on a sling), showing that both were in use at the time, and that at least sometimes Cleghorn confusingly used 'jhula' for both.

By the mid-1860s Himalayan exploration was no new activity, and Cleghorn made use of publications from a previous generation, among the best of which were Alexander Gerard's *Account of Koonawar in the Himalaya* and the *Travels in the Himalayan Provinces* by William Moorcroft and George Trebreck. Both of these works relate to journeys undertaken in the late teens and early twenties of the century, were posthumously edited and, coincidentally, appeared in 1841, Moorcroft's being edited by the Sanskrit scholar Horace Hayman Wilson. The two journeys were taken with very different ends in mind. Moorcroft was a vet, in charge of the Company's horse-breeding stud in Bengal, and the goal of his travels was to end up at the fabled horse-market of Bukhara. Alexander Gerard was a military surveyor, from a distinguished Aberdonian academic family, whose surveys were aimed at assessing natural resources with a view to more efficient revenue collection. Moorcroft and his young companion George Trebreck took several years, and a very roundabout route, to get to Uzbekistan (where they both died in 1825), via Ladakh, which took in places of interest to Cleghorn such as Kullu and Lahul. Cleghorn annotated many passages, for example on the tea trade to Ladakh, but the most interesting addition, inserted into the Lahul section, is a newspaper cutting discussing the inaccurate reports of the twig bridge across the Chandra River on which the Viceroy, Lord Elgin, had a soon-to-be-fatal heart attack, giving its true dimensions rather than the wildly exaggerated ones that had been in circulation.

The expeditions of Gerard, described in his book on Kinnaur,[47] took place in 1817 and 1818 (one describing his other travels had been issued the previous year). The first of these was in the company of Dr George Govan, the first superintendent of the Saharunpur Botanic Garden (whom Cleghorn knew later in Govan's later life, by which time Govan had retired to Pilmuir Cottage beside the St Andrews golf links). On the second of Gerard's journeys he was accompanied by his medical brother James, a notable surveyor. Kinnaur is the region around the Sutlej valley to the east of Simla which Cleghorn explored in 1862, at least partly in the company of Mabel in her early Indian days of good health. This is one of the areas where edible seeds are collected from the conifer *Pinus gerardiana*, whose name commemorates Patrick, the third Gerard brother, a soldier in the Bengal Native Infantry. To his copy of the book Cleghorn added the prices paid for these large and delicious pine nuts at Chini (now Kalpa), and also those for Pangi walnuts.

The fourth of the travel books is by one of Cleghorn's own friends, a fellow Scottish, botanically-minded, Company Surgeon, whose father was the Glasgow Professor of Chemistry. In the early 1860s, when Cleghorn was using Thomas Thomson's *Western Himalaya and Tibet* (1852), its author had recently retired from the post of Superintendent of the Calcutta Botanic Garden, where Cleghorn had visited him in December 1855 prior to embarking upon his own forestry work in Madras. This was also the year of publication of the *Flora Indica*, written by Thomson with Joseph Hooker, his friend from Glasgow University days. The travels described were undertaken between May 1847 and October 1848, when Thomson was one of the commissioners for demarcating the boundary between Kashmir and Chinese Tibet. The excursions were largely in the Kashmir territories, during which Thomson reached as far as Iskardo and the Karakorum range, and it included the first crossing by a Westerner of the Sach Pass while heading north from Chamba – a route that Cleghorn would himself follow in July 1862. The resulting book, published by Hooker's publisher Lovell Reeve, for which Cleghorn paid 15 shillings, has been patronisingly described in the *Oxford Dictionary of National Biography* as 'well received though prosaic',[48] but as the work of a botanist it was useful to

Cleghorn for its descriptions of forests and plants. Cleghorn made numerous annotations on his copy, for example on the use of the young leaves of *Eremurus* as 'spinage', and additions to the index with page references to *Daphne* (for paper-making) and jhula bridges. Unfortunately, as in many cases, the book has been cheaply and crudely rebound, its pages ruthlessly trimmed, with consequent destruction of the extremities of the marginalia.

While seeking Cleghorn's books in the RBGE library, one of the most evocative discoveries was a copy of *Practical Hints on Planting Ornamental Trees* (1852) by the Berkshire nurserymen John Standish and Charles Noble of Sunningdale Nursery (the nursery where Hooker's Sikkim rhododendrons had been propagated) (Plate 12.i). The book was intended for British estate owners, but includes descriptions of many of the Himalayan conifers that, by then, were in common cultivation in Britain. The interest of the copy lies in the unexpectedness of its provenance and annotations, which link trees/forestry and a personal connection from two dramatically contrasted worlds. Its original owner was Lord William Hay (Plate 12.ii), Superintendent of the Hill States, and was signed by him 'Simlah – 10/2/56', and later 'To Dr Cleghorn …'. Hay, who later succeeded his ornithologist brother Arthur as 10th Marquess of Tweeddale, used the rear endpapers of this manual to record local Indian names of the conifers (Plate 12.iii), and the pocket-sized volume is an encapsulation of the two worlds that were Cleghorn's as much as Hay's – of Scottish land-owners and their wooded estates, and their role in the India of the Company period.

Trees were not Cleghorn's only botanical concern in the Himalaya and he also took an interest in less significant economic products. His copy of R.H. Davis's *Report on the Trade and Resources of the Countries on the North-western Boundary of British India* (Lahore, 1862), which contains his own small publication on the economic plants of Lahul,[49] is interleaved, and bears notes copied from literature on the umbelliferous drug-plant *asafoetida*. Cleghorn never completely give up his original medical interests, and the library includes a fascinating work relating to the Punjab and Kashmir by the Transylvanian physician John Martin Honigberger entitled *Thirty-five Years in the East* (London, 1852). Fifteen of those years (1829–33, 1839–49) were spent in Lahore, the ones prior to the Maharaja's death in 1839 at the Court of Ranjit Singh, and the first part of the book concerns the history and ethnography of the Sikh kingdom. The other parts of the book are medical, comprising lists of diseases and their treatments. Honigberger had been introduced to homoeopathy during a European interlude, so the doses of some of the medicines are quaintly given in 'decillionth parts', although he personally favoured a 'smooth and middle course' taking the best from the 'opposite poles' of allopathy and homoeopathy. The book includes a medical vocabulary in four European and four Asian languages, but of greatest interest to Cleghorn was a substantial and largely botanical Materia Medica relating mainly to Kashmir (of which he also owned a separately bound, second-hand copy, heavily annotated by an unidentified botanist/medic).

In addition to studying books written by other Himalayan travellers, Cleghorn also needed to consult topographical and botanical reference works. For the latter, to assist with plant identification, he had Hooker and Thomson's *Flora Indica* and Wight and Arnott's *Prodromus*, but more relevant (and, more to the point, complete) was J.F. Royle's handsomely produced *Illustrations of the Botany ... of the Himalayan Mountains*, published in eleven parts between 1833 and 1840. Cleghorn's copy, bound in two volumes (text and plates), must have been bought second-hand in India, as it bears a purchase price of 70 Rupees, and the list of Latin bird names has many manuscript corrections in a hand that is not his. It does, however, also bear marks made by Cleghorn, for example in the section on the wild species of rhubarb, in which he took great interest in the Sutlej and Chenab Valleys in 1862.[50] The botanical parts of the Afghanistan section in Cleghorn's copy of Griffith's posthumously published *Journals* (1847) are also heavily annotated (the copy bears the stamp of the Madras Revenue & Judicial Department, beside which Cleghorn has written 'purchased at auction', lest anyone think he had stolen it). Also in the library are two strictly topographical works, both (like 'Royle') published in London by Cleghorn's own publisher W.H. Allen – the *Gazetteer of the Countries Adjacent to India on the North-West* (1844) by Edward Thornton, head of the Statistical Department at India House, and the *Map of the Punjab, Western Himalaya and Adjoining parts of Tibet* (1854) by the EIC Geographer John Walker. It is easy to picture Cleghorn planning journeys while poring over this linen-mounted map, which though unannotated, is weather-stained and clearly much-used.

One of the most interesting finds amongst Cleghorn's books was his copy of George Marsh's *Man and Nature* (the London printing of 1864), a work that was probably first read by Cleghorn in Lahul in August 1864 (Plate 6.iii). Reading this remarkable work probably rekindled Cleghorn's interest in climate and the physical consequences of deforestation; it is certainly hard to imagine a more spectacular landscape in which to read it, surrounded by the processes its author – a nineteenth-century Jared Diamond – described and used to predict (though with the hope that it could be avoided), the spectre of environmental catastrophe due to deforestation. The copy is copiously annotated, with underlinings and marginal lines against passages that struck a particular chord, relating to aspects of forests, climate, flooding, and also against items in Marsh's bibliography, of some of which Cleghorn owned his own copies. But there are also a few additional notes, including a reference to the invasion of European waterways by *Anacharis alsinastrum* (later called *Elodea canadensis* – the book is extremely digressive!), and to diseases of grapes that Cleghorn had observed in Bashahr in the Sutlej valley. The section on the use of coal in Europe is marked up as if for publication as an excerpt, with a 'Begin' and several 'omits'.[51] The connections of the notes, however, relate not only to India: Cleghorn clearly had the copy with him in Sicily and Malta on his homeward journey in 1867/8, as there is a note on the fossil remains in Sicilian caves marked 'see also Geol. Mus. Palermo'. In Palermo he must have shown the book to Henry Yule, as there are four marginal comments that, while not in Yule's hand, seem almost beyond question to be quotations of observations made by him, two of which are credited to 'Y' (Plate 6.iv). One gives a Bengali name for a type of saltmarsh, another queries the reliability of an apparent increase in the number of plant species on St Helena ('can Botany be relied on?'); there is an observation of a vine with a stem nine inches in diameter 'I saw one on Stromboli' (where Cleghorn never went). The clincher for the identification of 'Y', however, relates to an observation on the 'Cintra Orange … mentioned by Abulfeda', a reference that Yule would later cite in his classic Anglo-Indian dictionary, *Hobson-Jobson*. It is intriguing enough to picture Yule and Cleghorn discussing Marsh's visionary book in Sicily, but this also had consequences, as when Cleghorn visited Marsh in Florence shortly thereafter he effected an epistolary introduction between the two philologists.[52] From Rome, in 1874, Marsh sent Cleghorn a copy of an appendix to the second edition of his great work, which Cleghorn had carefully stitched into his copy, along with the covering letter in Marsh's scarcely legible hand (Plate 12.iv, v); and, although uninscribed, he probably also sent Cleghorn the copy of the Italian edition, *L'Uomo e la Natura* (Florence, 1870) now in the EUL collection.

The Punjab period culminated in Cleghorn's own second book, his *Report on the Forests of the Punjab* (1864), of which his own copy is the most heavily annotated in his library, with numerous corrections and additions (Plate 6.v, vi). Stuck into the front is a clipping of an anonymous review of the book, from the *Friend of India*, to which Cleghorn has added the initials 'D.B.' showing the otherwise unknown fact that it was written by Brandis. In a pocket at the back is a miscellaneous assemblage of documents: an exquisite manuscript map (covering the area from Peshawar in the north-west to Kalpa in the south-east) drawn on silk, based on the one by John Walker in Cunningham's *Ladak*, which the present author used to retrace Cleghorn's travels in 2014; a substantial newspaper cutting from the *Lahore Chronicle* of 11 July 1866, doubtless included for its notes on Kashmir, but, more bizarrely, also containing a news item on the sale of Sir Edwin Landseer's painting of Lady Godiva; a printed map of the section of the Himalaya north of Kangra; and a note from Peter Stark Lumsden about the forests near Peshawar.[53] On the back end-papers is to be found a pencilled list of the 27 individuals or bodies to whom Cleghorn sent presentation or review copies of the book, revealing his patronage network. In India these included the Viceroy (Sir John Lawrence), Sir William Denison, Sir Robert Montgomery, G.H.K. Thwaites, the *Friend of*

India, the Asiatic Society, Dr [Dietrich] Brandis, Colonel [Richard] Strachey and, in Britain, Lord Harris, Dr J.D. Hooker, Thomas Thomson, Charles Cowan (his father-in-law), St Andrews University and six learned Societies (Linnean, Edinburgh Botanical, Pharmaceutical, Highland and Royal Asiatic).

National Indian Forest Policy

After a period of secondment to the Punjab Government, Cleghorn worked for the Government of India between 1863 and 1867, in collaboration with Brandis, on national forest policy and legislation, and overseeing the development of regional Forest Departments. This period was mainly office-based, with summers in Simla and the rest of the year in Calcutta. There are several French and German works in the library from the 1860s, though these could have been acquired later. The French ones include three textbooks used at the Nancy forest school, two by Henri Nanquette on management (1860) and harvesting (1859), the third by Bernard Lorentz and Adolphe Parade on sylviculture (1860), which give the appearance of having been entirely unused by Cleghorn. A work on pruning by the Vicomte de Courval (1861) seems similarly unread, but a historical work by Louis Alfred Maury, *Les forêts de la Gaule et de l'ancienne France*, does bear annotations, though these might relate to Cleghorn's later *Encyclopaedia Britannica* articles. The German work is a classic textbook, the three-volume *Lehrbuch für Förster* by George Ludwig Hartig, founder of one of the earliest German forest schools, as revised by his son Theodor, a professor of forestry at Braunschweig, but this also seems to be unused, though Cleghorn probably admired its handsome plates, one of wood anatomy, one of tools and two on insect pests. The stodgy textbooks appear to be unread, and are certainly devoid of annotations, so it is hard to know what Cleghorn made of them. Although today it is possible to be cynical about the relevance in India of methods devised for temperate European forests, they were all that was then available and Brandis was convinced of the basic similarity of all forests and therefore the principles to be used for their management. In Burma he had already used statistical survey methods for assessing timber resources and working out felling regimes, which now started to be employed in India. Cleghorn must have been persuaded of their value, enough to be a keen supporter of the idea of training Indian foresters at Nancy in Alsace.

It tends to be Cleghorn's national role in the 1860s that has been best remembered, but this entire period was undertaken as a secondment from his Madras post, where during his long periods of absence, he was deputised for by Richard Henry Beddome. Between 1865, and leaving India for the last time in October 1867, Cleghorn returned to his Madras post on three occasions, two months in early 1865 preparing for sick leave, then two periods each of six months, in winter 1865/6 and from April to October 1867. The shorter visit involved packing up his herbarium and library to send home to Scotland, so his last two years were spent largely without access to his beloved books. The organising of his herbarium in 1865 must have brought his mind back to taxonomy, and although Cleghorn himself never described so much as a single new species this was a time of considerable taxonomic activity on Indian plants by others, notably Beddome who had taken over the employment of the artist Govindoo from Cleghorn, and the example of Govindoo's original employer, Robert Wight, in the matter of illustrated floristic publications. Beddome was particularly interested in ferns and during his period of deputising had started to write his *Ferns of British India* (Madras, 1866–8), illustrated by Govindoo. Unfortunately, as with so many of Cleghorn's copies of floristic works, the *Ferns* is no longer extant at RBGE. Beddome's other great works date from after he had succeeded as Conservator, following Cleghorn's departure from India. His contemporaries appear to have judged Beddome a disaster in this official role, perhaps because much of his time must have been devoted to taxonomy producing a series of impressive Wight-inspired illustrated works: the *Flora Sylvatica of South India* and *Icones Plantarum Indiae Orientalis*, both of which Cleghorn had copies of. In the latter is stuck a review from the *Gardeners' Chronicle*; although anonymous this is clearly by Cleghorn himself – it reveals the fascinating and otherwise unrecorded information that Govindoo's son continued to produced drawings for Beddome, accounting for what had previously seemed a surprisingly long period of activity for 'Wight's' Govindoo.

During these last Madras interludes Cleghorn retained his interest in economic and medical botany and it was in December 1865 that he accompanied Clements Markham on part of the latter's second Indian quinine excursion. The project and the friendship are both represented in the collection – by copies of W.G. McIvor's *Notes on the Propagation and Cultivation of the Medicinal Cinchonas* (Madras, 1867), and two of Markham's works, his *Travels in Peru and India* (London, 1862) and *The Chinchona Species of New Granada* (London, 1867). Cleghorn also owned Robert Brown's copy of an offprint of H.A. Weddell's 1848 monograph of the genus. Another book written at this time by a friend was of a taxonomic nature: Heber Drury's three-volume

Handbook of the Indian Flora. The first two volumes, of which Drury inscribed copies to Cleghorn, were printed in Trivandrum in 1864 and 1866 and the third in London in 1869 after they had both retired. The last contains a wistful letter from the author, one of only a handful of such tippings-in to books in the collection:

> … I suppose you are going to return to India or are you home for good? We are coming to stay with some friends in Linlithgow in the Autumn. I wish I thought we could meet. Sanderson I find still a satellite attendant on the Marquess of Tweeddale. Goodbye – I shall be rather curious to know if this ever reaches you & more particularly glad to know that you are well and thriving …

By this time (May 1869) Cleghorn had decided to stay in Britain, having left Madras for the last time in October 1867, with a European tour with Mabel *en route*.

EUROPEAN GRAND TOUR

Although lasting only a few months, traces of this European tour are to be found in Cleghorn's library. Some background reading in the form of Vivant Denon's *Travels through Sicily and Malta* could conceivably have belonged to his grandfather, as it dates from 1790 and is one of an extensive list of travel books published by the Perth publisher Robert Morison. The single work that must certainly represent a souvenir of the couple's three-month stay in Malta would appear, from its sheer fishy incongruity in the library, to be the sort of publication pressed upon travellers as a gift that it would seem rude to spurn while at the same time knowing that it will sit, forever unread, on a bookshelf – Gavinus Gulia's pamphlet *Tentamen Ichthyologiae Melitensis* (Malta, 1861). Another travel book relates to the next stage of the tour – the Comte de Marcellus' *Vingt Jours en Sicile* (1841), though as this was published in Paris it might have been acquired in retrospect on the next stage of the homeward journey. In any case Cleghorn clearly read it, as he marked passages on the Palermo botanic garden and on a spectacular blue lizard. Cleghorn's agricultural and botanical interests in Sicily, and some of the people he met, are represented by a *Florula Medica Siciliana* by Pietro Calcara (1851), and two agricultural works probably given to him by Giuseppe Inzenga. There is Inzenga's own description of his agricultural institute at Castelnuovo (1863), which Cleghorn visited, and a single part of the *Annali di Agricoltura*

Siciliana (1852). In Palermo Cleghorn was interested in the local seventeenth-century botanist Paulo Boccone, though there is no indication as to where or when he acquired that author's *Icones et Descriptiones Rariorum Plantarum Siciliae, Melitae, Galliae et Italiae* (which, under the name '*Fungus melitensis*', includes a description and illustrations of the strange parasitic flowering plant *Cynomorium*, in which Cleghorn took an interest). Its acquisition, however, is more likely to have occurred later, as the book was not published locally. Boccone left Sicily for a wandering life around Europe, and it was William Sherard who sponsored the publication of this small book in Oxford in 1674.

One of the specialities of the botanic garden in Naples was the introduction of exotic conifers and Giuseppe Pasquale, one of the assistants who showed Cleghorn around, presented him with a copy of a paper he had written on cones. The next stop was Florence, where he had written ahead and asked George Marsh to recommend some works relating to Italian forestry. Although none of the Italian forestry books described above bear inscriptions from this visit, these could represent gifts made by Marsh on this occasion, as certainly are some from a second visit by Cleghorn in 1875. In Florence Cleghorn also met Filippo Parlatore, who may have given him the (no longer extant) copy of his then recent monograph on cotton, with handsome folio plates, *Le Specie dei Cotoni* (1866), but in the Italian capital (as it then temporarily was) what particularly pleased him were the contents and affordability of the antiquarian bookshops. In the library are two early works, illustrated quarto catalogues of the Renaissance botanical gardens of Bologna and Florence, which could possibly represent souvenirs of the visit. Some of the plates in the *Istoria Botanica* of Giacomo Zanoni (Bologna, 1675) depict Indian plants, which Cleghorn has annotated with their Linnaean names (e.g. *Coix Lacryma* [*-Jobi*] and *Guilandina Bonduc*). The superintendent of the Florence botanic garden under the last two Medici Grand Dukes was Pier Antonio Micheli, known as the 'father of Mycology', though his *Catalogus Plantarum Horti Caesarei Florentini* was published posthumously, edited by J.T. Tozzetti, in 1748. While in Italy and France Cleghorn appears to have been thinking of the future, and plans for development of the Stravithie garden, which accounts for the presence in the library of obscure works such as Antonio Casabono's *Indicatore teorico-pratico d'orticoltura* (Genoa, 1862) and a little book by Marcellino and Giuseppe Roda on asparagus cultivation, *Coltivazione naturale e forzata degli Sparagi* (1868).

From Italy Hugh and Mabel continued northwards to Switzerland and France. One interesting book in the library relates to the former, Johann Jacob Scheuchzer's *Ouresiphoites Helveticus, sive Itinera Alpina Tria* (London, 1708) though, as it bears the bookplate of R.H. Alexander Bennet of Beckenham, it was probably acquired later in Britain. Described in this work are three journeys to investigate the artificial productions and natural history of

Switzerland. Indicative of the international reputation of its author, it was published by the Royal Society in London, illustrated with engravings of subjects including landscapes, mining activities, minerals and plants, each sponsored by a different FRS – the botanical ones include Sir Hans Sloane, James Petiver, Jacob Bobart and Edward Lhuyd. After Switzerland came Nancy, and Cleghorn's only visit to the famous École des Eaux et Forêts, then under the direction of Henri Nanquette, and it may have been here that he acquired the French forestry textbooks already discussed. Paris was the next stop, where Mabel consulted Marion Sims, an American gynaecologist recommended by Mrs Marsh, while Hugh visited the Jardin des Plantes, Villmorin the seed-merchant, and several bookshops. As in Italy, his thoughts were by now clearly looking towards retirement and Stravithie, as shown by two recently published horticultural works probably bought in Paris at this time, perhaps at F. Savy, a bookseller in the rue Hautefeuille, whom he wrote of visiting – an *Essai sur l'entomolgie horticole* by J.A. Boisduval (1867), and Alphonse Breuil's *Instruction élementaire sur la conduite des arbres frutiers* (seventh edition, 1868). Judging by a group of books, all published by the firm the previous year (1867), another Paris bookseller whom Cleghorn appears to have visited was Jules Rothschild in the rue de St André-des-Arts. Rothschild was bookseller to the Société Botanique de France but also specialised in arboriculture, and all four of the books purchased were pocket-sized forestry manuals: Charles de Kirwan's two-volume work on indigenous and exotic conifers, Eugène Robert's on the insect pests of plantations, Alfred Puton's on forest management, and one by the Comte Des Cars on pruning. This last, titled *Les élagage des arbres*, went into several French and German editions, and was illustrated in an unusual manner with plates showing the silhouettes of trees with the branches that were to be pruned printed in red, and the desired final tree-profiles punched out from stiff, card overlays. It was probably also in Paris that Cleghorn bought his copy of the up-to-date French forest laws, Charles Jacquot's *Les Codes de la législation forestière* (1866). Such forestry works would be relevant for the continued involvement he probably already intended to maintain with the India Office, but at this point he could only have suspected that this would concern the selection of students to be trained, largely at Nancy, prior to careers in the Indian forest service.

India office and late forestry work

During the 1870s and '80s Cleghorn continued to accumulate books on a substantial scale, at about the same rate as he had in India,[54] resulting in what may have been the most extensive private forest library in Scotland: it must certainly have been unique in its range, and its strengths in Indian and European material. Given the paucity of his publications from this period it is hard to say how, or to what extent, Cleghorn used this outstanding resource, but he certainly drew on it for the two articles, on Forestry and on Arboriculture, he contributed to the great Ninth Edition of the *Encyclopaedia Britannica*,[55] and for the evidence he gave in 1885 to Sir John Lubbock's Select Committee on the training of foresters in Britain. Given his readiness to open his library to a group of forestry-students from Nancy, refugees from the Franco-Prussian War in 1870 (among whom was James Sykes Gamble, who became one of the leading Indian foresters of the next generation), it is likely that he made it available to other interested groups or individuals. The relative remoteness of Stravithie must have limited this, which is doubtless one of the reasons he ensured that its future existence would be in the Scottish capital.

There are simply too many books, periodicals and Government of India publications from this period in Cleghorn's library to give more than a taste of their range. By this time Brandis's vision for a national forest service was in full swing, achieved by means of training a small number of élite foresters in Europe, while concurrently fostering in India a corporate professional spirit by means that included conferences and publications and, from 1878, the establishment, at Dehra Dun under Frederick Bailey, of a training school for more junior employees. Cleghorn was closely involved in the European part of this system, for which he personally interviewed every candidate, and was kept abreast with the Indian end of operations through the resulting publications – such as the prolific works of Brandis and the reports of the forestry conferences at Allahabad (1874) and Simla (1875); he also subscribed to the service's newly established professional journal, *The Indian Forester*, from its first volume in 1876. From 1880 onwards he also received large numbers of Government of India reports, covering the whole of the subcontinent from Madras to Baroda and Assam – not only those relating to the Forest Department and the Public Works Department (under whose auspices forestry came while Cleghorn was still in India), but 'Selections' on particular topics from those of the Home and Foreign Departments. These were presumably donations from the Government and it is hard to imagine that Cleghorn would ever have read most of them. He did, however, read a handsomely bound, gold-tooled, set of the *Parliamentary Papers* on Indian forestry, published by the House of Commons in 1871, which cover the period of his national work in the 1860s, in which are included many of his own reports and memoranda (including some that had not been reprinted in his own *Forests of the Punjab*) (Plate 8.iv).

Brandis had interests beyond the science of forestry and, given the botanical training of his youth, he was also interested in the taxonomy of trees. It fell to him to complete the work of the Punjab forester John Lindsay Stewart (a medical graduate of Glasgow, who died at Dalhousie in 1873) and, by means of a sabbatical at Kew, to publish Stewart's *Forest Flora of North-West and Central India* (1874), together with a companion volume of exquisitely clear lithographs by John Nugent Fitch. Cleghorn had repeatedly pressed the authorities for funds for the publication of this work, as he had while in India for the continuation of Joseph Hooker's encyclopaedic work on the plants of the Subcontinent. Though *Flora Indica* was not continued, it must have given Cleghorn immense pleasure when in 1894 he received the penultimate, sixth volume of the *Flora of British India* (the last would not come out until 1897, two years after his death).[56] A regional Indian floristic work from this period is J.E.T. Aitchison's *Catalogue of the Plants of the Punjab and Sindh* (London, 1869), the work of an Indian surgeon who was also a connection-by-marriage of Mabel Cleghorn. Brandis wanted to publicise his Indian achievements internationally, as part of which an extensive set of samples of Indian timbers was sent to the 1878 Paris Exhibition. It was Cleghorn's protégé J.S. Gamble who curated this collection, leading to Gamble's authorship of his outstanding *Manual of Indian Timbers* (1881), which must have given Cleghorn a glow of satisfaction when he received a copy (though, disappointingly, neither of his two extant copies bears a dedicatory inscription, and Cleghorn would not live to see the later, greatly expanded editions).

What of Europe? The stream of text-books from Nancy continued with works by Gustave Bagneris, Lucien Boppe, Eugène Reuss and Eugène Bartet, the last three of whom Cleghorn met on an excursion made by them in 1881 to investigate the state of British forests. But Cleghorn also acquired books on European forests and their management, including works by two forest officers who had returned from India and were well known to him – George Falconer Pearson and Inches Campbell-Walker. However, the most prolific author of such works, sharing Cleghorn's concern to establish a forest school in Britain, was the Rev Dr John Croumbie Brown. Cleghorn owned Brown's regional works on English, Finnish and Norwegian forests, his work on *Reboisement in France* (1876), his *Forests and Moisture* (1887) and *Hydrology of South Africa* (1875) – and even a rare pamphlet on *Welwitschia mirabilis* dating from Brown's days as Colonial Botanist at the Cape of Good Hope. But as none of these is inscribed it suggests that the pair were not close, despite the apparent similarity of their interests and religious outlook. Two other foresters, Wilhelm Schlich and Frederick Bailey, returned from Indian careers to become actively involved in forest education when, belatedly, it became established in Britain. The first European-trained foresters taken to India by Brandis in 1867 had been Schlich and Berthold Ribbentrop, and it was Schlich who in 1885 started the forest school at Cooper's Hill, Surrey. Cleghorn owned the first three volumes of Schlich's comprehensive *Manual of Forestry* (1889–95) which, unlike the European text-books, and for the first time, incorporated the results of Indian practical experience. Cleghorn also owned three works by Ribbentrop – one on Oudh, and two editions of one on the Punjab. Closer to home was Bailey's appointment to the forest lectureship at Edinburgh in

1892, in which Cleghorn had taken a great interest and personally contributed £1,000. It is therefore hardly surprising that Bailey's works on French and Hungarian forests were in Cleghorn's library, though these copies are no longer extant – Bailey's own copies of his works appear to have been kept at RBGE in preference.

Cleghorn's forestry interests were not restricted to Europe and India, and he also owned works relating to Australia and North America, including ones by Charles Sprague Sargent among the latter. The Australian interest had been present since Indian days – the introduction of eucalyptus and acacias to the Nilgiris as quick-growing fuel crops – and this interest continued, as represented by Ferdinand von Mueller's finely illustrated *Report on the Forest Resources of Western Australia* (1879). Showing how wide was the phenomenon of eucalyptus-worship, Cleghorn also had a copy of Ellwood Cooper's *Forest Culture and Eucalyptus Trees* published in San Francisco (1876), in which he made marginal marks against references to G.P. Marsh and to his own Punjab reports.

Another significant activity of his later years was Cleghorn's involvement with the ground-breaking International Forestry Exhibition held in Edinburgh in 1884. This is represented in his library by the exhibition's anonymous, and doubtless multi-authored, *Official Catalogue*; by William K. Rose's *Handguide*; and by a volume of related prize essays on *Forestry and Forest Products* edited by John Rattray and Hugh Mill (1885). By this date an interest in the origins of forest conservancy in India was being taken, as expressed by Sir George Birdwood in the introduction to the *Catalogue of the Indian Exhibit*,[57] written at the request of Colonel James Michael, a colleague of Cleghorn in his early Madras days. That there was interest in such matters, and not only in Britain, is shown by another book in the library, published in Madras in 1884. *Forestry in Southern India* is by another of Cleghorn's early colleagues Henry Rhodes Morgan, edited by John Shortt, one of the most successful alumni of the Madras Medical School. One can but regret that in old age Cleghorn himself made no contribution to this historical literature.

LAIRD OF STRAVITHIE

The great love of his retirement, the fulfilment of his grandfather's aspirations, was Cleghorn's ability, through conspicuous thrift, to occupy and improve the position of Laird of Stravithie. This period is richly represented in his extant library with books concerning agriculture and horticulture. The agricultural books include works from a previous generation, perhaps already at Stravithie, such as *Baxter's Agricultural and Horticultural Gleaner* (1836) and Edward

Lance's *Cottage Farmer* inspired by the Enlightenment principles of Henry Home, Lord Kames.[58] Also from an earlier period is the Rev. John Walker's *Essays on Natural History and Rural Economy* (1812), but Cleghorn must have purchased for himself a more up-to-date work in this genre, the anonymous *Gardener's and Farmer's Reason Why* (1860). There are also works on agriculture relating to what might be called the 'hardware' and 'software' of farming – of the former is John Ewart's *Land Drainer's Calculator* (1862), and of the latter two editions of William Curtis's *Practical Observations on British Grasses* (1805, 1824) and two of the *Agrostographia* (1853, 1877) published by the Edinburgh seed-merchant firm of Peter Lawson & Co.

A group of books relates to Cleghorn's responsibility to his tenantry – both the care of their homes and the land they farmed on his behalf, but also the legal framework under which this operated. Much loved as a laird as he appears to have been, this was a hierarchical world, and one in which Cleghorn as a magistrate was greatly concerned with the upholding of the law on matters such as poaching. In this context it was enlightening when examining his copy of the *Farmer's Lawyer* of 1841 (by an anonymous Writer to the Signet, possibly Thomas Gordon, dedicated to the 8th Marquess of Tweeddale) to find tipped into it a clipping from the *Gardeners' Chronicle* on leases, and more pointedly one from an un-named newspaper ominously entitled 'What gamekeepers may do to trespassers'. This, however, is the only strictly legal book and more numerous are titles that perhaps suggest a more caring side to Cleghorn's lairdly responsibilities, such as Robert Skirving's *Landlords and Labourers* (Edinburgh, 1862), Edward Smith's *The Peasant's Home* (1876) and the Earl of Onslow's *Landlords and Allotments* (1886). However, the passages of T.E. Kebbel's *The Agricultural Labourer* (1870) that he has marked are to be found in the chapter 'On hiring'. These relate to the undesirability of small farms though 'the hope of obtaining them tends to thrift, sobriety and steadiness', and that hiring labourers weekly and providing for their boarding 'checks early marriages, and prevents a redundant population, though at a considerable cost to morality'! Cleghorn's 'county duties' are represented in his library by Henry Burdett's 1877 work on *The Cottage Hospital, its Origin, Progress, Management and Work, with an Alphabetical List of every Cottage Hospital at present opened, and a Chapter on Hospitalism in Cottage Hospital Practice.*

At Stravithie the Cleghorns developed a garden, even if of a rather rudimentary nature: the major elements were terraced lawns with specimen trees, and a walled, kitchen garden/orchard, though Mabel was surely allowed some flowerbeds near the mansion, which would account for the presence in the library of a small pamphlet by Joseph Dale *On the Chrysanthemum*. In the library were copies of many of the classic works of horticulture, some of which (such as those by Evelyn and Dillenius) have been discussed in the context of his Madras activities, but there were other early works that may have been at

Stravithie since his grandfather's time – such as William Marshall's *Planting and Ornamental Gardening* (1785) and *Planting and Rural Ornament* (1796). The grandson, however, kept up to date with books such as John Lindley's *Theory and Practice of Horticulture* (1855), George Glenny's *Handbook to the Flower Garden and Greenhouse* (1861) and William Robinson's *Gleanings from French Gardens* (1868). Appealing to Cleghorn's devotion to parsimony (if somewhat ironic for someone who owned a thousand-acre estate, and left shares worth £39,000) is his copy of Samuel Wood's *Multum-in-Parvo Gardening* (1877), subtitled: 'How to make One Acre of Land produce £620 a year, by the cultivation of fruit and vegetables; also How to Grow Flowers in Three Glass Houses, so as to realise £176 per annum in clear profit'.

With specific interests in trees – willows to plant along the burns and in hedgerows, conifers for the lawns, and fruit trees for the walled-garden – these are all well represented. On sallows he had William Scaling's *The Salix or Willow*, and on conifers he had bought Kirwan's small two-volume work in Paris, and from India he had brought back Lord William Hay's gift of Standish and Noble's *Practical Hints*. Later he would acquire four more comprehensive works: the *Pinaceae ... a Handbook of the Firs and Pines* (1866) by John Nelson (publishing under the pseudonym 'Johannes Senilis'), and the *Synopsis of the Coniferous Plants Grown in Great Britain* (1850), by Joseph Knight and Thomas Perry, based on trees sold at their Exotic Nursery at Chelsea. This nursery was taken over by James Veitch, who also specialised (among much else) in conifers, resulting in his *Manual of the Coniferae* (1881) which Cleghorn also owned. The fourth conifer book was more taxonomic, the Austrian Stephan Endlicher's *Synopsis Coniferarum* (1847), which the Laird annotated with botanical synonyms. Orchards and fruit trees also figure largely among the horticultural books and, like those on general gardening, include a mixture of the old and the new – for example, Ralph Austen's *A Treatise of Fruit Trees* (Oxford, 1665), and one acquired in what was surely a fit of optimism, the *Manuale del fruitticoltore italiano* (1874) by the brothers Roda. Judging from four works in the library, and more realistically given the climate of Fife, Cleghorn in his orchard in the walled garden appears to have decided to concentrate on apples, as represented by Henry Phillips' *Pomarium Britannicum* (1820), Robert Hogg's *British Pomology* (1831), John Lindley's three-volume *Pomologia Britannica* and Archibald Farquharson Barron's *British Apples* (1884).

The recent discovery of his pamphlet collection has provided tangible links to several other aspects of Cleghorn's later life as a scholar-laird. In this period he took an active role in several Edinburgh-based Scottish societies connected with botany and forestry. One of the duties of the president of the Botanical Society of Edinburgh was to give an annual address and in 1869 Cleghorn used this as an opportunity to review British botanical research undertaken during the course of the year. This explains the presence of a series of six reprints on fossil botany that he had requested from William Carruthers, Keeper of Botany at the British Museum (Natural History), which came with a covering letter from Henry Trimen explaining that their author was prevented from sending them himself due to a whitlow on his right hand. More surprisingly, in 1885 and 1887, Cleghorn was a member of a British Association for the Advancement of Science (BAAS) committee on fisheries, which explains the presence of two reprints on a disease of the salmon (Stirling, 1879/80; Simpson, 1884). As a philanthropist Cleghorn donated £1,000 to each of his old universities – to St Andrews for the establishment of a botanical lectureship or chair, and to Edinburgh for one in forestry. At St Andrews John Hardie Wilson, had already been lecturing on botany and started a botanic garden (for which Cleghorn had donated plants and attended the opening), so it is touching to find copies of two of Wilson's earliest papers inscribed to one whom he must have regarded as a patron.

OTHER LIBRARY TREASURES

This biographical approach to bibliography has allowed mention of only a small proportion of the works in Cleghorn's library and has required the omission of some extremely interesting items. Of those that have not fitted into the scheme so far, it is possible to cite only a further handful, of interest for a variety of reasons, including provenance – one of his three sixteenth-century titles, two of the 18 works dating from the seventeenth century, one of 42 from the eighteenth, two nineteenth-century works, ending with an extremely important bound, two-volume set of original drawings of 'Trees & Plants of Malabar'.

The *Materia Medica* of Dioscorides, a first-century Greek doctor who worked in the Roman army, had a profound, if not always a positive, influence on the history of botany – some of the problems arose from attempts to equate Mediterranean plants (those known to Dioscorides) with those of northern Europe (where many of the significant Renaissance botanists worked). Many authors had tried to work out the identity of Dioscorides' plants but the *Commentarii in Libros Sex Pedanii Dioscoridis de Materia Medica* of the sixteenth-century Italian botanist Pietro Andrea Mattioli went much further, including descriptions and handsome woodcut illustrations of all the plants known to him. Cleghorn had a copy of one of the finest folio editions of Mattioli, published in Venice in 1560 by Vincenzo Valgrisi (Plate 7.vi). When looking at the title page of this book, Valgrisi's typographic symbol, a serpent twined around a Tau cross, the base of which is clasped by a pair of hands each emerging from a billowing cloud, evoked a sense of *dèja vu* from my travels in southern India in search of Cleghorn and his predecessor Wight. In the Travancore royal family's wooden Padmanabhapuram Palace on the Malabar Coast is a remarkable carved bed, given to the raja of the day by Hendrik van Rheede on behalf of the Dutch East India Company, possibly in 1665. The bed is said to be made of 16 different timbers, each with an ayurvedic property, and is today referred to as a 'medicinal' bed. The profuse carving on the head- and foot-boards, almost certainly the work of an indigenous craftsman, was clearly inspired by western book illustrations but, with a medical subtext in mind, what might initially be taken as a staff of Aesculapius at the centre of the foot-board proves to be none other than Valgrisi's Tau cross.[59] Rheede's *Hortus Malabaricus* was based on a precursor, a manuscript 'Viridarium Orientale' by Father Matthew of St Joseph (c. 1617–1691), a discalced Carmelite Friar who had studied medicine in Naples. Is it going too far to imagine that he might have taken a copy of this edition of Mattioli with him to India, which was then used as a model for the wood carvers? It is unlikely that Cleghorn ever saw the bed, but he was certainly interested in the *Hortus Malabaricus*; much further work requires to be done on this remarkable piece of furniture and its iconography, but it certainly represents a fascinating hybridity of culture and the connections that can sometimes be made (not least in India) between apparently diverse subjects such as bibliography, botany and the applied arts.

The greatest European botanist of the sixteenth century was, arguably, Carolus Clusius (1526–1609) who in 1593 went to work in Leiden, where he ended his career as superintendent of the Hortus Botanicus. It was in Leiden in 1605 that Francis van Ravelingen (one of Plantin's sons-in-law) published, in folio, the second part of Clusius's collected works, the *Exoticorum Libri Decem*. This must have been of particular interest to Cleghorn as among much original material (relating to animals as well as plants), it includes Clusius's translations of the classical works on Indian botany by Garcia da Orta and Cristobal Acosta. Cleghorn's copy must have been obtained from the London antiquarian book trade, as it is stamped 'Museum Britannicum 1831 duplicate for sale' and it may have been this version of Orta's *Aromatum et Simplicium Aliquot* that he read on the ship *Trafalgar* in 1851, when returning to India from his first sick-leave.[60]

The *Flora seu de Florum Cultura, Libri IV*, by the Jesuit botanist and Hebrew scholar Giovanni Battista Ferrari was first published in Rome in 1633. A handsome quarto on gardening and the plants in the garden of the author's patron Cardinal Francesco Barberini, its scientific significance lies in one of its plates, the first illustration of the seed of a plant (*Hibiscus mutabilis*) drawn with the help of a microscope.[61] Through his patron, Ferrari was in the circle of Cassiano dal Pozzo and the Academia dei Lincei, which accounts for the quality of the illustrations commissioned for the book from major artists such as Pietro da Cortona and Guido Reni, engraved by Johann Friedrich Greuter and Cornelis Bloemart. Cleghorn had a copy of the 1646 Amsterdam edition of *Flora* edited by Bernhard Rottendorf. The greatest interest of his copy, however, lies in its provenance: it bears the bookplate of the Earl of Moira and is signed on the contents page by 'Sr. John Rawdon' (Plate 13.ii). This signature must date between 1724 and 1750, when Rawdon held a baronetcy inherited from his father, but before he was created successively Lord Rawdon, then first Earl of Moira. Rawdon, his (eponymous) father, and his grandfather all had strong horticultural interests. The grandfather, Sir Arthur (the second baronet and a friend of Sir Hans Sloane), had developed renowned gardens at the family's Ulster seat of Moira, Co. Down. The book, however, probably travelled to India in the baggage of the second Earl of Moira, Francis Rawdon-Hastings, later the first Marquess of Hastings, a notable Governor-General of India (1813–23), whose work on the Plantation Committee in Bengal Cleghorn had commended in his 1851 British Association report on deforestation. In Calcutta, with his Scottish wife the Countess of Loudon, Hastings had also been a keen supporter of botany through the Agri-Horticultural Society of India. It seems possible that his volume escaped from Hastings's library in Calcutta, entered the second-hand book trade, to be acquired forty years later by Cleghorn. One weeps, however, to see what happened to it after reaching RBGE: rebound in 1962 in the cheapest and nastiest buckram imaginable (its cream colour surely explicable only as a crude parody of a vellum original), the beautiful plates trimmed to within millimetres of their lives.

The history of natural classification of plants owes much to the Jussieu family and the Jardin des Plantes in Paris, but its pre-history might be said to go back to Joseph Pitton de Tournefort. Tournefort's classification of flowering plants was not a natural one, but his use of floral characters to define genera was influential, and many of his genera were maintained even in Linnaeus's artificial system. His great work, with fine illustrations of floral parts by Claude Aubriet, was first published in French, and later in Latin as the *Insitutio Rei Herbariae*. Cleghorn owned a handsome three-volume, quarto edition posthumously edited by Tournefort's successor at the Jardin des Plantes, Antoine de Jussieu (Paris, 1719). But it is the provenance of these volumes that is of interest, as they bear the armorial bookplate of 'William Morehead' (Plate 5.iv), almost certainly the Madras civil servant William Ambrose Morehead (1805–1863), with whom Cleghorn worked on the committee of the 1855 Madras Exhibition. Morehead came from a similar Scottish background to Cleghorn's, and when Morehead acted as Governor of Madras, during two inter-regnums, in 1860 and 1860/1, he was the younger man's ultimate boss. The Moreheads owned the bizarrely named estate of Herbertshire, near Falkirk; William's maternal grandfather, Charles Wilson as professor of Church History at St Andrews had been a colleague of Hugh Cleghorn senior, and William's brother Charles was a Bombay surgeon.[62] Due to ill-health Morehead retired to Edinburgh where he died in 1863, commemorated by a large Celtic cross of red granite in the Dean Cemetery and a stained glass window in the former Episcopal church of Holy Trinity, Dean Bridge (his father had been Dean of the Diocese of Edinburgh). It is not know where Cleghorn acquired the volumes: it could have been either in Madras or, perhaps, much later in an Edinburgh bookshop.

The last of the books with interesting provenances are two titles sent by Sir William Hooker from Glasgow to the intrepid botanist Anna Maria Walker in Ceylon, with the aim of inspiring her to take an interest in cryptogams. The copy of Hooker's own two-volume *Musci Exotici* (London, 1818–20), which she received in August 1834, is the large-paper edition with hand-coloured plates, engraved by William Edwards (who also worked on Roxburgh's *Plants of the Coast of Coromandel*), based on Hooker's own drawings. The volumes bear the bookplate of her husband Colonel George Warren Walker, and manuscript indexes in his or her hand. The second work is the *Genera Filicum* (London, 1838–42), an incomplete copy with the first 100 (of 120) plates, many of which are based on exquisite drawings by Francis Bauer, lithographed in Glasgow (some on stone, others on zinc) by Allan & Ferguson. The volume is inscribed by Mrs Walker 'A. W[arren] Walker from Sir W.J. Hooker'. After the death of her husband Anna Maria stayed on in India; she died in Mangalore in 1852, where her son the engineer George Warren Walker lived, as did her daughter Selina who was married to the judge Findlay Anderson (who at one point was on the committee of the Madras Agri-Horticultural Society with Cleghorn). After his mother's death her son sent the copy of *Genera Filicum* to Madras adding the dedication 'Dr Hugh Cleghorn with kind regards from George Warren Walker 1853' along with a (regrettably no longer extant) volume of correspondence between his 'good old mother' and Cleghorn's own old teachers Robert Graham and Robert Christison relating to gamboge; doubtless the volumes of *Musci Exotici* accompanied these. It is fascinating to reflect on the journeys of these much-travelled volumes: from Glasgow to Ceylon; on Mrs Walker's travels around India, including Meerut in the north, then south to Mangalore; and, after her death, to Madras; followed by Cleghorn's own travels to northern India; only to end up at Stravithie, just over a mile from Mrs Walker's birthplace of Kinaldy.

The final treasure of Cleghorn's library to be described is a set of original drawings of 'Trees and Plants of Malabar', bound in two volumes, at EUL.[63] These contain 280 plates of graphite drawings (only the first few are coloured), showing the plant habit accompanied by minute floral dissections and, despite the very unusual medium, are clearly the work of an Indian artist, with the plant names given in Tamil script and Roman transliteration. These volumes make a remarkable connection with Cleghorn family history as they bear the armorial bookplate of Alexander Walker of Bowland, who in the late 1770s had been a pupil of the elder Cleghorn at St Andrews University. The presence of a cutting from a late nineteenth-century antiquarian bookseller's catalogue shows, however, that these were almost certainly purchased (for 16 shillings) by the younger Hugh Cleghorn. How they became separated from the rest of Walker's library is unknown, and the related text for the first 140 plates is with Walker's rich collection of manuscripts in the National Library of Scotland, labelled 'Arbores et Herbae Malabaricae vol 1'.[64] This manuscript contains a preface (transcribed much later, in 1826, when Walker was Governor of St Helena), with an explanation of how Walker came to commission the drawings. In this he is at pains to establish the drawings' originality: that they were not made in imitation of Rheede's work, which he states scarcely to have been aware of when he commissioned them from a native artist. He was equally keen to establish their authenticity, by stating that they were made 'in my presence' and that the accompanying information was made with the 'assistance of some intelligent natives' – that is, it was a project extremely similar to, but thought up independently of, and a century later, than Rheede's. This must have been in the 1790s, when Walker was stationed in Malabar, at the very time he was corresponding with the elder Hugh Cleghorn, then in India on the expedition that led to his acquisition of Ceylon for Britain. Later on Walker did, however, become seriously interested in the *Hortus Malabaricus*, as in the same collection is his own manuscript English translation of Rheede's important Latin preface to the third volume of that great work.

ENDNOTES

1. Noltie, 2016a.

2. Noltie, 2016b.

3. 1000 acres of land (including numerous farms, and the fully furnished Stravithie House), with almost £40,000 in moveable assets (shares, etc.).

4. *Transactions & Proceedings of the Botanical Society of Edinburgh* 19: 41. 1891.

5. Shelf List in the Library Accessions Register (Guard Book), copy kindly provided by Dr Joseph Marshall.

6. Anon, 1918–23.

7. Anon, 1889.

8. Anon, 1897.

9. Museum of Science & Art, Library Accession Book, 1895, copy kindly provided by Mark Glancy.

10. http://www.bonhams.com/auctions/15132, consulted 8 May 2015.

11. Grant, 2008.

12. RBGE BC 4/179 HC to JHB 26 Jan 1856.

13. Clark, 1992.

14. One of the few known for certain is John Hill's *Review of the Works of the Royal Society of London*, 1751 – Grant, 2008, subsequently, after an Antipodean sojourn, acquired in 2016 by the author.

15. Her first husband, Charles Hope-Weir, was a third-cousin of John Hope; she undertook serious botany in South Africa and, after her second marriage, in Bengal where she appears to have had links with two of Hope's pupils, James Kerr and James Robertson.

16. Cleghorn's copy, of the second edition, bears a dedication from Knight to Alexander Dauney, professor of Civil Law at King's College, Aberdeen.

17. The first botanical illustrations to be reproduced in Scotland by lithography; however, the fact that Cleghorn's copy has manuscript corrections in Hooker's hand suggests a later date of acquisition: it seems unlikely that there would have been a personal connection while Cleghorn was an undergraduate.

18. I am grateful to Graham Bradshaw for information about this.

19. A keen botanist whose daughter Catherine Heriot Maitland was married to Sir David Brewster's son James – in the Brewster Album of calotypes are photographs of Heriot, as well as of the young Cleghorn – see Smith, 1990.

20. RBGKew HC f. 111 HC to JSH 5 Dec 1850.

21. Cleghorn's complete set was sold by RBGE in the late 1980s, and was offered for sale on the internet by a Low Countries book dealer for many years in the late 'noughties'.

22. MacDonell was evidently a friend of Cleghorn's father Peter, and a supporter of Cleghorn in his early Indian days – see StA CP 2/8/20 PC to HC 1 Jul 1845.

23. The Vepery Mission in Madras was run by the SPCK; Rottler transferred to it from Tranquebar in 1803 and died there in 1836, where he is buried in the mission church of St Mathias.

24. At this point Harvey was working as a botanist in Dublin, but from 1836 to 1842 he had been Colonial Treasurer at the Cape. Cleghorn continued to take an interest in Harvey later obtaining a copy of his *Memoirs* (1869) and the three-volume *Flora Capensis* of Harvey and Sonder (1859–65).

25. Named by George Bentham for her brother-in-law, Dr George Leith Roupell.

26. Advertisement *Musical Times* 3: 184, 1849.

27. Cleghorn, 1856h.

28. StA CP 9/4/7(iii).

29. Grant, 2008, now in the author's collection.

30. StA CP 9/4/6(ii).

31. Its three volumes are bound as one, the colouring is slightly crude, and it bears a surprising Karlsruhe bookseller's label.

32. Cleghorn, 1856l.

33. Many of Horsefield's drawings, specimens and nature prints still await study in the collections of Kew and the Natural History Museum, London.

34. I am grateful to David Mabberley for drawing Kippist's letter to my attention; it is now stored as EUL Gen 1729-1732.

35. She later divorced her bankrupt husband Rawack, returned to Vienna, and married the pianist and editor Julius Epstein, friend of Brahms and mentor of Mahler.

36. StA CP 9/4.

37. See KDC 82/256 HC to Thistleton-Dyer 5 Jan 1894.

38. The RBGE copy of *Hortus Madraspatensis* is one presented by Cleghorn to his friend George Lawson, at one point a teaching assistant to J.H. Balfour.

39. Cleghorn had paid Pamplin 7/6 for these in 1859 – StA CP 9/4/9(ii).

40. The manuscript of the paper must have been kicking around in Madras for some time, as Ingledew had retired in 1821 – Crawford 1930.

41. Robert Flower Riddell, c. 1798–1866, who had a medical degree from Glasgow had worked in Hyderabad, and was also the author of one of the first Anglo-Indian Cookery books.

42. RBGE BC 4/176 HC to JHB 13 Oct 1855.

43. Curiously the extant set is one obtained from John Rohde.

44. Cleghorn, 1861a, p. 21.

45. Cleghorn, 1861a.

46. Much later on, knighted and as a Lieutenant General, Torrens was one of the old India hands who would end up as a Governor of Malta.

47. The modern spelling.

48. Woodward & Grout, 2004.

49. Cleghorn, 1862d.

50. Cleghorn, 1862c.

51. Its place of publication by Cleghorn has not yet been traced.

52. According to Lowenthal 2003: 367, Yule had a hand in the edition of excerpts from *Man and Nature* for Indian foresters published in Madras in 1882, but the basis of this assertion is not known and the work came out under the authorship of the Madras civil servant Andrew John Stuart.

53. Peter Stark Lumsden (1829–1910), a soldier, had been based on the NW Frontier 1852–7.

54. Judging from dates of publication, which seems reasonable for books that were acquired new, there are 96 titles from the 1850s, 104 from the 1860s, 96 from the 1870s and 77 from the 1880s.

55. Cleghorn, 1875d, 1879.

56. In 1871 Hooker had clearly asked Cleghorn if he might contribute to the work, but the reply was that other matters 'for some years have interrupted Botanical pursuits and habits of thought – so that with all the will, I would find it difficult to work steadily at Descriptive Botany' KDC 157/209 HC to JDH 20 Jan 1871. Cleghorn pushed Hooker's case for financial support for what was still being called 'Flora Indica' with M.E. Grant-Duff at the India Office in 1871 – see KDC 157/210 HC to JDH 27 Mar 1871.

57. Strangely this was not among the material left to the Museum or Edinburgh, though Cleghorn must certainly have had a copy.

58. Hugh Cleghorn senior had a copy of Lord Kames's *Gentleman Farmer* of 1802 in his library – Grant, 2008.

59. I am indebted to Michael Bury for discussions on this subject.

60. RBGE HC to JHB 12 xii 1851.

61. See Freedberg, 2002.

62. Morehead's maternal grandmother's first cousin was George Bogle, the Tibetan traveller whose works were edited by Clements Markham.

63. EUL Mss Gen 2018/9.

64. NLS Ms 13817.

PLATE I

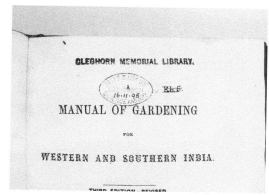

ii.

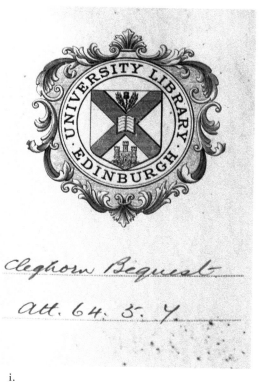

i.

PLATE 2

i.

ii.

iii.

PLATE 3

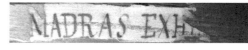

PLATE 4

iii.

ii.

i.

iv.

v.

PLATE 5

i.

iv.

iii.

ii.

PLATE 6

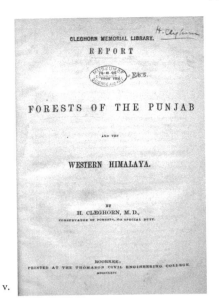

v.

vi.

ii.

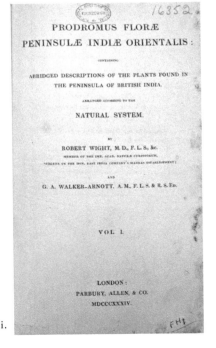

i.

iv.

iii.

PLATE 7

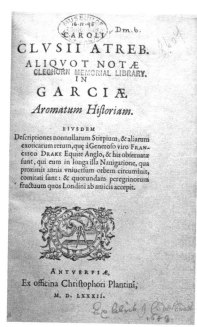

CAROLI
CLVSII ATREB.
ALIQVOT NOTÆ
IN
GARCIÆ
Aromatum Historiam.

EIVSDEM

Descriptiones nonnullarum Stirpium, & aliarum exoticarum rerum, quæ à Generoso viro FRANCISCO DRAKE Equite Anglo, & his observatæ sunt, qui eum in longa illa Nauigatione, qua proximis annis vniuersum orbem circumiuit, comitati sunt: & quorundam peregrinorum fructuum quos Londini ab amicis accepit.

ANTVERPIÆ,
Ex officina Christophori Plantini,
M. D. LXXXII.

iv.

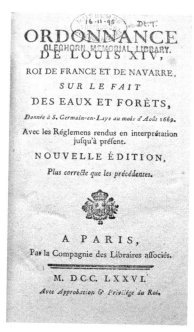

ORDONNANCE
DE LOUIS XIV,
ROI DE FRANCE ET DE NAVARRE,
SUR LE FAIT
DES EAUX ET FORÊTS,
Donnée à S. Germain-en-Laye au mois d'Août 1669.

Avec les Réglemens rendus en interprétation jusqu'à présent.

NOUVELLE ÉDITION,
Plus correcte que les précédentes.

A PARIS,
Par la Compagnie des Libraires associés.

M. DCC. LXXVI.
Avec Approbation & Privilège du Roi.

v.

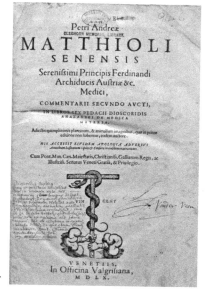

Petri Andreæ
MATTHIOLI
SENENSIS
Serenissimi Principis Ferdinandi
Archiducis Austriæ &c.
Medici,
COMMENTARII SECVNDO AVCTI,
IN LIBROS SEX PEDACII DIOSCORIDIS
ANAZARBEI DE MEDICA
MATERIA.

Adiectis quamplurimis plantarum, & animalium imaginibus, quæ in priore editione non habentur, eodem auctore.

HIS ACCESSIT EIVSDEM APOLOGIA ADVERSVS
Amathum Lusitanum: quin & Censura in eiusdem enarrationes.

Cum Pont. Max. Cæs. Maiestatis, Christianiss. Galliarum Regis, ac Illustriss. Senatus Veneti Gratia, & Priuilegio.

VENETIIS,
In Officina Valgrisiana,
M D L X.

vi.

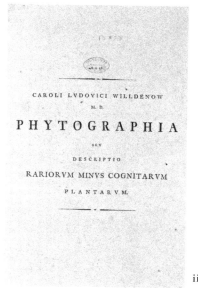

CAROLI LVDOVICI WILLDENOW
M. D.

PHYTOGRAPHIA
SEV
DESCRIPTIO
RARIORVM MINVS COGNITARVM
PLANTARVM.

ii.

iii.

i.

PLATE 8

iv.

v.

iii.

i.

ii.

PLATE 9

KEW GARDENS;

A POPULAR GUIDE

TO THE

ROYAL BOTANIC GARDENS OF KEW;

BY

SIR W. J. HOOKER,

K.H. D.C.L. F.R.A. & L.S.

&c. &c.

Director.

"Soft roll your incense, *Herbs* and *Fruits* and *Flowers*,
In mingled clouds, to Him, whose sun exalts,
Whose breath perfumes you, and whose pencil paints."

LONDON:

PRINTED FOR

LONGMAN, BROWN, GREEN, AND LONGMANS,

PATERNOSTER-ROW.

1847.

i.

ii.

Dawson Turner Esq
July 14 1847

KEW GARDENS.

iii.

A

TREATISE

ON

The MANNER of Raising

FOREST TREES, &c.

In a Letter from the Right Honourable,
The Earl of —— to his Grandson.

To which are added,

TWO MEMOIRS; the one on Preserving
and Repairing FORESTS; The other
on the Culture of FORESTS.
Both translated from the FRENCH of
M. DE BUFFON of the Royal
Academy at Paris.

Thomas Hamilton, 6th Earl of Haddington

EDINBURGH:

Printed for G. HAMILTON and J. BALFOUR.

M,DCC,LXI.

v.

Dunse July 30. 1768

Mr Ainslies Complements to Mr Thos with a Coppy of the Late Earle of Haddinton's Treaties on Forest Trees which is the Shortest and Best on the Subject, in proof of which the author had more Success that way than any other in Britain — and hope the knowledge proceeding from the Reading of this will be a Mean of beautifying part of the waste ground of Teviotdale —

v.

PLATE 10

vi.

LEONARDI PLUKENETII

PHYTOGRAPHIA

Sive

Stirpium Illustriorum, & minus cognitarum

ICONES.

TABULIS ÆNEIS,

Summâ diligentiâ elaboratæ,
Quarum unaquæq; Titulis descriptorys
& Notis Suis propriis, & Characteristicis
desumptis, insignita, ab usus ejusdem
Sortis facilè discriminatur.

PARS PRIOR.

MEMINISSE JUVABIT.

LONDINI. MDCXCI.
SUMPTIBUS AUTORIS.

v.

HORTUS
INDICUS MALABARICUS

AMSTELODAMI, Sumptibus { JOANNIS VAN SOMEREN, et JOANNIS VAN DYCK. Anno cIɔIɔCLXXVIII.

i.

33 George Square
July 16. 1851.

My dear Cleghorn—

ii.

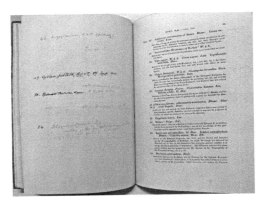

iii.

PLATE 11

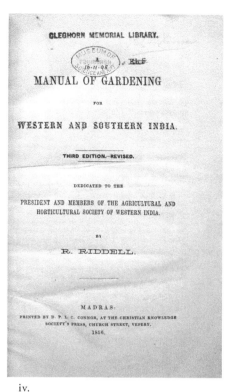

MANUAL OF GARDENING

FOR

WESTERN AND SOUTHERN INDIA.

THIRD EDITION.—REVISED.

DEDICATED TO THE

PRESIDENT AND MEMBERS OF THE AGRICULTURAL AND
HORTICULTURAL SOCIETY OF WESTERN INDIA.

BY

R. RIDDELL.

MADRAS:
PRINTED BY D. P. L. C. CONNOR, AT THE CHRISTIAN KNOWLEDGE
SOCIETY'S PRESS, CHURCH STREET, VEPERY.
1856.

iv.

i.

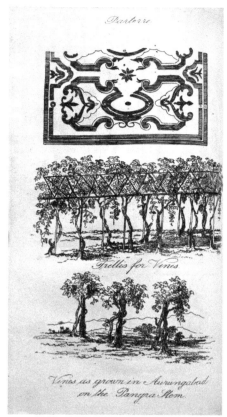

Parterre

Trellis for Vines

Vines as grown in Aurungabad
on the Pangra Stem

v.

SPECIMENS

OF

NATURE PRINTING

FROM

UNPREPARED PLANTS,

ETC. ETC.

BY

HENRY SMITH,

SUPT. OF THE GOVERNMENT PRESS, MADRAS

MADRAS:
PRINTED AND PUBLISHED BY H. SMITH, AT THE FORT SAINT GEORGE GAZETTE PRESS
1857.

SPECIMENS

OF

NATURE PRINTING

FROM

UNPREPARED PLANTS,

ETC. ETC.

ii.

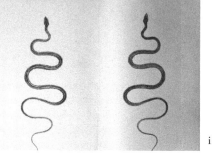

iii.

PLATE 12

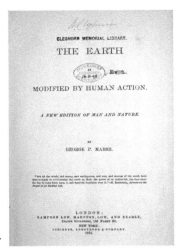

iv.

v.

i.

ii.

iii.

PLATE 13

iv.

iii.

ii.

i.

Photographs of items in the collection of the University of Edinburgh are reproduced with their kind permission, and designated 'EUL'. Others are of items in the collection of the Royal Botanic Garden Edinburgh.

PLATE 1. Posthumous Cleghorn book stamps
i. Cleghorn Bequest, Edinburgh University (EUL).
ii. Cleghorn Memorial Library, Museum of Science and Art, now at RBGE.

PLATE 2. Cleghorn bookplates
i. H. Cleghorn (the commonest label, found in dozens of Cleghorn's books).
ii. Hugh Cleghorn (from Lee, 1788).
iii. Wakefield gilt stamp on front board (from Hill, 1751).

PLATE 3. The Stravithie library today, showing one of Cleghorn's original bookcases, with labels in his hand showing the original locations of some of his pamphlets and periodicals in the cupboards below the open shelves (with the kind permission of David Chalmers).

PLATE 4. Booksellers' labels
i. Henry Ormston, Edinburgh (from Hooker, 1838. EUL).
ii. J.R. Hogg, Madras (from Porteus, 1811).
iii. Inscription from William Pamplin (from Dillwyn, 1839. EUL).
iv. Pharoah & Co., Madras (from Kinloch, 1853).
v. J. Higginbotham, Madras (from Skinner, 1862).

PLATE 5. Bookplates of earlier owners (1)
i. Sir John Anstruther (from Hermann, 1687).
ii. James Heriot of Ramornie (from Linnaeus ed. Smith, 1792. EUL).
iii. Vepery Mission, Madras (from Fleming, 1810. EUL).
iv. William Morehead (from Tournefort, 1719).

PLATE 6. Cleghorn's working copies
i. Wight and Arnott, 1834 – title page.
ii. Wight and Arnott, 1834 – showing Cleghorn's additions and annotations.
iii. Marsh, 1864 – title page.
iv. Marsh, 1864 – annotation with information from Henry Yule.
v. Cleghorn, 1864b – title page.
vi. Cleghorn, 1864b – additional material.

PLATE 7. Some rare books
i. Annotations by J.P. Rottler in Fleming, 1810 (EUL).
ii. Willdenow, 1794.
iii. Annotations by J.P. Rottler in Willdenow, 1794.
iv. Clusius, 1582
v. Chaussepierre & Rousselet (eds), 1776.
vi. Mattioli, 1560.

PLATE 8. Bindings and binders' labels
i. Rowbotham, London (Roupell and Harvey, 1849).
ii. Gilt stamp on Rowbotham binding.
iii. American Mission Press, Madras (from *Botanical Gazette*, 1850–1).
iv. India Office presentation binding, from *East India* (ed Phillimore), 1871.
v. Fletcher & Co., St Andrews (from Baillon, 1876–92).

PLATE 9. Dedications to previous owners
i. W.J. Hooker, 1847.
ii. Inscription in the hand of Dawson Turner.
iii. Dedication to Turner in Hooker's hand.
iv. Hamilton, 1761.
v. Letter from Robert Ainslie.

PLATE 10. Gifts to Cleghorn from other botanists (1)
i. Titlepage of Rheede, 1678.
ii/iii. Letter of gift from R.K. Greville accompanying vols 1–6 of *Hortus Malabaricus*.
iv. Cleghorn's annotated copy of Dillwyn, 1839.
v. Plukenet, 1691.
vi. Dedication by Robert Wight in Plukenet's *Opera*.

PLATE 11. Two Madras publications
i. Smith, 1857.
ii. Label on front board.
iii. Nature printed snake.
iv. Riddell, 1856.
v. Etched illustration by pupils of Alexander Hunter's School of Art.

PLATE 12. Gifts to Cleghorn from other botanists (2)
i. Standish & Noble, 1852.
ii. Dedication from Lord William Hay.
iii. Notes by Hay on Himalayan trees.
iv. G.P. Marsh, 1874.
v. Letter of gift from Marsh.

PLATE 13. Bookplates of earlier owners (2)
i. J.M.W. Baumann (from Roth, 1821. EUL).
ii. Earl of Moira (from Ferrari, 1646).
iii. Duke of Sussex (from Lingard, 1819).
iv. Lewis Balfour (from Muller, 1846).

References

Manuscript

Edinburgh University Library: Master shelf catalogue (EUA Acc.2010/018).

National Museums of Scotland: Museum of Science & Art, Library Accession Book, 1895.

RBGE: John Hutton Balfour's incoming correspondence (cited in form: RBGE BC 4/179 HC to JHB 26 Jan 1856).

RBGE: 'List of Books and Pamphlets 34001 [1940 to 39169, 1957]'.

RBGE: 'Cleghorn Memorial Library' typescript listing of books by J.T. Johnstone [1940].

RBG Kew – Henslow Correspondence (cited in form Kew HC f. 111 HC to JSH 5 Dec 1850).

University of St Andrews: Cleghorn papers (cited in form StA CP 2/8/20).

Printed

Note: the letters following the date of publication of Cleghorn's own works refer to the bibliography of his publications in Noltie (2016a, Appendix 1).

Anon. (1889). Presentation to Hugh Cleghorn of Stravithie, M.D., LL.D., F.R.S.E. *Transactions of the Scottish Arboricultural Society* 12: 198–205.

Anon. (1897). *List of Books, &c., relating to Botany and Forestry, including the Cleghorn Memorial Library in the Library of the [Edinburgh] Museum [of Science and Art]*. Edinburgh: H.M.S.O.

Anon. (1918–23). *Catalogue of the Printed Books in the Library of the University of Edinburgh*. 3 vols. Edinburgh: T. & A. Constable.

Clark, Aylwin (1992). *An Enlightened Scot: Hugh Cleghorn 1752–1837*. Duns: Black Ace Books.

[Cleghorn, H]. (1856h). Report on timber and ornamental woods, in *Madras Exhibition of Raw Products, Arts, and Manufactures of Southern India, 1855, Reports of the Juries on the Subjects in the Thirty Classes into which the Exhibitions was Divided*, pp. 60–73, [(ed.) ?E. Balfour]. Madras: For the General Committee of the Madras Exhibition, by Messrs. Pharoah & Co.

[Cleghorn, H.] (1856l). Art. III. – 1. Flora Indica ... [Review of Hooker & Thomson's *Flora Indica* and other works]. *Calcutta Review* 26: 355–372.

Cleghorn, H. (1861a). *The Forests and Gardens of South India*. Pp. [i–]vi–xiv, [1–]2–412. London: W.H. Allen & Co.

Cleghorn, H.C. (1862c). Memoranda on Himalayan rhubarb, and daphne fibre. *Madras Quarterly Journal of Medical Science* 5: 465–472.

Cleghorn, H. (1862d). Extracts from letters from Dr. H.W. Bellew, of the Guide Corps, and Dr. H. Cleghorn, Conservator of Forests, to the Secretary to Government Punjab, regarding the produce of Salep, Asafoetida, &c., in *Report on the Trade and Resources of the Countries on the North-Western Boundary of British India*, ed. R.H. Davies, Appendix XXXIV pp. ccclxxiv-vii. Lahore: Government Press.

Cleghorn, H. (1875d). 'Arboriculture', in *The Encyclopaedia Britannica: a Dictionary of Arts, Sciences, and General Literature*, ed. 9 (ed. T.S. Baynes) 2: 314–24. Edinburgh: Adam & Charles Black.

Cleghorn, H. (1879). 'Forests', in *The Encyclopaedia Britannica: a Dictionary of Arts, Sciences, and General Literature*, ed. 9 (ed. T.S. Baynes) 9: 397–408. Edinburgh: Adam & Charles Black.

Crawford, D.G. (1930). *Roll of the Indian Medical Service 1615–1930*. London: W. Thacker & Co.

Freedberg, D. (2002). *The Eye of the Lynx: Galileo, his Friends, and the Beginnings of Modern Natural History*. London & Chicago: University of Chicago Press.

[Grant, A.] (2008). *Books from the Library of Hugh Cleghorn (1752–1837)*. Edinburgh: Grant & Shaw Ltd.

Lowenthal, D. (2003). *George Perkins Marsh: Prophet of Conservation* (paperback edition). Seattle & London: University of Washington Press.

Noltie, H.J. (1999). *Indian Botanical Drawings 1793 to 1868 from the Royal Botanic Garden Edinburgh*. Edinburgh: Royal Botanic Garden Edinburgh.

Noltie, H.J. (2016a). *Indian Forester, Scottish Laird: the Botanical Lives of Hugh Cleghorn of Stravithie*. Edinburgh: Royal Botanic Garden Edinburgh.

Noltie, H.J. (2016b). *The Cleghorn Collection: South Indian Botanical Drawings 1845 to 1860*. Edinburgh: Royal Botanic Garden Edinburgh.

Smith, G. (1990). *Disciples of Light: photographs in the Brewster Album*. Malibu: the J. Paul Getty Museum.

Woodward, B.B. & Grout, A. (2004). Thomson, Thomas (1817–1878) in (eds.) H.C.G. Matthew & B. Harrison *Oxford Dictionary of National Biography* 54: 459–60. Oxford: OUP.

The catalogue

As a major purpose of this catalogue is to throw light on Cleghorn's life and work as an Indian Forester and Scottish Laird, rather than arrange it as a single alphabetical sequence by author, it has seemed more useful to present it as a classified arrangement; within this are geographical subdivisions under which the books are listed alphabetically by author. Of greatest interest are those works that could have influenced his ideas on forest policy (initially for Madras, and later for the whole of India). Clearly such works must have been published before 1868 (the year he reached Britain after leaving India for the last time), and despite the fact that copies of at least some of these were undoubtedly acquired after leaving India, attention has been drawn to potentially relevant titles by printing them in **bold**.

The classification used (and page numbers on which the items appear) is as follows:

Forestry
    India, 73–83
    Britain, 83–9
    Continental Europe
        France, 89–93
        Germany, 93–4
        Italy, 94–5
        Other, 95
    Rest of world, 96–7

Agriculture and land tenure
    India, 97
    Britain, 97–9
    Continental Europe, 99–100
    Rest of world, 100

Brief notes are given on format, current location, binding, bookplates and significant annotations.

Abbreviations:

EUL Cleghorn Bequest, Edinburgh University Library

CML Cleghorn Memorial Library (originally at Museum of Science and Art, transferred to the Royal Botanic Garden Edinburgh (RBGE) 1940, though some items were subsequently disposed of as 'duplicates').

Forestry

ANDERSON, Thomas (1867). On the Cultivation of Mahogany in India. *Supplement to the Calcutta Gazette* **6 Feb 1867: 47–56. Folio. Pamphlet at RBGE**, ex Museum (CML). Minor annotations in pencil by Cleghorn.

ANDERSON, Thomas (1867). Introduction of the Mahogany Tree into Bengal. *Supplement to the Calcutta Gazette* **9 Mar 1867: 185–90. Folio. Pamphlet at RBGE** ex Museum (CML). No annotations by Cleghorn.

BADEN-POWELL, Baden Henry (1882). *Manual of Jurisprudence for Forest Officers*. Calcutta. 8vo. EUL. Original binding. Annotations: signed in pencil on title-page 'H Cleghorn'.

BADEN-POWELL, Baden Henry & GAMBLE, James Sykes (eds) (1874). *Report of the Proceedings of the Forest Conference, 1873–74, held at Allahabad*. Calcutta. 8vo. CML. At RBGE.

In original boards. Annotations: signed on front cover in ink 'H Cleghorn'.

BAGNERIS, Gustave (1876). *Manual of Sylviculture*. Translated from the French by E.E. Fernandez & A. Smythies. Nagpur. 8vo. CML. At RBGE. Original binding. No annotations, but of interest for being published in India, and translated by one of the early Nancy-trained Indian foresters (Fernandez was selected by Cleghorn, and worked in Central Provinces).

BALFOUR, Edward G. (1862). *The Timber Trees, Timber and Fancy Woods of India, and of Eastern and Southern Asia*. Ed 2. Madras. 8vo. EUL. Original binding. Annotations: flyleaf inscribed 'My dear Cleghorn, I do not know where this will reach you; but I hope it will find you well and strong, as I know it will do, in active labour: And I hope that it will be accepted by you, with the kind regards of Yrs very sincerely Edward Balfour. Madras 29 Octr. 1863'; no annotations by Cleghorn.

BALFOUR, Edward G. (1870). *The Timber Trees ... of India.* Ed 3. Madras. 8vo. CML. At RBGE. Original binding. No signature or annotations.

BEDDOME, Richard Henry (1869–70). *Forester's Manual of Botany for Southern India.* 4to [Madras]. CML. At RBGE. Rebound. No signature or annotations.

BOMBAY FOREST DEPARTMENT (1879–86). *Administration Reports 1877/8– 1885/6.* 9 vols. Bombay. Folio. EUL.

BRANDIS, Dietrich (1875). *Memorandum on Forest Legislation Proposed for British India other than the Presidencies of Madras and Bombay.* Simla. Folio. EUL.

BRANDIS, Dietrich (1876). *Suggestions Regarding Forest Administration in Central Provinces.* Calcutta. Folio. EUL.

BRANDIS, Dietrich (1876). *Suggestions Regarding Management of Forests in Jalpaiguri and Darjeeling.* Calcutta. Folio. EUL.

BRANDIS, Dietrich (1880). *Review of Forest Administration ... India, 1878–79.* Calcutta. Folio. EUL.

BRANDIS, Dietrich (1881). *Suggestions Regarding Forest Administration in British Burma 1876, 1881.* 2 vols. Calcutta. Folio. EUL.

BRANDIS, Dietrich (1882). *Suggestions Regarding Forest Administration in NW Provinces and Oude.* Calcutta. Folio. EUL.

BRANDIS, Dietrich & SMYTHIES, Arthur (1876). *Report of Proceedings, Forest Conference, Simla 1875.* Calcutta. Folio. EUL.

BRANDIS, Dietrich, STENHOUSE, William, BATCHELOR, C. & RIBBENTROP, Berthold (1875). *Preliminary Working Plan of the Sutlej Working Circle.* Calcutta. Folio. EUL.

[BRANDIS, Dietrich, STEWART, John L. & WOOD, E.S. (1865). *Report upon Deodar Forests.* Calcutta. Folio]. EUL.

BRANDIS, Dietrich, STEWART, John Lindsay [& FITCH, John Nugent] (1874). *Illustrations of the Forest Flora of NW and Central India.* London. 4to. EUL. Original binding. No signature or annotations.

CLEGHORN, H. (1861). *Forests and Gardens of South India.* London. 8vo. EUL. Rebound. A working copy, signed in ink on title-page 'H Cleghorn'; some newspaper clippings inserted. Marginal lines and corrections

79

on pp 13, 44, 179, 216; on p 11, against *Calophyllum angustifolium* 'Lt. Beddome considers it to be an undescribed species of that genus', p 16 about coffee plantations 'Applications shd. be liberally responded to'. Plates bound in at back and numbered in ink by C.

CLEGHORN, H. (1864). *Report upon the Forests of the Punjab and the Western Himalaya.* **Roorkee. 8vo. CML.** At RBGE. Rebound. Cleghorn's heavily annotated and grangerised copy. In pocket at rear C's manuscript map, various printed maps and a letter from the engineer Peter Sandys Lumsden. On rear flyleaf a list of recipients to whom C sent complimentary copies.

CLEGHORN, H. (1864). *Report upon the Forests of the Punjab and the Western Himalaya.* **Roorkee. 8vo. EUL.** Original binding ('Thomason College Press, Roorkee' label on back pastedown), with two maps in back pocket. Verso of front flyleaf inscribed 'E G Balfour Esq Dy. Inspr. of Hospitals with Kind Regards of H Cleghorn Madras 6th March /65'.

DALZELL, Nicol Alexander (1869). *The Natural History and Biology of the Teak Tree.* London. 8vo. Original paper wrappers, printed with title. Pamphlet at RBGE, ex Museum (?CML). No annotations by Cleghorn.

EAST INDIA (Forest Conservancy) Parliamentary Papers on period 21 May 1862 to Aug 1871. **C.B. Phillimore (ed.) (1871). 4 vols: 1(1 & 2 – India), 2 (Madras), 3 (Bombay). London. Folio. CML.** At RBGE in fine, gold-tooled, presentation binding. Front pastedown of vol. 1(1) with engraved label 'Presented to Dr Cleghorn By Her Majesty's Secretary of State for India in Council. India Office London'. Pencil annotations on vol. 1 pp 323 (on continental training of foresters) for which corners of pp 324/4 and 325/5 turned down, 342/3 & 359 (on continental training).

FALCONER, Hugh (1852). *Report on the Teak Forests of the Tenasserim Provinces.* **Calcutta. 8vo. CML.** At RBGE. Original binding. Signed in pencil 'H Cleghorn' on title-page. Cutting from Allen's Indian Mail 29 April 1856 about McClelland's teak report. Annotations on p 5 and long note on p 7 'The unrestrained liberty accorded to any individual to appropriate to himself any unoccupied forest under such liberal conditions (1 Rs per log) contributed without doubt in the 1st instance to the prosperity of Moulmein but a continuance of the same system has led to the extermination of all available forests, & deprived Moulmein of this valuable resource it being now in great measure dependent upon the Shan States for the finest teak'. Minor annotations on pp 12, 14, 15, 24, 30, 38, 76, 83, 90, 234–7 etc. Long quote from J.W. Helfer on back flyleaf, and page references on back pastedown.

FOREST DEPARTMENT, INDIA (1886). *Code of Instructions.* Ed 3. Calcutta. 8vo. CML. Not found at RBGE.

GAMBLE, James Sykes (1878). *List of the Trees, Shrubs, and large Climbers found in the Darjeeling District, Bengal.* Calcutta. 8vo. CML. Not at RBGE (the copy kept is one sent by Govt. of India to the 1884 International Forestry Exhibition).

GAMBLE, James Sykes (1881). *A Manual of Indian Timbers.* Calcutta. 8vo. EUL. Two copies, in original bindings. Title-pages signed in pencil 'H Cleghorn', no notes.

GELL, Francis (1863). *Handbook for Use in the Jungles of Western India.* **Bombay. 12mo. EUL.** Rebound. No signature or annotations. (Note. This is a list of native plant names. Gell was a missionary. The book is dedicated to 'Dhoondie Mahar of Khandalla'. Conspicuous for its absence of any mention of Alexander Gibson – the *Bombay Flora* is attributed solely to its co-author N.A. Dalzell).

GIBSON, Alexander (1857). *Handbook to the Forests of the Bombay Presidency.* **Bombay. 8vo. CML.** At RBGE. Rebound. No signature, some marginal marks on pp 57 (ref. to Masulipatam and Rajahmundry), 58, 96 (timber agent's salary), and against forest rules pp 107–11.

[HENDERSON, G., STEWART, J.L., CLEGHORN, H.F.C. (eds) (1868)]. *Select Papers of the Agri-Horticultural Society of the Punjab.* **Lahore. 8vo.** Copy from Stravithie library at RBGE. In original leather binding. Many annotations, possibly by J.L. Stewart. (Note. This includes Lord Dalhousie's paper on tree-planting in Punjab with footnotes by Cleghorn).

INDIA FOREST DEPARTMENT (1872–78). *Report on Administration of Forest Department in the Several Provinces 1870/1, 1871/2, 1872/3 (in two), 1876/7.* 8 vols. Calcutta. 8vo. EUL.

INDIA FOREST DEPARTMENT (1877). *Code of Instructions.* Calcutta. 8vo. EUL. Original binding. No signature or annotations.

INDIA FOREST DEPARTMENT (1881). *Code of Instructions.* Ed 2. Calcutta. 8vo. EUL. Original binding. No signature or annotations.

INDIA FOREST DEPARTMENT (1884–87). *Review of Forest Administration in British India 1883/4, 1884/5, 1885/6,* by Wilhelm Schlich. Simla. Folio. EUL.

KURZ, Sulpiz (1875). *Preliminary Report on Forest Vegetation of Pegu.* Calcutta. Folio. EUL.

KURZ, Sulpiz (1877). *Forest Flora of British Burma.* 2 vols. Calcutta. 8vo. EUL. Original bindings. No signature or annotations.

MADRAS FOREST DEPARTMENT (1875–92). *Annual Administration Report 1873/4–1877/8, 1879/80, 1880/1, 1883/4, 1884/5, 1885/6, 1887/8, 1889/90, 1890/2, 1891/2.* Madras. Folio. EUL.

[MADRAS, *Denkenekotta Range, Salem Forests* – Map. 4to]. EUL.

MADRAS PRESIDENCY (1893). *Annual Administration Report of the Forest Department for the fifteen months ending 30th June 1893.* Madras. Folio. CML, but not found at RBGE.

MANN, Gustav (1890). *Progress Report of Forest Administration of the Province of Assam for the Year 1889–90.* Shillong. [Not part of CML]. At RBGE, original boards. Signed on front cover 'H Cleghorn'.

MONEY, William Taylor (1811). *Observations on the Expediency of Shipbuilding at Bombay.* **London. 8vo. CML.** At RBGE, bound by Cleghorn with Pering (1812) and Layman (1813). With Cleghorn's manuscript index to the three works on front pastedown.

MORGAN, Henry Rhodes (1884). *Forestry in Southern India.* Edited by John Shortt. Madras. 8vo. CML. At RBGE. Original binding. No signature or annotations.

[PHAYRE, Arthur Purves, McCLELLAND, John et al. (1855)]. *Papers on Teak Forests of Pegu.* **Calcutta. 8vo. CML.** At RBGE. Original binding. Signed in ink 'H Cleghorn' on title-page, numerous annotations by Cleghorn on front and back pastedowns, and throughout text.

PUNJAB STATUTES (1878). *The Punjab Code ... Rules for the Conservancy of Forests.* Calcutta. 8vo. EUL.

RIBBENTROP, Berthold (1873). *Hints on Arboriculture in the Punjab.* Calcutta. 8vo. EUL. Original binding. No signature or annotations.

RIBBENTROP, Berthold (1874). *Hints on Arboriculture in the Punjab.* Lahore. 8vo. EUL.

RIBBENTROP, Berthold (1886). *Note on the Inspection of the Forests in Oudh*. Simla. Folio. EUL.

SKINNER, Thomas William (1862). *Description and Strength of some of the Indian and Burman Timbers*. Madras. 8vo. CML. At RBGE. In original boards. Signed on front cover and title-page 'H Cleghorn', with bookseller's stamp J. Higginbotham, Madras, no annotations.

STRETTELL, George W. (1876). *The Ficus elastica in Burma Proper*. Rangoon. 4to. CML. The copy at RBGE is not Cleghorn's (the copy kept is one sent by Govt. of India to the 1884 International Forestry Exhibition).

STEWART, John Lindsay (1868). *Selections from the Records of the Punjab Public Works Department. No 1, Forest and Fuel Plantations in the Punjab*. Lahore. 8vo. EUL. Original wrappers. Front wrapper signed in pencil 'H Cleghorn', no annotations.

STEWART, John Lindsay (1874). *The Forest Flora of North-West and Central India*. London. 8vo. EUL. Original binding. Signed on title-page 'Private copy H. Cleghorn St Andrews N[orth] B[ritain]'; marginal marks on pp ix, x; corrections on pp 3, 17, 504; p 130 note against *Moringa*.

BRITAIN

ABLETT, William H. (1880). *English Trees and Tree-Planting*. London. 8vo. CML. At RBGE. In original binding. No signature or annotations.

"AGRICOLA" [James Anderson] (1777). *Miscellaneous Observations on Planting and Training Timber-Trees; particularly calculated for the Climate of Scotland*. Edinburgh. 8vo. CML. At RBGE. Rebound. No signature or annotations.

AIKIN, John (1820). *The Woodland Companion or, a Brief Description of British Trees*. Ed 3. London. 12mo. CML. At RBGE. Rebound. No signature or annotations.

BAGNERIS, Gustave (1882). *Manual of Sylviculture*. Translated from the second French edition. London. 8vo. CML, but not at RBGE.

BALFOUR, John Hutton (1857). *On the Structure and Growth of Timber* (reprint

from **Architectural Institute Edinburgh). Edinburgh, 22 April 1857. 8vo. EUL.** Pamphlet bound with works by G.A. Hight and J.F. Duthie (Att 66.5.9–11). Signed on title-page in pencil 'H Cleghorn', no annotations.

BLAIKIE, Francis (1814). *Treatise on the Planting and Management of Forest Timber Trees adapted to the System of Farm Clump Planting.* **Ed 2. Burton-upon-Trent. 8vo. CML.** At RBGE. Original boards. No signature or annotations.

BONER, Charles (1861). *Forest Creatures.* **London. 8vo. CML.** At RBGE. Original binding. No signature or annotations. (Note. This concerns game animals and birds, dedicated to Ernst, Duke of Saxe-Coburg-Gotha).

BROWN, James (1851). *The Forester.* **Ed 2. Edinburgh. 8vo. CML.** At RBGE. Rebound. Signed 'H Cleghorn' on flyleaf; annotation on p 86 (about fence-posts).

BROWN, James (1861). *The Forester.* **Ed 3. Edinburgh. 8vo. Copy at RBGE**, but not part of CML. Rebound. Signed 'H Cleghorn' on flyleaf; marginal marks against items of Chapter 5 on p ix of Contents (but not in main text).

BROWN, John Croumbie (1883). *The Forests of England.* Edinburgh. 8vo. EUL. Original binding. No signature or annotations.

BURROWS, A.J. (1884). *Science for Foresters.* London. 8vo. CML. At RBGE. In original boards. No signature or annotations.

[CAMPBELL-WALKER, Inches (1872). *Report on English and Scotch Forests.* London. Folio]. EUL.

CREE, Gavin (1851). *Essays on the Scientific Management of Forest Trees.* **Biggar. 8vo. CML.** At RBGE. In original boards. No signature or annotations.

CRUICKSHANK, Thomas (1830). *The Practical Planter.* **Edinburgh. 8vo. CML.** At RBGE. Rebound. No signature or annotations.

[*DEAN FOREST* (?1884). 2o]. EUL.

'DOYLE, Martin' [the Rev. William Hickey] (1830). *Hints to Small Holders on Planting, etc.* **Dublin. 12mo. CML.** At RBGE. Rebound. No signature or annotations.

EMMERICH, Andrew (1789). *The Culture of Forests.* **London. 8vo. CML.** At RBGE. Rebound. No signature or annotations. (Note: Emmerich was Deputy-Surveyor-General of Royal Woods and Parks).

EVELYN, John (1670). *Sylva.*
**Ed 2. London. (Bound with
Pomona or an Appendix
concerning Fruit-Trees in
relation to Cider). Folio. CML.**
At RBGE. Original binding.
No signature; marginal mark on
p. 127 (toxicity of yew to cattle).

EVELYN, John (1812). *Silva,*
with notes by A. Hunter, M.D.
to which is added, The Terra,
a Philosophical Discourse of
Earth. **Ed 4. 2 vols. York. 4to.
CML.** At RBGE. Rebound.
Obscure pencil annotation
on flyleaf, which shows that
Cleghorn acquired it in India
'Chocalin gum 2 v[ols] 50 Rs.'
'2/24/33'. 'No 366 – 2
Vol – 20 Rs'.

GRIGOR, James (1841). *The*
Eastern Arboretum [Norfolk].
**London and Norwich. 8vo.
CML.** Not at RBGE (another
copy kept).

GRIGOR, John (1868).
Arboriculture. Edinburgh. 8vo.
CML. Not at RBGE (two other
copies kept, one belonging to
R. Hutchison of Carlowrie).

GRINDON, Leopold Hartley
(1870). *The Trees of Old England.*
Ed 2. London. 8vo. CML.
At RBGE. Original binding.
Signed 'H Cleghorn' on title-
page; blind stamp 'The Gore.
Bournemouth' on flyleaf; no
annotations.

**[HAMILTON, Thomas, 6th Earl
of Haddington (1761)].**
Treatise on the Manner of
Raising Forest Trees, etc.
Edinburgh. 12mo. CML. At
RBGE. Rebound. No signature
or annotations; bound in after
flyleaf a letter 'Dunse July 30
1768. Mr Ainslies Compliments
to Mr Ker with a Coppy of the
Late Earle of Hadinton's Treaties
on Forest Trees – which is the
shortest and Best on the subject,
in proof of which the author had
more success that way than any
other in Britain – and hope the
knowledge proceeding from the
Reading of this will be a means
of Beautifying part of the wast
ground of Teviotdale'. (Note
'Mr Ainslie' is the Indian
surgeon Whitelaw Ainslie's
father – 'Mr Ker' may be one
of the Lothian family).

HANBURY, William (1758).
An Essay on Planting and
a Scheme for Making it
Conducive to the Glory of God.
Oxford. 8vo. EUL. Pamphlet in
modern binding. No ownership
or annotations.

[HAYES, Samuel] 'S .H.' (1794).
Practical Treatise on Planting
and the Management of Woods
and Coppices. **Dublin. 8vo.
CML.** At RBGE. Rebound. No
signature or annotations.

HEATH, Francis George (1883).
Burnham Beeches. Ed 5. London.
8vo. CML. At RBGE. Rebound.
No signature or annotations.

HEMSLEY, William Botting (1877). *Handbook of Hardy Trees, Shrubs, and Herbaceous Plants*. London. 8vo. CML. At RBGE. Rebound. No signature or annotations.

HORTON, Richard (1863). *Table showing the Solidity of Hewn or Eight-sided Timber.* **London. 8vo. CML.** At RBGE. In original leather binding. Signed 'H Cleghorn' in pencil on flyleaf.

HUCKVALE, Graily (1878). *Timber, Plantations, and Underwood; their Uses, Measurement, and Valuation.* London. 8vo. CML. At RBGE. Original paper wrappers. No annotations.

JOHNS, the Rev Charles Alexander (1846). *Forest Trees of Britain. Nos 1–2*. London. 12mo. EUL. Original wrappers, bound with Chaytor's *Agricultural & Trade Depression*.

[KENT, Elizabeth] (1831). Sylvan Sketches. London. 8vo. CML. Not at RBGE (copy of a 1825 edition kept).

KNIGHT, Joseph & PERRY, Thomas Aloysius [1850]. *Synopsis of the Coniferous Plants grown in Great Britain.* **London. 8vo. CML.** At RBGE. Original binding. No signature or annotations; inscribed on verso of flyleaf 'With Knight & Perry's respectful duty'. Purple ink-stamp on front board 'R.J.

Mitchell & Sons 52, Parliament St., S.W.' looks later, suggesting that Cleghorn bought it in London later in life.

LAYMAN, Captain William (1813). *Precursor to an Exposé on Forest Trees and Timber.* **London. 8vo. CML.** At RBGE, bound by Cleghorn with Money (1811) and Pering (1812). With Cleghorn's ms index to the three works on inside front board. (Note: Layman promoted the use of Malabar Teak to the Royal Navy).

LINGARD, John (1819). *A Philosophic and Practical Inquiry into the Nature and Constitution of Timber.* **London. 8vo. CML.** At RBGE. Rebound. With bookplate of the Duke of Sussex [i.e. Prince Augustus Frederick] on front pastedown (Plate 13.iii). Inscribed in pencil on flyleaf 'H Cleghorn purchased of W. Pamplin' (presumably in case someone thought he had stolen it from the Duke – no other book is annotated with the bookseller's name). Inscribed on title-page 'His Royal Highness the Duke of Sussex K.G. & K.C.B. &c President of the Society of Arts with the Author's humble respects'.

McINTOSH, Charles (1860). *The Larch Disease*. **London. 16mo. CML.** At RBGE. Original binding. Signed in pencil 'H Cleghorn' on title-page, no annotations.

MANWOOD, John (1665). *A Treatise of the Laws of the Forest.* **Ed 3. London. 8vo. CML.** At RBGE. Rebound. Flyleaf inscribed 'Ex libris Johanis Bworkett … 1675'.

MITCHELL, James (1827). *Dendrologia, or a Treatise of Forest Trees; with Evelyn's Silva revised, corrected, and abridged.* **Keighley. 8vo. CML.** At RBGE. Original binding. No signature or annotations.

MONTEATH, Robert (1820). *The Forester's Guide.* **Stirling. 8vo. CML.** At RBGE. In old binding. No signature or annotations.

MONTEATH, Robert (1824). *The Forester's Guide and Profitable Planter.* **Ed 2. Edinburgh. 8vo. CML.** In original boards. No signature or annotations.

[NELSON, John] 'Johannes Senilis' (1866). *Pinaceae: being a Handbook of the Firs and Pines.* London. 8vo. CML. Not at RBGE (the copy kept was previously owned by A.W. MacTier, presented by Royal Scottish Arboricultural Society 1895).

PERING, Richard (1812). *A Brief Enquiry into the Causes of Premature Decay in our Wooden Bulwarks.* **Plymouth. 8vo. CML.** At RBGE, bound by Cleghorn with Money (1811) and Layman (1813). With

Cleghorn's manuscript index to the three works on front pastedown.

PHILLIPS, Henry (1823). *Sylva Florifera.* **2 vols. London. 8vo. CML.** Not at RBGE (another copy kept).

PONTEY, William (1808). *The Forest Pruner.* **Ed. 2. London. 8vo. CML.** At RBGE. Original binding. No signature or annotations.

PONTEY, William (1826). *The Forest Pruner.* **Ed. 4. Leeds. 8vo. CML.** At RBGE. Rebound. No signature or annotations.

PONTEY, William (1828). *The Profitable Planter.* **Ed. 4. London. 8vo. CML.** At RBGE. Original binding. No signature, marginal marks pp 161–171 (but not certainly made by C).

PRIDEAUX, Thomas Symes [1853]. *The Economy of Fuel.* **London. 12mo. CML.** At RBGE. No signature or annotations.

RAIT, James (1862). *The Relative value of Round and Sawn Timber.* **Edinburgh. 8vo. CML.** At RBGE. Rebound. No signature or annotations.

RATTRAY, John & MILL, Hugh Robert (1885). *Forestry and Forest Products, Prize Essays of the Edinburgh International Forestry Exhibition, 1884.* Edinburgh. 8vo. EUL. Original full calf binding. No signature or annotations.

ROGERS, W.H. [c. 1878]. Guide to the New Forest.. Southampton. 16mo. CML. At RBGE. In original paper wrappers. Signed in pencil on front wrapper; no annotations.

SCALING, William (1871). *The Salix or Willow in a Series of Papers. Part 1* (ed. 2). London. 8vo. Original printed wrapper. Pamphlet at RBGE, ex Museum (CML). Signed in ink on front cover 'H. Cleghorn'. Note. Bound with it is a 12-page catalogue of willows for sale by Scaling 'Willow Nurseryman, Basford, Notts'.

SEEMANN, Berthold (1856). Popular History of the Palms and their Allies. London. 8vo. CML. At RBGE. Rebound. With 'H Cleghorn' signature on title-page; annotation on p 158.

SELBY, Prideaux John (1842). *History of British Forest Trees*. London. 8vo. CML. Not at RBGE (the copy kept was previously owned by A.W. MacTier, presented by Royal Scottish Arboricultural Society 1895).

[SINCLAIR, George] (1832). *Useful and Ornamental Planting, with an Index*. London. 8vo. CML. At RBGE. Rebound. Signed in pencil 'H Cleghorn' on title-page; marginal lines on pp iii, 70 (chlorosis), 71 (lichens/ mosses on trees), 131 (seeking information on Himalayas), 132 (*Platanus*), 133 (spanish chestnut), 140 (deodar), etc.

[SOCIETY for the DIFFUSION of USEFUL KNOWLEDGE] (1829). Library of Entertaining Knowledge, vol. 42 *Timber Trees: Fruits*. London. 12mo. CML. Not at RBGE.

[SOCIETY for the PROMOTION of CHRISTIAN KNOWLEDGE] (1851). *The British Sylva, and Planters' and Foresters' Manual*. London. 8vo. CML. At RBGE. In original binding. No signature or annotations.

STANDISH, J. & NOBLE, Charles (1852). *Practical Hints on Planting Ornamental Trees*. London. 12mo. CML. At RBGE. Original binding. Purchased from 'Smith Elder & Co East India Agents Cornhill London [label on front pastedown]' by Lord William Hay, signed by him on flyleaf 'Wm Hay Simlah 10/2/56' to which he has later added 'To Dr Cleghorn from …'. With many annotations (local names, etc) by Hay on Simla trees, especially on back endpapers.

STRUTT, Jacob George (1826). *Sylva Britannica*. London. Folio. CML. At RBGE. Original binding. No signature or annotations.

STRUTT, Jacob George [1830].
Sylva Britannica; or Portraits of Forest Trees. **London. 8vo.**
CML. At RBGE. Rebound. No signature or annotations. (Note: The plates are chine colle etchings).

TAYLOR, Joseph (1812). *Arbores Mirabiles.* **London. 12mo. CML.** Not at RBGE.

VEITCH, James and Sons (1881). *Manual of the Coniferae.* London. 8vo. CML. At RBGE. Original binding. No signature or annotations.

EUROPE

France

BAGNERIS, Gustave (1873). *Manuel de Sylviculture.* Paris & Nancy. 8vo. CML. At RBGE. Original binding. No annotations.

BAILEY, Frederick (1886). *Forestry in France.* Edinburgh. 8vo. CML. At RBGE. Original paper wrappers. No annotations. (Note: A reprint from *Transactions of the Scottish Arboricultural Society* vol. 11(2)).

BAILEY, Frederick (1887). *A Forest Tour among the Dunes of Gascony.* Edinburgh. 8vo. CML. At RBGE. Original paper wrappers. No annotations. (Note: A reprint from *Transactions of the Scottish Arboricultural Society* vol. 11(3)).

BAILEY, Frederick (1887). *A Forest Tour in Provence and the Cevennes.* Edinburgh. 8vo. CML. At RBGE. Original paper wrappers. Signed in ink on front wrapper, no other annotations.

(Note: A reprint from *Transactions of the Botanical Society of Edinburgh* vol. 16(3)).

BAUDRILLART, Jacques-Joseph (1808). *Nouveau Manuel Forestier.* **2 vols. Paris. 8vo. CML.** At RBGE. Rebound. No signature or annotations.

BECQUEREL [Antoine Cesar] (1853). *Des Climats et de l'Influence qui exercent les Sols boisés et non boisés.* **Paris. 8vo. CML.** At RBGE. Original binding. No signature or annotations.

BONARD (1826). *Des Forêts de la France, considérées dans leurs Rapports avec la Marine Militaire.* **Paris. 8vo. CML.** At RBGE. Rebound. No signature or annotations.

BOPPE, Lucien (1882–3). *Création de peuplements artificiels et boisement des terrains nus.* Nancy. 4to. EUL. Lithographed ms, in original paper wrappers. Front wrapper inscribed 'Docteur Cleghorn Hommage de l'auteur L. Boppe'.

BOPPE, Lucien (1882–3). *Exposé des faits généraux relatifs à la production forestière*. Nancy. 4to. EUL. Lithographed ms in original paper wrappers. Front wrapper inscribed 'Dr Cleghorn Hommage de l'auteur L. Boppe'.

BREUIL, Alphonse du (1857). *Cours elémentaire, théorique et pratique, d'arboriculture.* **2 vols. Ed. 4. Paris. 8vo. CML.** At RBGE. Vol. 1 rebound; vol. 2 in original binding. Vol. 1 signed in pencil 'H Cleghorn' on title-page; with H Cleghorn bookplate on front pastedown; vol. 2 with bookplate, signed 'Dr Cleghorn' on half-title, no annotations in either.

BROWN, John Croumbie (1876). *Reboisement in France*. London. 8vo. EUL. Original binding. Signed 'H Cleghorn' in pencil on title-page; marginal mark on p. 48.

CALVEL, Etienne (1825). *Manuel pratique des plantations.* **Nouvelle édition. Paris. 8vo. CML.** At RBGE. In old binding (rebacked). No signature or annotations.

CANNON, David (1877). *Le propriétaire planteur*. Orleans. 8vo. EUL. Original paper wrappers. Signed on front wrapper 'H. Cleghorn' in ink; flyleaf inscribed 'To Dr

Cleghorn an old and valued friend of his family souvenir of the author D. Cannon'; pages uncut, no annotations.

[CHAUSSEPIERRE, Charles Georges Coqueley de & ROUSSELET, Michel Louis (eds)] (1776). *Ordonnance de Louis XIV, sur le fait des eaux et forêts.* **Nouvelle édition. Paris. 12mo. CML.** At RBGE. Original binding. No signature or annotations.

COURVAL, Ernest Alexis, Vicomte de (1861). *Taille et conduite des arbres forestiers.* **Ed. 2. Paris. 8vo. CML.** At RBGE. Rebound. No signature or annotations. (Note: Concerns tree pruning).

DES CARS, A.J. de P. (1867). *L'élagage des arbres.* **Ed. 6. Paris. 12mo. CML.** At RBGE. Rebound. Signed 'H Cleghorn' on title-page, no annotations.

DES CARS, A.J. de P. (1870). *L'élagage des arbres*. Ed. 7. Paris. 12mo. EUL. Original paper wrappers. No signature or annotations.

EAUX et FORÊTS (1877–78). *Annuaire pour 1877 et 1878*. 2 vols. Paris. 16mo. CML. At RBGE. Original paper wrappers. 1877 report signed 'H. Cleghorn' in ink on front cover.

HERBIN de HALLE, Pierre-Etienne (1815). *Des bois propres au service des arsenaux*

de la marine et de la guerre.
Paris. 8vo. CML. At RBGE.
Original leather binding
(rebacked). No signature or
annotations.

JACQUOT, Charles (1866).
Les codes de la législation
forestière. **Paris. 8vo. EUL.**
Original boards. Signed in
pencil 'H Cleghorn' on
title-page.

KIRWAN, Charles de (1867–68).
Les conifères indigènes-
exotiques. **2 vols. Paris. 12mo.**
CML. At RBGE, rebound, but
enclosing original card boards.
No signature or annotations.

LE CAMUS de MÉZIÈRES,
Nicolas (1782). *Traité de la*
force des bois. **Paris. 8vo. CML.**
Not at RBGE.

LESBAZEILLES, Eugène (1884).
Les forêts. Paris. 8vo. CML. At
RBGE. Original binding. No
signature or annotations.

LORENTZ, Bernard & PARADE,
Adolphe L.F. (1860). *Cours*
elémentaire de culture des bois.
Ed. 4. Paris & Nancy. 8vo.
CML. At RBGE. Rebound.
Signed in pencil on title-page
'H Cleghorn'; annotations on
pp v, vii, 3 (sustainable yield and
regeneration); 553–561 English/
Latin names for trees.

MANTEUFFEL, Baron Hans
Ernst de (1874). *L'art de*
planter plantations en général
– plantations en butte. Ed. 12.

Paris. 12mo. CML. At RBGE.
Rebound. No signature or
annotations.

MATHIEU, Auguste (1858).
Flore forestière. Description …
des vegetation ligneux. Nancy.
8vo. EUL. Original binding.
Front flyleaf signed in pencil 'H
Cleghorn, purchased 1873', no
annotations.

MAURY, Louis Ferdinand Alfred
(1867). *Les forêts de la gaule*
et de l'ancienne france. **Paris.**
8vo. CML. At RBGE. Rebound.
No signature; marginal marks
pp 77 (Hartz), 81 (French v
German forests), 83 (white
poplar), 85 (vines), 87 (Roman
law); 128, 207, 210 (Haguenau
forest); 392 (forests of
Pyrenees), 401 (an abbey
responsible for destroying
forest); 417 (game animals);
468–9 (French forest law).

MEAUME, Edouard (1857).
Introduction à l'étude
de la législation et de la
jurisprudence forestières.
Nancy. 8vo. CML. At RBGE.
Rebound. Signed 'H Cleghorn'
on title-page; half-title with an
illegible signature (?French);
French annotations on pp 9,
10, 12–15.

MILLET D'AUBENTON, Charles
(1837). *Notice sur la culture*
des oseraies dans le département
de l'aisne. Lyon. 8vo. Original
wrappers. Pamphlet at RBGE,
ex Museum (CML). Signed

on front wrapper in pencil 'H. Cleghorn', and in an older hand, in ink, 'M. Guillemin'.

NANQUETTE, Henri (1859). *Exploitation, débit, et estimation des bois.* **Nancy. 8vo. CML.** At RBGE. Rebound. No signature or annotations.

NANQUETTE, Henri (1860). *Cours d'aménagement des forêts.* **Paris & Nancy. 8vo. CML, EUL.** At RBGE. Original binding (with gilt-stamped coat of arms that is damaged and illegible, likewise lettering at base of spine – who had this binding made, or did it come thus from Nanquette?). Flyleaf inscribed 'Dr Cleghorn care of A. Cowan & Son 38 W. Register St [Edinburgh]'.

NOIROT[-BONNET, Louis] (1832). *Traité de la culture des forêts.* **Paris & Dijon. 8vo. CML.** At RBGE. Rebound. Pencil signature 'H Cleghorn' on half-title, no annotations.

'ONIMUS' (1866). *Mémoire sur l'aliénation de la forêt … de la Harth.* **Colmar. 8vo. EUL.** Original paper wrappers. No signature or annotations.

PAILLET, Jean Baptiste Joseph [c. 1835]. *Le code forestier expliqué.* **Paris. 8vo. CML.** At RBGE, in old binding (rebacked). No signature or annotations.

PERTHUIS de LAILLEVAULT, L. de (1803). *Traité de l'aménagement et de la restauration des bois et forêts de la France.* **Paris. 8vo. CML.** At RBGE. In early binding (rebacked). Signed on flyleaf 'G.L. Meason Lindertis', no annotations.

PUTON, Alfred (1867). *L'aménagement des forêts.* **Paris. 12mo. CML.** At RBGE, in original boards. No signature or annotations.

PUTON, Alfred (1874). *L'aménagement des forêts.* Ed. 12. Paris. 12mo. CML. At RBGE. Rebound. Signed in pencil 'H Cleghorn' on title-page, no annotations.

RENDU, Victor (1876). *Les insectes nuisibles à l'agriculture, aux jardins, et aux forêts de la France.* Paris. 12mo. CML. At RBGE. Original binding. No signature or annotations.

RIBBE, Charles de (1857). *La Provence au point de vue des bois etc.* **Paris. 8vo. EUL.** Rebound but enclosing original paper wrappers. No signature or annotations.

ROBERT, Eugène (1867). *Les destructeurs des arbres d'alignement.* **Paris. 12mo. CML.** At RBGE. Rebound. No signature or annotations.

ROTHSCHILD, Jules (1865). *L'aliénation des forêts de l'état.* **Paris. 8vo. EUL.** Rebound, but enclosing original paper wrappers. Signed 'H Cleghorn' in ink on front wrapper; no annotations.

SECONDAT, Jean-Baptiste de (1785). *Mémoires sur l'histoire naturelle du chêne.* **Paris. Folio. CML.** At RBGE. In Cleghorn's boards. No signature or annotations.

TELLÈS D'ACOSTA, Dominique Antoine (1782). *Instruction sur les bois de marine et autres.* **Paris. 12mo. CML.** At RBGE. Original binding. No signature or annotations.

TROY, Paul (1861). *Études sur le reboisement des montagnes.* **Paris. 8vo. EUL.** Original paper wrappers. No signature or annotations.

VARENNE de FENILLE, Philibert Charles (1807–08). *Mémoires sur l'administration forestière.* **Parts 1–3. Ed. 2. Paris. 8vo. CML.** Not at RBGE (the CML set was accessioned by the Museum in 1894, so cannot have been Cleghorn's).

Germany

BRANDIS, Dietrich (1888). *Notes on Forest Management in Germany.* London. Folio. EUL.

CAMPBELL-WALKER, Inches (*et al.*) (1873). *Reports on Forest Management in Germany, Austria and Great Britain.* London. 8vo. CML. At RBGE. In original binding. Flyleaf inscribed 'Dr Cleghorn with Dr B[randis]'s aff. regard. July 1873'.

CAMPBELL-WALKER, Inches (1873). *Reports on Forest Management in Germany.* London. 8vo. EUL. Original binding. Flyleaf inscribed 'Dr Cleghorn with Campbell Walker's Compts. India Office 14ᵗʰ Augᵗ. 1873'.

DES CARS, A.J. de P. (1868). *Das Aufästen der Bäume. Frei in's deutsche übertragen durch C. Haber.* **Köln. 12mo. CML.** At RBGE. Rebound. No signature or annotations.

HARTIG, Georg Ludwig (1861). *Lehrbuch für Förster,* **revised by Theodor Hartig. 3 vols. Stuttgart. 8vo. CML.** In old binding, three in one. No signature or annotations.

HIGHT, George Ainslie (1894). *Report on Forest Administration in Germany.* Calcutta. 8vo. EUL. Pamphlet bound with works by J.H. Balfour and J.F. Duthie. No signature or annotations.

PEARSON, George Falconer. (*et al.*) (1873). *Supplement to Reports on Forest Management in Germany, Austria and Great Britain.* London. 8vo. CML. At RBGE. In original binding. No signature or notes.

REUSS, Eugène & BARTET, Eugène (1884). *Étude sur l'experiméntation forestière … en Allemagne et in Autriche.* Nancy. 8vo. EUL. Original paper wrappers. Front wrapper inscribed 'A Monsieur le Dr Cleghorn souvenir […] des auteurs Bartet & Reuss'; no signature or annotations.

Italy

ANON (Ministero di Agricoltura) (1866). *Raccolta delle leggi forestali che sono in vigore nel regno d'Italia.* Prato. 8vo. EUL.

BÉRENGER, Adolfo di (1859–63). *Dell' antica storia e giurisprudenza forestale in Italia.* Treviso & Venezia. 8vo. CML. At RBGE. In original binding. Flyleaf inscribed 'A Monsieur Dr. Cleghorn Conservateur de Forets homage de l'Auteur. Vallombrosa 15/5 1875'. With it is bound the 'Indici Generali' (1867) to the work, separately inscribed to Cleghorn, who must have had the two bound together.

[BÉRENGER, Adolfo di] (1869). *'Ispettore-Generale dei boschi del regno d'Italia'. Paradossi forestale esaminati e discussi.* Prato. 8vo. CML. At RBGE. In old binding. No signature or annotations.

BÉRENGER, Adolfo di (1871). *Nuovo metodo di tassare i boschi ed assestarne l'economia.* Forli. 8vo. CML. At RBGE. Rebound. No signature or annotations.

BÉRENGER, Adolfo di (1871–72). *Giornale di economia forestale, ossia raccolta di memorie lette nel R. Istituto Forestale di Vallombrosa.* Vol. 1. Firenze. 8vo. CML. At RBGE. In old binding, but enclosing original front paper wrapper. Front wrapper inscribed 'A Monsieur Dr Cleghorn Conservateur des forests, homage de l'Auteur' [clearly given on C's visit to Vallombrosa in 1875], no annotations.

BÉRENGER, Adolfo di (1880). *Guida per il coltivatore di vivai boschivi.* Firenze & Roma. 8vo. CML. At RBGE. In old binding. No signature or annotations.

FAVERO, L. (1875). *La selva del Montello nel Trivigiana*. Milano. 8vo. EUL. Original wrappers. Front wrapper inscribed 'Sir Hugh Cleghorn M.D. Stravithie St Andrews', no signature or annotations.

FORNAINI, Antonio (1825). *Saggio sopra l'utilitá di ben governare e preservar le Foreste del Sacerdote.* **Firenze. 8vo. CML.** At RBGE. Rebound. No signature or annotations.

NOCE, Giuseppe del (1849). *Trattato istorico, scientifico, ed economico delle macchie e foreste del Gran-Ducato Toscano.* **Firenze. 4to. CML.** At RBGE. Rebound. No signature or annotations.

RABBENO, Aronne (1872). *Le selve e le innondazioni: studi di legislazione forestale*. Torino.

8vo. CML. At RBGE. Modern binding enclosing original paper covers. No signature or annotations.

RICCI, Jacopo (1821). *Della cultura del boschi.* **Firenze. 12mo. EUL.** Original paper wrappers. No signature or annotations.

SIEMONI, Giovanni Carlo (1864). *Manuale teorico-pratico d'arte forestale.* **Firenze. 8vo. EUL.** Original binding. Signed in pencil 'H Cleghorn' on title-page, no annotations.

SIEMONI, Giovanni Carlo (1872). *Manuale d'arte forestale*. Firenze. 8vo. CML. At RBGE. Rebound. Flyleaf inscribed 'Dr Hugh Cleghorn with sincere regards of George P. Marsh. May 5 1875'.

Other European Countries

BAILEY, Frederick (1887). *Forestry in Hungary*. Edinburgh. 8vo. CML. At RBGE. Original paper wrappers. No annotations. (Note: A reprint from *Transactions of the Scottish Arboricultural Society* vol. 12(1)).

BROWN, John Croumbie (1883). *Finland, its Forests etc*. Edinburgh. 8vo. EUL. Original

binding. No signature or annotations.

BROWN, John Croumbie (1884). *Forestry in Norway*. Edinburgh. 8vo. EUL. Original binding, pages uncut. No signature or annotations.

BROWN, John Croumbie (1887). *Forests and Moisture*. Edinburgh. 8vo. EUL. Original binding. Signed in pencil 'H Cleghorn' on title-page, marginal lines on pp 82, 94.

BROWNE, Daniel Jaye (1846). *The Trees of America*. New York. 4to. CML. At RBGE. Original binding. Signed 'Dr Hugh Cleghorn' on flyleaf [not in his hand, might this have been written on by a bookseller, marking it for him?], no annotations.

CHALONER [Edward] & FLEMING [Quintin] [1850]. *The Mahogany Tree*. Liverpool and London. 8vo. CML. Not at RBGE (the copy kept was accessioned by RBGE in 1908).

COOPER, Ellwood (1876). *Forest Culture and Eucalyptus Trees*. San Francisco. 12mo. CML. At RBGE. Original binding. No signature, marginal lines on pp 48–51, 52 (beside references to G.P. Marsh and Cleghorn's Punjab Reports). But annotation on p 110 (Mauritius) and a manuscript index following the errata page at the end is not in Cleghorn's hand, so it probably belonged to someone else before him.

COULTAS, Harland (1860). *What May Be Learned from a Tree*. New York. 8vo. EUL.

EMERSON, George Barrell (1846). *Report on the Trees and Shrubs growing naturally in the Forests of Massachusetts*. Boston. 8vo. CML. At RBGE. Rebound. No signature or annotations. Bought by Cleghorn from Pamplin for 8 shillings in 1857.

FULLER, Andrew S. (1866). *The Forest Tree Culturist; a Treatise on the Cultivation of American Forest Trees*. New York. 12mo. CML. At RBGE. Original binding. Inscribed 'Dr Hugh Cleghorn' on flyleaf [not in his hand, might this have been written on by a bookseller, marking it for him?], no signature or annotations.

KÖLLAR, Vincent (1840). *Treatise on Insects injurious to Gardeners, Foresters, and Farmers*. Translated from the German by Jane and Mary Loudon, with notes by J.O. Westwood. London. 8vo. CML. At RBGE. Rebound. No signature or annotations.

MUELLER, Ferdinand von (1879). *Report on the Forest Resources of Western Australia*. London. 4to. CML. At RBGE. Original binding. No signature or annotations. [Note: Includes fine plates of eucalypts].

OHIO STATE FORESTRY
BUREAU (1886). *First Annual
Report (1885)*. Columbus. 8vo.
CML. Not at RBGE (the copy
kept was presented by Royal
Scottish Arboricultural
Society, 1895).

**PAPPE, Ludwig (1862). *Silva
Capensis*. Ed. 2. London &
Cape Town. 8vo. CML.** Not
at RBGE.

SARGENT, Charles Sprague
(1884). *Report on the Forests
of North America (exclusive of
Mexico)*. Washington. 4to.

CML. At RBGE. Original
binding. No annotations.

SARGENT, Charles Sprague
(1885). *The Woods of the United
States*. (Jesup Collection,
American Museum of Natural
History). New York. 8vo. CML.
Not at RBGE.

SCHLICH, Wilhelm (1889–95).
Manual of Forestry, vols 1–3.
London. 8vo. EUL. Original
bindings. Vol. 1 signed in pencil
'H Cleghorn' on title-page; no
annotations.

Agriculture (and land tenure)

INDIA

**ANON (1864). *Correspondence
relating to the Deterioration
of Lands from the Presence
in the Soil of Reh*. Calcutta.
8vo. CML.** At RBGE. Original
paper wrappers. No signature or
annotations.

**GREENAWAY, Thomas (1864).
*Farming in India, considered
as a Pursuit for European
Settlers of a Superior Class*.
London. 8vo. CML.** At RBGE.
Original binding. Signed in
pencil 'H Cleghorn' on title-
page, no annotations.

BRITAIN

ANON (1860). *The Gardener's and
Farmer's Reason Why*. London.
8vo. CML. Not at RBGE.

BAKER, John L. (1852). *Essay on
Farming of Northamptonshire*.
London. 8vo. EUL. Original
paper wrappers. No signature or
annotations.

BAXTER (1836). *Baxter's Agricultural And Horticultural Gleaner*. London. 8vo. EUL. Original binding. No signature or annotations.

CHAYTOR, Henry (1880). *Agricultural and Trade Depression*. London. 8vo. EUL. Original wrappers, bound with the Rev. C.A. Johns' *Forest Trees*. No signature or annotations.

CURTIS, William (1805). *Practical Observations on the British Grasses*. Ed. 4. London. 8vo. CML. At RBGE. Rebound. On flyleaf with many notes by previous owner 'Rob: Harriott B..., Lincolnshire'.

CURTIS, William (1824). *Practical Observations on the British Grasses*. Ed. 6, with additions by John Lawrence. London. 8vo. CML. At RBGE. In old binding. No signature or notes.

DONALD, James (1861). *Land Drainage, Embankment, and Irrigation*. Ed. 3. London. 8vo. CML. Not at RBGE.

EWART, John (1862). *The Land Drainer's Calculator*. London. 12mo. CML. At RBGE. In original card boards. No signature or annotations.

GREG, Robert Hyde (1842). *Scotch Farming in England*. London. 8vo. EUL.

HOLDITCH, Benjamin [?1836]. *Essay on the Weeds of Agriculture*. Ed. 4. London. 8vo. EUL.

Pamphlet bound by Cleghorn with works by G. Inzenga, J.A. Guillemin, Cleghorn & J.H. Balfour. No signature or annotations.

KEBBEL, Thomas Edward (1870). *The Agricultural Labourer*. London. 8vo. EUL. Original binding. Signed in pencil 'H Cleghorn' on title-page. Chapter 5 on 'Hiring', with marginal lines, e.g., passage on small farms not being desirable but the 'hope of obtaining them tends to thrift, sobriety and steadiness'; on weekly hiring and boarding 'checks early marriages, and prevents a redundant population, though at a considerable cost to morality'. (Note: The author was a Tory lawyer of the Inner Temple).

LANCE, Edward Jarman [1833]. *The Cottage Farmer, with portrait of Lord Kames*. London. 8vo. EUL. Original paper wrappers. No signature or annotations.

LAWSON, Peter & Son (1853). *Agrostographia*. Ed. 4. Edinburgh. 4to. EUL. Pamphlet bound by Cleghorn with works by A.W. Eichler, R.H. Greg, Scott & Redgrave. No signature or annotations.

ONSLOW, William Hillier, Earl of (1886). *Landlords and Allotments*. London. 8vo. EUL. Original binding. No signature or annotations.

SKIRVING, Robert Scot (1862). *Landlords and Labourers*. Ed. 2. Edinburgh. 8vo. EUL. Rebound, but enclosing original wrappers. No signature or annotations.

SMITH, Edward (1876). *The Peasant's Home*. London. 8vo. EUL. Original binding. Title-page stamped 'Presented by the Publisher', no signature or annotations. Second copy, in original binding, with no signature or annotations.

SYME, David (1877). *Agrostographia: a Treatise on the Cultivated Grasses and other Herbage and Forage Plants*. Edinburgh. 4to. CML. At RBGE. In original card boards. No signature or annotations.

WALKER, the Rev. John (1812). *Essays on Natural History and Rural Economy*. London. 8vo. CML. At RBGE. Original binding. Signed 'Robert Travers M.B. Trin. Coll. Dublin' on verso of title-page'; no Cleghorn annotations.

'WRITER to the SIGNET' [Thomas Gordon?] (1841). *The Farmer's Lawyer*. Edinburgh. 8vo. CML. At RBGE. Original binding. With H Cleghorn bookplate on front pastedown. Stuck on back pastedown newspaper clippings 'What gamekeepers may do to trespassers' and from the *Gardeners' Chronicle* on leases. Clearly used by Cleghorn.

EUROPE

ANNALI DI AGRICOLTURA SICILIANA (1852). Anno 1, Trimestre 4. Palermo. 8vo. EUL. Pamphlet bound by Cleghorn with works by G. Inzenga, B. Holditch, Cleghorn & J.H. Balfour. Original paper wrappers. Signed in ink 'H Cleghorn' on front wrapper.

ANON (1844). *Prospectus and Proposed Laws and Regulations of the Agricultural and Commercial Society of British Guiana*. Georgetown, Demeraray (sic).

8vo. Bound with Ingledew (1837) and Proceedings of Agri-Horticultural Societies of Bombay and Madras. H Cleghorn bookplate on flyleaf. Not in CML, acquired by RBGE from Cleghorn's library c. 2008 (ex Stravithie Sale).

BANFIELD, Thomas Charles (1846). *Agriculture on the Rhine*. London. 12mo. CML. At RBGE. Rebound. No signature, many annotations, e.g. p 10 (reference to India), pp 99–122.

CLEGHORN, H.F.C. (1870). *Notes on Agriculture of Malta and Sicily*. Edinburgh. 8vo. EUL. Pamphlet bound by Cleghorn with works by J.A. Guillemin, G. Inzenga, B. Holditch & J.H. Balfour.

HEHN, Victor (1870). *Kulturpflanzen und Hausthiere in ihrem Übergang aus Asien nach Griechenland und Italien, sowie in das übrige Europa*. Berlin. 8vo. CML. At RBGE. In old binding, but enclosing original boards. Inscribed on front board 'Dr H Cleghorn with best regards of Geo. P. Marsh Rome May 8 75'.

INZENGA, Giuseppe (1863). *Descrizione della istituto agrario Castelnuovo*. Palermo. 8vo. EUL. Pamphlet bound by Cleghorn with works by J.A. Guillemin, B. Holditch, Cleghorn & J.H. Balfour. Original wrappers. Signed on front wrapper 'Cleghorn' in pencil.

REST OF WORLD

SAINT-DENYS, Leon d'Hervey (1850). *Recherches sur l'agriculture et l'horticulture des Chinois*. Paris. 8vo. CML. At RBGE. In old binding. No signature or annotations.

SHIER, John (1847). *Report on Thorough Drainage*. Demerara. 8vo. EUL. Pamphlet bound by Cleghorn with works by Cleghorn, & Biasoletto (Att 65.4.8–12). Original wrappers. Front wrapper inscribed 'William [Hunter] Campbell Esquire W.S. Edinburgh from the Author'.

Horticulture (including botanic gardens)

INDIA

ANDERSON, Thomas (1869). List of Acanthaceae cultivated in Royal Botanical Gardens, Calcutta. *Journal of the Agricultural and Horticultural Society of India* 1(n.s.): 265–89. 8vo. Pamphlet (reprint, paginated 2–25) at RBGE, ex Museum (?CML). No marks to show Cleghorn's ownership.

BONAVIA, Emanuel (1890). *The Cultivated Oranges and Lemons of India and Ceylon*. London. Text 8vo; Atlas oblong. CML. Not at RBGE (another copy kept).

CLEGHORN, H.F.C. & REID, Francis Archibald [1853]. *Report and Proceedings of the Agri-Horticultural Society of Madras, 1853*. **[Madras]. 8vo.** At RBGE bound with Ingledew (1837) and Proceedings of Agri-Horticultural Society of Bombay. With H Cleghorn bookplate on flyleaf. Not in CML, acquired by RBGE from Cleghorn's library c. 2008 (ex Stravithie Sale).

GRIFFITH, William (1843). *Report on the Honb'le Company's Botanic Gardens, Calcutta. Parts I, V, VII.* **Calcutta. Folio. CML.** At RBGE. Flyleaf annotated 'Presented to the Medical Society Madras by the Medical Board 11 January 1844'; bound with Wallich's 1840 Report.

GRIFFITH, William (1845). On some plants in the H.C. Botanic Gardens. *Calcutta Journal of Natural History* 5: 355–73 + tt 24–26. 8vo. Pamphlet at RBGE, ex Museum (?CML). No Cleghorn annotations, but plates stitched to text in C's manner.

INGLEDEW, William & WIGHT, Robert (1837). *Treatise on the Culture of the Red Rose,*

Strawberry, Brazil Gooseberry, Peach, Mango and Grape Vine. **Madras. 8vo.** At RBGE bound with Proceedings of Agri-Horticultural Society of Bombay. With H Cleghorn bookplate on flyleaf. Not in CML, acquired by RBGE from Cleghorn's library c. 2008 (ex Stravithie Sale).

JENNINGS, Samuel (1867). The cultivation of orchids adapted to the climate of Calcutta. *Journal of the Agricultural and Horticultural Society of India* 14: 121–65. 8vo. Pamphlet (reprint, paginated 2–48) at RBGE, ex Museum (CML). Signed in pencil on front page 'H. Cleghorn'.

RIDDELL, Robert (1856). *Manual of Gardening for Western and Southern India.* **Ed. 3. Madras. 8vo. CML.** At RBGE. Rebound. Signed 'H. Cleghorn' on title-page. Corrections to native names on pp 122, 123; a letter pasted onto flyleaf 'Christian Knowledge Society's Office, Madras. 27 Sept. 1856. H.F.C. Cleghorn Esqre. M.D. Sir, By desire of Dr R. Riddell I have the pleasure to send you a bound copy of his "Manual on Gardening" recently printed at our Press; and beg the favour of an acknowledgement for the same. I am, Sir, Your most obedient Servt. [?B.] Mailer Supt. C.K.S.'

SAHARUNPUR & MUSSOORIE (1874–94). *Report on Progress of Botanical Gardens, 1879–89, 1892–94.* 14 vols. Allahabad. Folio. EUL.

SCOTT, John, (1869). A list of the higher cryptogams cultivated in Royal Botanical Gardens, Calcutta. *Journal of the Agricultural and Horticultural Society of India* 1(n.s.): 200–64. 8vo. Pamphlet (reprint, paginated 2–66) at RBGE, ex Museum (?CML). No Cleghorn annotations.

SPEEDE, George Thomas Frederic (1842). *The Indian Handbook of Gardening.* Ed. 2. Calcutta. 8vo. CML. At RBGE. Rebound. With H Cleghorn bookplate on front pastedown, signed 'H Cleghorn' in pencil on title-page, minor marginal lines on pp 20, 24, 25, 33 (plant growth). At back, advertisements by Thacker & Co for books on horticulture & agriculture, 1842 – Wight & Arnott 10 Rs, Wight's Contributions Rs 4/11, Lindley's Intro to Botany Rs 11/4, Loudon's Arboretum & Fruticetum 8 vols Rs 125.

VOIGT, Joachim Otto (1845). *Hortus Suburbanus Calcuttensis.* Calcutta. 8vo. EUL. Original binding. Front paste-down signed 'Charles Drew H.E.C.S. Madras Jany. 1856', title-page signed in pencil 'H Cleghorn', no annotations.

WALLICH, Nathaniel (1840). [*Report of Calcutta Botanic Garden*]. [Calcutta]. Folio. CML. At RBGE. Stamped on front page 'Madras Literary Society'; bound with Griffith's 1843 *Report*.

BRITAIN

AUSTEN, Ralph (1665). *A Treatise of Fruit-Trees.* Oxford. 12mo. CML. At RBGE. Rebound. No signature or annotations.

BALFOUR, John Hutton (1849). On the *Aconitum ferox* (Wall.,) which has recently flowered in the garden of the Edinburgh Horticultural Society. *Edinburgh New Philosophical Journal* 47: 366–9 + t. 5. 8vo. Pamphlet (reprint, paginated 2–6) at RBGE, ex Museum (?CML). No marks to show C's ownership.

BALFOUR, John Hutton (1849). On the *Aconitum ferox* … another copy, at EUL, bound by Cleghorn with works by L. Pappe, W.B. O'Shaughnessey, E.J. Waring, T.W.C. Martius, Cleghorn & R. Lyell (Att 65.5.1). With H Cleghorn bookplate on front paste-down, with C's ms contents list on flyleaf.

BALFOUR, John Hutton (1860).
Notice of the Palm-House
in the Royal Botanic Garden
Edinburgh. *Transactions of the
Botanical Society [of Edinburgh]*
6: 128–36. 8vo. Pamphlet at
RBGE, ex Museum (?CML).
Not found.

BALFOUR, John Hutton (1860).
Notice of the Palm-House …
Another copy at EUL, bound by
Cleghorn with works by
L. Pappe, W.B. O'Shaughnessey,
E.J. Waring, T.W.C. Martius,
Cleghorn & R. Lyell. Bookplate
on front paste-down, with C's
ms contents list on flyleaf.

BARRON, Archibald Farquharson
(1884). *British Apples*. London.
8vo. CML. At RBGE. In
old binding. No signature or
annotations.

BRADLEY, Richard (1717). *New
Improvements of Planting and
Gardening*. London. 8vo.
CML. At RBGE. Rebound. No
signature or annotations.

[BURBIDGE, Frederick William
(1877). *Horticulture*. London.
8vo.]. EUL. Original binding.
No signature or annotations.

DALE, Joseph (c. 1875) *On
the Chrysanthemum* (ed. 3).
London. 12mo. Original paper
wrappers, printed with title.
Pamphlet at RBGE, ex Museum
(?CML). No annotations by
Cleghorn.

DILLEN, John Jacob (1732).
Hortus Elthamensis. 2 vols.
London. Folio. CML. At
RBGE. Original binding. With
bookplate of John Duncanson
MD [possibly J.D. (1825–1876)
of Alloa] on front pastedown;
no Cleghorn signature, plates
annotated with names but not
by Cleghorn.

DRUMMOND, N. (1873). The
red fir of Oregon at Rossie
Priory. *Dundee Advertiser*.
Pamphlet at RBGE, ex Museum
(?CML). Not found.

EVELYN, John (1669).
Kalendarium Hortense. Ed 3.
London. 4to. CML. Not at
RBGE (other copies kept).

GLENNY, George (1861).
*Handbook to the Flower Garden
and Greenhouse*. Ed 5. London.
8vo. CML. At RBGE. Rebound
(ruthlessly trimmed). No
annotations.

HEREMAN, Samuel (1840).
*Blight on Flowers: or Figures and
Descriptions of the Insects infesting
the Flower Garden*. London. 8vo.
CML. At RBGE. Rebound. No
annotations.

HOGG, Robert (1851). *British
Pomology: the Apple*. London.
8vo. CML. At RBGE. Rebound.
Signed 'H Cleghorn' on title-
page, marginal line on pp 5
(reference to T.A. Knight), 104
(reference to Scotland).

HOOKER, William Jackson (1847). *Kew Gardens: a Popular Guide*. London. 8vo. CML. At RBGE. Original binding rebacked. Inscribed by Hooker on half-title 'Dawson Turner Esqr. July 14 1847', and on flyleaf by Dawson Turner 'one of a very few copies printed on large & thick paper. That presented to the Queen was precisely like this, except in having the Royal arms on the cover.– A present from Sir W.J. Hooker, whose Autograph see on the following leaf'. Several cuttings tipped in (including one of Decimus Burton's new gates from Kew Green, 1846). Note: Presumably given by Hooker to C at some point after Turner's death (which took place in 1858), though C had purchased a copy of the work from Pamplin in 1856.

JACKSON, Benjamin Daydon (1876). *Catalogue of Plants cultivated in the garden of John Gerard in the years 1596–99*. Privately printed. London. 4to. CML. At RBGE. Original boards. Numbered copy 84, inscribed to 'Dr Cleghorn St Andrews N[orth] B[ritain] … B. Daydon Jackson 9 July 1878'.

KEW, ROYAL BOTANIC GARDENS [1880]. *Records of the Gardens* (J. Smith). London. 8vo. EUL.

KNOWLES, George Beauchamp & WESTCOTT, Frederick (1837–38). *The Floral Cabinet*. 2 vols. London. 4to. CML. At RBGE. Original binding. With H Cleghorn bookplate in both volumes.

LINDLEY, John (1841). *Pomologia Britannica*. 3 vols. London. 8vo. CML. At RBGE. Rebound. No signature or annotations.

LINDLEY, John (1855). *The Theory and Practice of Horticulture*. London. 8vo. CML. At RBGE. Rebound. With H Cleghorn bookplate in front paste-down, and signed in pencil on title-page. On back flyleaf some page references given for 'Frost' 'Peat' and some illegible annotations, one about ?spruce bark. 1856 Longman's catalogue bound in at end. Purchased by Cleghorn from Pamplin in 1856.

LODDIGES, Conrad & Sons (undated). *Orchideae*. London. 12mo. CML. At RBGE. Rebound. No signature or annotations.

LOUDON, John Claudius [1832]. *Catalogue of all the Plants Indigenous, Cultivated in, or Introduced to Britain*. New edition. London. 8vo. CML. At RBGE. Original binding. No signature or annotations.

LOUDON, John Claudius (1843). *On the Laying out, Planting, and Managing of Cemeteries*. London. 8vo. CML. At RBGE. Original binding (rebacked). Signed 'H Cleghorn' in pencil on flyleaf; bookplate of Thomas Sopwith on front pastedown, inscribed on title-page (presumably to Sopwith) 'From the Author'.

LOUDON, John Claudius (1844). *Arboretum et Fruticetum Britannicum*. 8 vols. Ed. 2. London. 8vo. CML. At RBGE. 4 text vols rebound, 4 of plates in original bindings. Stamped on flyleaf 'J. Rohde'.

LOUDON, Jane (1843–44). *The Ladies' Flower-Garden of Ornamental Perennials*. 2 vols. London. 4to. CML. Not at RBGE (another copy kept).

LOUDON, Jane (1844–54). *The Ladies' Flower-Garden of Ornamental Annuals*. 3 vols. London. Vols. 1 and 2, 4to, Vol. 3, 8vo. CML. Not at RBGE (another copy kept).

[MARSHALL, William] (1785). *Planting and Ornamental Gardening*. London. 8vo. CML. Not at RBGE.

[MARSHALL, William] (1796). *Planting and Rural Ornament*. 2 vols. London. 8vo. CML. At RBGE. Original leather binding. No signature or annotations;

a bookplate has been removed from front pastedowns of both volumes.

MOORE, David (1875). On the successful establishment of *Loranthus europeus* [sic] on oak trees in the Botanic Garden, Glasnevin. *Journal of the Royal Dublin Society* 6: 383–7. 8vo. Original wrappers, with title printed on front. 8vo. Pamphlet (reprint, paginated 4–8) at RBGE, ex Museum (?CML). No Cleghorn annotations.

PHILLIPS, Henry (1820). *Pomarium Britannicum*. London. 8vo. CML. Not at RBGE (copy of an 1821 edition kept).

SUTHERLAND, James (1683). *Hortus Medicus Edinburgensis; or a Catalogue of the Plants in the Physical Garden at Edinburgh*. Edinburgh. 8vo. CML. Not at RBGE.

WOOD, Samuel (1877). *Multum-in-Parvo Gardening*. London. 8vo. CML. At RBGE. Original binding. Signed in pencil on title-page; no other annotations.

WOOD, Sara (1877). *The Dwellers in our Gardens*. Ed. 2. London. 8vo. CML. At RBGE. Original binding. No signature or annotations.

BARJAVEL, Casimir François Henri (1830). *Traité complet de la culture de l'olivier*. Marseille & Paris. 8vo. CML. At RBGE. In old binding. No signature or annotations.

BOISDUVAL, Jean Alphonse (1867). *Essai sur l'entomologie horticole*. Paris. 8vo. CML. At RBGE. Rebound. No signature or annotations.

BREUIL, Alphonse du (1868). *Instruction elémentaire sur la conduite des arbres fruitiers*. Ed. 7. Paris.12mo. CML. At RBGE. Rebound. No signature or annotations.

CASABONO, Antonio (1862). *Indicatore teorico-pratico d'orticoltura*. Genova. 8vo. EUL. Original paper wrappers, pages uncut. No signature or notes.

COMMELIN, Caspar (1715). *Horti Medici Amstelaedamensis Plantae Rariores et Exoticae*. Lugduni Batavorum. Bound with *Praeludia Botanica, Lugduni Batavorum*, 1715. 4to. CML. At RBGE. Rebound. No signature.

FERRARI, Johan Battista (1646). *Flora seu de Florum Cultura, Libri IV*. Editio nova by Bernh. Rottendorf. Amsterdam. 8vo. CML. Rebound. With bookplate of Earl of Moira transferred to front pastedown.

Index, following dedication, signed 'Sr. John Rawdon'.

HERMANN, Paul (1687). *Horti Academici Lugduno-Batavi Catalogus*. Lugduni Batavorum. 8vo. CML. Bookplate of Sir John Anstruther of Anstruther on verso of title-page; signed in pencil on flyleaf 'Hugh F.C. Cleghorn 1840'.

MARTINS, Charles (1866). *Floraison en pleine terre du* Dasylirion gracile *Zucc. au Jardin des Plantes de Montpellier comparée a celle du* Phormium tenax *et de l'*Agave americana. Montpellier. 8vo. Pamphlet (reprint from *Annales de la Societé d'horticulture et de botanique de l'Hérault*, paginated 4–5 + t) at RBGE, ex Museum (?CML). No Cleghorn annotations.

MICHELI, Petrus Antonius & TOZZETTI, Johannis Targioni (1748). *Catalogus Plantarum Horti Caesarei Florentini*. Florentiae. 4to. CML. At RBGE. In Cleghorn's boards (rebacked). No signature or annotations.

[NEILL, Patrick] (1823). *Journal of a Horticultural Tour through Flanders, Holland, and the North of France in 1817, by a Deputation of the Caledonian Horticultural Society*. Edinburgh. 8vo. CML. At RBGE. In old binding. No signature or annotations.

ROBINSON, William (1868). *Gleanings from French Gardens*. London. 8vo. CML. At RBGE. Rebound. Marginal line on p 222 about how to take cuttings of oleander.

RODA, Marcellino & Giuseppe (1868). *Coltivazione naturale e forzata degli sparagi*. Ed. 2. Torino & Napoli. 8vo. CML. At RBGE. Rebound. No signature or annotations.

RODA, Marcellino & Giuseppe (1874). *Manuale del frutticoltore italiano*. Roma, Torino, Milano & Firenze. 8vo. CML. At RBGE. Original binding. No signature or annotations.

SAVI, Gaetano (1832). Sul ciliegio pendulo (*Prunus Semperflorens* Wild). *Giornale Agrario Toscana* 6: 467–72. 8vo. Pamphlet (reprint, with title printed on front cover, paginated 4–8) at RBGE, ex Museum (?CML). No Cleghorn annotations.

TINEO, Vincenzo (1827). *Catalogus Plantarum Horti Regii Panormitani*. Palermo. 8vo. EUL. Rebound, but enclosing original paper wrappers. Front wrapper inscribed 'Dr Walker Arnott from M Tineo'. (Note. Doubtless lent to him by Arnott in 1868, immediately after C had been in Sicily and while C was lecturing for him in Glasgow, but not returned as Arnott died).

Geographical (physical, geography, travels, zoology, etc.)

India & Ceylon

ABREU, Robert (1858). *Journal of a Tour through the Pegu and Martaban Provinces.* **Maulmain. 8vo. CML.** At RBGE. Rebound. Verso of flyleaf inscribed 'To, the Madras Spectator, Madras. This volume is presented with much respect by his most obdt. servant The Author. Maulmain 30th Jany. 1858', and by Cleghorn 'Recd.

from Mr Wray, HC'; annotation on p 51. (Note. Abreu was John McClelland's assistant).

ACOSTA, Joseph d' (1600). *Histoire naturelle et moralle des indes, tant orientalles qu' occidentalles.* **Composée en Castillan et traduite en François par R.R. Cauxois. Paris. 8vo. CML.** Not at RBGE (Hope's copy kept).

ADAMS, Andrew Leith (1867). *Wanderings of a Naturalist in India.* **Edinburgh. 8vo. CML.** At RBGE. Rebound. Signed 'H Cleghorn' on title-page, no annotations.

BAIKIE, Robert (1857). *The Neilgherries.* **Ed. 2, edited by W.H. Smoult. Calcutta. 8vo. CML.** At RBGE. In original binding (map missing from back pocket). Signed on recto of flyleaf 'H Cleghorn to Forest Dept', no annotations.

BARNES, George Carnac (1862). *Report on the Settlement in Kangra.* **Lahore. 8vo. EUL.** Original paper wrappers. Signed on front wrapper 'H Cleghorn' in pencil, no annotations.

[BENTLEY, John] (1823). *Essays Relative to the Habits, Character, and Moral Improvement of the Hindoos.* **London. 8vo. CML.** Not at RBGE.

CARTER, Henry John (1857). *Atlas to Geological Papers on Western India.* **Bombay. 8vo (oblong). EUL.** No signature or notes.

COTTON, Arthur & CAUTLEY, Proby T. (1864). *The Ganges Canal.* **[London]. 4to. CML.** Not at RBGE.

COTTON, Frederik Conyers (1856). *Report of a Tour of Inspection of the Northern Littoral Districts of the* *Madras Presidency ... with Observations Thereon by C.E. Faber.* **Madras. Folio. EUL.** Original binding. Signed in pencil 'H Cleghorn' on title-page, no annotations.

CUNNINGHAM, Alexander (1854). *Ladák.* **London. 8vo. CML.** At RBGE. Original binding. Signed by Cleghorn on title-page; annotations pp 71, 116, 167 etc.

FORBES, Gordon S. (1855). *Wild Life in Canara and Ganjam.* **London. 8vo. CML.** At RBGE. Original binding. No signature or annotations.

GERARD, Alexander (1841). *Account of Koonawur in the Himalaya.* **Edited by George Lloyd. London. 8vo. CML.** In old binding (though not original as pages savagely trimmed). Signed 'H Cleghorn' on title-page; annotations on pp 70 (price of pine nuts at Chini May '62 '2 seers for 4 as i.e. ... ana per pound'), 72 (price of walnuts at Pangi), 73, 82, 84, 87, 118 (prayer beads), 199, 216–8, 234–5, 299–304 etc.

GRIFFITH, William (1847). *Journals of Travels in Assam, Burma, Bootan, Affghanistan, etc.* **Calcutta. 8vo. CML.** At RBGE. Rebound. Signed 'H Cleghorn' in pencil on flyleaf, occasional annotation – p 31 (on tobacco 'difft. from My[?sore]'), spelling corrections.

GRIFFITH, William (1847). *Journals of Travels in Assam, Burma, Bootan, Affghanistan, etc.* **Calcutta. 8vo. EUL.** Original binding. With H. Cleghorn bookplate on front pastedown, title-page stamped 'Revenue & Judicial Department Madras', beside which C has added 'H Cleghorn by purchase at auction', pages 313–502, relating to Afghanistan, are heavily annotated, especially with plant names, e.g. p 337 (a reference to 'covered with an Artemisioid odoriferous plant') to which he has added 'Chota Lahul like this'.

[HAIG, T.F. (1856). *Report on Navigability of the River Godavery.* **(2 pts – text + maps). Madras. Folio]. EUL.** Original binding. No signature or annotations.

HAMILTON, Francis (*né* BUCHANAN) (1819). *Genealogies of the Hindus.* Edinburgh. 8vo. EUL. Original binding. Title-page inscribed 'From the author' (presumably to Hugh Cleghorn senior).

HAMILTON, Francis (*né* BUCHANAN) (1819). *An Account of the Kingdom of Nepal.* Edinburgh. 4to. CML. Not at RBGE (Sir George Watt's copy kept).

HAMILTON, Francis (*né* BUCHANAN) (1833). *A Geographical, Statistical and* *Historical Description of the District of Dinajpur.* **Calcutta. 8vo. EUL.** Original binding. Signed in pencil 'H Cleghorn' on title-page, no annotations.

HARKNESS, Henry (1832). *Description of a Singular Aboriginal Race Inhabiting the Summit of the Neilgherry Hills.* **London. 8vo. EUL.** Original boards. Flyleaf signed in pencil 'Dr Cleghorn Wakefield', and on title-page in pencil 'H Cleghorn', no annotations. (Note: With lithographs based on drawings by McCurdy; bookseller's catalogue of Smith Elder bound in at end).

HENDERSON, George & HUME, Allan Octavian (1873). *Lahore to Yarkand.* **London. 8vo. CML. At RBGE.** In original binding. Signed by I[saac] A[nderson] Henry on title-page, with copious annotations presumably by Henry.

HOFFMEISTER, Werner (1848). *Travels in Ceylon and Continental India.* **Translated from the German. Edinburgh. 12mo. CML.** At RBGE. Rebound. No signature or annotations.

HONIGBERGER, John Martin (1852). *Thirty-five Years in the East.* **2 vols. London. 8vo. CML.** At RBGE. Rebound as one volume. No signature or annotations.

HOOKER, Joseph Dalton (1854). *Himalayan Journals,* **2 vols. London. 8vo. CML.** Not at RBGE (another copy kept). Note: Cleghorn paid £1 16 shillings for this from Pamplin in October 1854.

HÜGEL, Baron Charles (1845). *Travels in Kashmir and the Punjab, with notes by Major T.B. Jervis.* **London. 8vo. CML.** At RBGE. Rebound. No signature, some marginal marks and annotations, but almost certainly not by C, as these relate to Kashmir where he never went.

KELAART, Edward Frederick (1852). *Prodromus Faunae Zeylanicae.* Ceylon. 8vo. EUL. Original binding American Missionary Press Bindery Madras. H Cleghorn bookplate on front pastedown, no notes.

KNIGHT, Captain [William Henry] (1863). *Diary of a Pedestrian in Cashmere and Tibet.* **London. 8vo. CML.** At RBGE. Rebound. No signature, title-page stamped 'Officers Mess 90th LI', Persian annotation on p 73 (probably not by Cleghorn).

LAHORE (undated). *Maps connected with report on Land Revenue Settlement … 1865–69.* **Folio. EUL.** Original binding. Label on front board inscribed 'Dr Cleghorn' in ink.

[LISBOA, J.C., GRAY, W., WILSON, G.H.D. and McRAE, J.G.] (1886). *Gazetteer of the Bombay Presidency. Vol. XXV Botany.* Bombay. 8vo. CML. Not at RBGE (another copy kept).

MACKAY, Alexander (1853). *Western India: Reports Addressed to the Chambers of Commerce of Manchester, Liverpool, Blackburn, and Glasgow.* **London. 8vo. EUL.** Original binding. With H Cleghorn bookplate on front pastedown, title-page also signed in pencil. (Note: Concerns cotton and the development of railways).

McIVOR, William Graham (1865). *Description of an Invention for Overcoming the Inertia of Heavy Bodies.* **'Unpublished'. Ootacamund. 4to. EUL.** In original boards. Front board signed in ink 'Dr Cleghorn', illustrated with four photographs of composite drawings.

MALLOCH, Daniel Edward (1852). *Siam … Imports and Exports.* **Calcutta. 8vo. EUL.** Original binding. Flyleaf inscribed in pencil 'H Cleghorn', first flyleaf inscribed illegibly 'Mr […] Acklutee…[?] presented by the Author August 1852'.

MARKHAM, Clements Robert (1862). *Travels in Peru and India.* London. 8vo. CML. At RBGE. In original binding. No signature or annotations.

MARKHAM, Clements Robert (1876). *Narratives of the Mission of George Bogle to Tibet, and of the Journey of Thomas Manning to Lhasa.* London. 8vo. CML. At RBGE. Rebound. Signed 'H Cleghorn' on title-page, no annotations.

MARSHALL, Henry (1846). *Ceylon.* London. 8vo. EUL. Rebound. No signature or annotations.

MARTIN, Robert Montgomery (1838). *History of Eastern India.* Vol. 3. London. 8vo. EUL. Original binding. With H. Cleghorn bookplate on front pastedown, flyleaf inscribed 'B. Ogilvie' 'Purchased H Cleghorn' (lest someone think he had stolen it?).

MONTGOMERIE, Thomas George (1874). *Routes in the Western Himalayas, Kashmir etc.* Dehra Doon. 8vo. EUL. Rebound, but enclosing original paper wrappers. Note: One of relatively few with EUL armorial bookplate annotated in ink 'Cleghorn bequest', no signature or annotations. (Note: Includes an interesting 'Polymetric Table' at end – a 2D chequerboard of distances).

MOORCROFT, William & TREBECK, George (1841). *Travels in the Himalayan Provinces, etc.* **Edited by H.H. Wilson. 2 vols. London. 8vo. CML.** At RBGE. Rebound. With Cleghorn's signature on title-page of vol. 1; vol. 1 annotated by Cleghorn on pp 261, 267, 350–2 (tea trade); pp 178–80, 82, 84 (Kulu); newspaper cutting about Elgin's crossing of Chandra stuck in p 193, 248, 267, 328–9; vol. 2 annotated by Cleghorn pp 47, 256, but title-page signed 'P. Elwin Williams, Amritsar, May 30th 61'.

MOUAT, Frederic John (1863). *Adventures and Researches among the Andaman Islanders.* **London. 8vo. CML.** At RBGE. Rebound. Signed 'H Cleghorn' on title-page, the title-page also inscribed 'Officers Library 98th Regt. No 3', no annotations.

MULLER, C.F. (1846). *History of the Sikhs.* **Calcutta. 8vo. CML.** At RBGE. In original binding. With grand armorial bookplate of 'Lewis Balfour Merchant Calcutta' and annotated by him 17 February 1847. Cleghorn must have bought this in Calcutta. Balfour (1817–1870) was Robert Louis Stevenson's maternal uncle (Plate 13.iv).

[MURDOCH, Dr John] (1888). *Pictorial Tour Round India.* **Madras. Folio. CML.** Not at RBGE.

PURDOM, W. (1860). *Report on Navigation of the Punjab Rivers*. London. 8vo. EUL.

ST JOHN, Spenser (1862). *Life in the Forests of the Far East*, Vol. 1 only (of 2). London. 8vo. At RBGE, in original binding. Not in CML, acquired 2016 from Alan Grant (ex Stravithie sale). Signed in pencil on front flyleaf 'Dr Cleghorn Stravithy St Andrews'.

THOMSON, Thomas (1852). *Western Himalaya and Tibet*. London. 8vo. CML. At RBGE. Rebound. Signed in pencil 'H Cleghorn Stravithy' on title-page, many marginalia most minor, pp 335, 337 343 about *Eremurus* ' abundant Fl early young leaves used as spinage By ...' [savagely trimmed], 361; 390 (against plant list), 'all in Lahul'; 455 (hemp) etc; 496–7 (additions to index including *Daphne*, jhula). This book cost 15 shillings new (L. Reeve catalogue).

THORNTON, Edward (1844). *Gazetteer of the Countries adjacent to India on the North-West.* 2 vols. London. 8vo. CML. At RBGE. Rebound. No signature, a few annotations in vol. 2 – p 128 (plant names) and geographical ones on pp 83, 122, 124, 125, 150–2 and possibly others.

TORRENS, Henry D'Oyley (1862). *Travels in Ladák, Tartary, and Kashmir*. London. 8vo. CML. At RBGE. Rebound. Signed 'H Cleghorn' on title-page.

TREVELYAN, Charles E. (1860). *Minutes Relating to Tour in South India*. [Madras]. Folio. EUL. No wrappers. No signature or annotations.

VIGNE, Godfrey Thomas (1840). *Personal Narrative of a Visit to Ghuzni, Kabul, and Afghanistan*. London. 8vo. CML. At RBGE. Rebound. No signature or annotations.

WALKER, John (1854). *Map of the Punjab, Western Himalaya, and adjoining parts of Tibet*. London. CML. At RBGE. No annotations, but evidently heavily used.

BRITAIN AND EUROPE

CHARDON, C.A. (1857). *Des inondations*. Paris. 4to. EUL. Pamphlet bound by Cleghorn with works by A.W. Eichler, R.H. Greg, P. Lawson, Scott & Redgrave. No signature or annotations.

DENON, Dominique Vivant (1790). *Travels through Sicily and Malta*. Perth. 8vo. EUL.

GULIA, Gavinus (1861). *Tentamen Ichthyologiae Melitensis*. Malta. 8vo. EUL. Rebound, but enclosing original wrappers. On front wrapper Cleghorn has added '1861' in pencil as the date of publication.

LANDSBOROUGH, the Rev. David (1847). *Arran*. Ed 2. Edinburgh. 8vo. CML. Not sent to RBGE.

MARCELLUS, Marie-Louis-Auguste Demartin du Tyrac, Comte de (1841). *Vingt jours en Sicile*. Paris. 8vo. EUL. In original wrappers. Signed on front wrapper 'H Cleghorn' in pencil; marginal marks on pp 72 (beside account of Palermo botanic garden) and 153 (description of a blue lizard).

MORREN, Charles François Antoine (?1838). *Huit jours à Newcastle* [for British Associaion meeting at which the author read paper on pollination of *Vanilla*] *en 1838*. 8vo. EUL. A collection of 17 pamphlets by Morren, bound, with armorial bookplate with the motto 'Naturae Donum' [Peacock family arms] on front pastedown, no signature or annotations. Other titles: De la spécialité des cultures propres aux établissements horticoles de Liège. Les femmes et les fleurs. Horticulture et philosophie. Mémoires pour servir aux éloges biographiques des savans de la Belgique. Rapport sur le mémoire de Mr A. Trinchinetti de Monza. Nouvelles remarques sur la morphologie des ascidies. Notes sur l'excitabilité et le mouvement des feuilles chez les Oxalis. Notice sur l'histologie de l'Agaricus epixylon. Observations sur l'anatomie des Hedychium. Note sur ... "Recherches sur le mouvement de l'anatomie du style du Goldfussia anisophylla". Expériences et observations sur la gomme des cycadées. Observations sur l'anatomie des Musa. Observations sur l'épaisseur de la membrane végétale dans ... l'appareil pileux. Observations sur la formation des huiles dans les plantes. Notes sur les fruits aromatiques due Leptotes bicolor. (Various publishers, Liège and Brussels).

PERTH MUSEUM (1881). *Catalogue of the Vertebrate Animals*. Perth. 8vo. CML. Not sent to RBGE by Museum.

ROZET, C.A. (1856). *Moyens de forcer les torrents*. **Paris. 8vo. EUL.** A pamphlet, in original paper wrappers. No signature or annotations.

SCHEUCHZER, Johann Jacob (1708). *Ouresiphoites Helveticus, sine Itinera Alpina Tria*. London. 4to. CML. At RBGE. In old binding (rebacked). With bookplate of R.H. Alexander Bennet (of Beckenham, Kent). Has this been transferred from the correct original book when rebacked? No signature.

SCOTT & REDGRAVE, Messrs (undated). *Sewage Tracts. Nos 1–5*. London. 8vo. EUL. Pamphlet bound by Cleghorn with works by A.W. Eichler, C.A. Chardon, R.H. Greg, P. Lawson. No signature or annotations.

SIMPSON, James (1884). *Notes accompanying a microscopical demonstration of* Saprolegnia ferax. Edinburgh. 8vo. Pamphlet at RBGE, ex Museum (?CML). No Cleghorn annotations, but it could reflect his late fishery interests.

STIRLING, Archibald Buchanan (1879–80). Additional observations on the fungous

disease affecting salmon and other fish [2 & 3]. *Proceedings of the Royal Society of Edinburgh* 10: 232–50; 370–8. 8vo. Two pamphlets at RBGE, ex Museum (?CML). No Cleghorn annotations; both inscribed on front covers 'With the Authors Compliments'.

TARTINI, F. (1838). *Memorie sul bonificamento della maremme toscane.* **Florence. 8vo. EUL.** Original paper wrappers, pages uncut. No signature or annotations.

TENORE, M. (1827). *Essai sur la geographie physique etc*. Naples. 8vo. EUL. In original paper wrappers, pages uncut. No signature or annotations.

-

REST OF WORLD

BROWN, John Croumbie (1875). *Hydrology of South Africa*. Kirkcaldy. 8vo. EUL. Original binding. No signature or annotations.

BROWNE, Patrick (1756). *The Civil and Natural History of Jamaica*. London. Folio. CML. At RBGE. Rebound. No signature, annotations on pp 200 (*Achras*), 245 (*Grias cauliflora* and a *Botanical Magazine* reference), 262 (*Duranta ellisii*), 300 (switches of 'Brya' for 'the scourging of

refractory slaves' is, unusually for C, marked with '!!!'), 352 (*Hura crepitans*) etc; the plates (of which many are by G.D. Ehret) mostly annotated with Linnaean names by C.

DANVERS, Frederick Charles (1878?). *A Century of Famines*. [London]. Folio. EUL. Original wrappers. No signature or annotations.

ELLIS, Henry (1817). *Journal of the Proceedings of the late Embassy to China*. London. 4to. CML. At

RBGE. Rebound. No signature or annotations.

GARDNER, George (1849). *Travels in the Interior of Brazil.* Ed. 2. London. 8vo. CML. At RBGE. Rebound. With T.C. Archer's signature on title-page, no annotations. This cost 12 shillings new (L. Reeve catalogue).

GUILLEMIN, Jean Antoine (1839). *Rapport sur sa mission au Brésil.* Paris. 8vo. EUL. Pamphlet bound by Cleghorn with works by G. Inzenga, B. Holditch, Cleghorn & J.H. Balfour (Att 65.4.14–19). Original wrappers. Inscribed on front cover 'a Monsieur R. Brown Hommage de l'Auteur'.

HECTOR, James (1883). *Handbook of New Zealand.* Ed. 3. Wellington. 8vo. CML. At RBGE. In original binding. No signature or annotations.

HERBERT, Sir Thomas (1677). *Some Years' Travels into divers Parts of Africa and Asia the Great.* London. 4to. CML. At RBGE. In Cleghorn's binding. On front pastedown a long biography of Herbert copied by Cleghorn from *Athenae Oxoniensis*.

KAEMPFER, Engelbert (1712). *Amoenitatum Exoticarum Politico-Physico-Medicarum Fasciculi V.* Lemgoviae. 4to. CML. At RBGE. Rebound. Flyleaf with H Cleghorn bookplate, and signed in pencil

'H Cleghorn', with old signature 'H Hastings'; C has added Linnaean names pp. 761–907 (and some *Botanical Magazine* references).

[KINLOCH, Charles Walter] (1853). *Die Zieke Reiziger [The Invalid Traveller]; or Rambles in Java and the Straits in 1852 by a "Bengal Civilian".* London. 8vo. CML. At RBGE. In original binding. With H Cleghorn bookplate on front pastedown, signed on title-page, no annotations, with bookseller's label 'sold by Pharoah & Co. Ath[enaeum]. Library Madras'.

MARSH, George Perkins (1864). *Man and Nature or Physical Geography as Modified by Human Action.* London. 8vo. CML. At RBGE. Rebound. Signed in ink 'H Cleghorn' on title-page. Annotations on pp 60 (vine on Stromboli) 'I saw one at Stromboli, which unless my memory fails, was 9" in diameter Y'and 64 (name of oranges) 'It is applied I think to a particular orange – the large egg orange? Y The Cintra Orange is mentioned by Abulfeda. Although not in his hand these are almost certainly by Henry Yule, who refers to the latter in Hobson-Jobson. Also pp 65 [apparent increase in flora of St Helena] 'could Botany be relied on'; 339 [formation of grassland from tidal mud] 'Bengal chur' [not-C] pp vii–xv – many marks including '2' and

'3' against items of bibliography; 18 [skeletons in Sicilian caves] 'see also Geol. Mus. Palermo' [C]; 68 on invasive *Anacharis alsinastrum* 'see Proc. Edin Bot Soc' [C]; 72 [diseases of grapes] 'also Bussahir' [C]; 74 [olives] '... Paul' [not-c]; 184, original Latin from Sandys 1611 quote about cotton on Malta, apparently correcting an English translation [C]; 221–2 on coal in England marked up for quoting 'Begin' 'omit' (3 omits); 554 'Holinshed p. 222' added to index [C]. Numerous underlinings, marginal lines and double lines, and a curious tick/ sideways S (more than in most of his books) against passages about deforestation, climate, floods etc.

MARSH, George Perkins (1870). *L'uomo e la natura*. Firenze. 8vo. EUL. Original paper covers. Signed on front cover 'H Cleghorn' in ink, pages uncut, no dedication, no annotations.

MARSH, George Perkins (1874). *The Earth as Modified by Human Action*. London. 8vo. CML. At RBGE. Original binding. With letter sent by Marsh with Appendix (which is attached at end) from Rome Dec 18 1874. Signed in pencil 'H Cleghorn' on title-page. With Marsh additions/corrections on pp vi, 25, 194, 195, 208, 441 etc. Marginal lines (by C) on p 92 (extinction of wolf), 306, 307

SONNERAT, Pierre (1776). *Voyage à la Nouvelle Guinée.* **Paris. 4to. CML.** At RBGE. Rebound. No signature or annotations.

SONNERAT, Pierre (1782). *Voyage aux Indes Orientales et à la Chine.* **2 vols. Paris. 4to. CML.** At RBGE. Rebound. No signature; plates of plants in vol. 2 annotated with Linnaean names by C.

THÉVENOT, J. de (1687). *Travels into the Levant.* Translated from the French. London. Folio. CML. At RBGE. Rebound. No signature or annotations.

[TURGOT, Etienne François] (1758). *Mémoire instructif sur la manière de rassembler, de preparer, de conserver, et d'envoyer les diverses curiosités d'histoire naturelle.* Lyon. 8vo. CML. At RBGE, rebound. No signature or annotations.

WINTERBOTTOM, Thomas (1803). *Account of the Native Africans in the Neighbourhood of Sierra Leone.* 2 vols. London. 8vo. CML. At RBGE. Two vols rebound as one. No signature or annotations. (Note: Surely part of his grandfather's library).

WOLFF, Joseph (1848). *Narrative of a Mission to Bokhara in the years 1843–1845, to ascertain the fate of Colonel Stoddart and Captain Conolly.* Ed 5. Edinburgh. 8vo. CML. At

RBGE. In original binding. With dedication in Persian and English from the author 'As a token of regard to my friend Padre Robert Stevenson. Jos Wolff'.

WÜLLERSTORF-URBAIR, Bernhard Aloys von (1861–62). *Reise der Oesterreichischen Fregatte Novara um die Erde, in 1857–59.* **3 vols. Wien. 8vo. CML.** At RBGE. In original bindings. No signature or annotations.

Palaeontology

BAILEY, Jacob Whitman (1846). On the detection of spirally dotted, or scalariform ducts, and other vegetable tissues in anthracite coal. *American Journal of Science and Arts* 1 (ser. 2): 407–10. 8vo. Pamphlet (reprint, paginated 2–14) at RBGE, ex Museum (?CML). No marks to show Cleghorn's ownership.

BOWERBANK, James Scott (1840). On a new variety of vascular tissue found in a fossil wood from the London Clay. *Transactions of the Microscopical Society of London* 1: 16–18 + t. 2. 8vo. Original paper covers. Pamphlet (reprint, paginated 2–3) at RBGE, ex Museum (?CML). No marks to show Cleghorn's ownership; dedication on title-page 'R. Brown Esq. FRS with the Authors respects'.

CARRUTHERS, William (1866). On the structure and affinities of Lepidodendron.

Journal of Botany 4: 337–48 + tt 55, 56. 8vo. Original paper wrappers. Pamphlet (reprint, paginated 2–12) at RBGE, ex Museum (CML). Front cover inscribed by author 'Revd. R.T. Lowe with kind regards of Wm. Carruthers' and in pencil by Cleghorn 'Lepidodendron & Calamites (Carruthers)'. Marginal marks by Cleghorn. This and the following were requested by Cleghorn for his 1869 talk to the BSE reviewing botanical work of the year, inserted in this is a covering letter to Cleghorn from Henry Trimen: 'British Museum 8 Nov 1869. My dear Sir, As Mr Carruthers is prevented by a sort of whitlow from using his right hand he has asked me to answer your letter. He sends you some of his published papers on fossil botany; all he has by him – the results of his work in the Flora of the Coal Measures is given in the Royal Institution lecture afterwards printed in the Geological Magazine. The detailed account of the fruit of Calamites you will find in the "Journal of Botany" for 1867 p. 349. Of the memoirs sent, one or two bear upon the fossil plants of secondary rocks. The first of this series was published also in the Journal of Botany, 1867, p. 1. Mr Carruthers is sorry that he has no copy of this paper to send you– The important paper on fossil Cycadeae which he read at the Linnean Society's meeting in June 1868 is not yet printed, though the illustrative plates are finished & the whole is ready for the printers– In this two new extinct tribes of Cycadeae are established in addition to the existing ones– Trusting this will answer your purpose. I am, dear sir Yours faithfully Henry Trimen'.

CARRUTHERS, William (1867). On an Airodeous fruit from the Stonesfield slate. *Geological Magazine* 4: 146–8 + t. 8. 8vo. Original paper wrappers. Pamphlet (reprint, paginated [1–]2, lacking plate) at RBGE, ex Museum (CML). Front cover annotated by Cleghorn 'Aroideous Fruit (Carruthers) Geol. Mag. April 1867'.

CARRUTHERS, William (1867). On Cycadoidea yatesii, a fossil cycadean stem from the Potton Sands, Bedfordshire. *Geological Magazine* 4: 199–201 + t. 9. 8vo. Original paper wrappers. Pamphlet (reprint, paginated 2–3) at RBGE, ex Museum (CML). Front cover annotated by Cleghorn 'Geol. Mag. May 1867'.

CARRUTHERS, William (1868). British fossil Pandaneae. *Geological Magazine* 5: 153–6 + t. 9. 8vo. Original paper wrappers. Pamphlet (reprint, paginated 2–4) at RBGE, ex Museum (CML). Front cover annotated by Cleghorn 'Brit. Fossil Pandaneae (Carruthers). Geol. Mag. April 1868'.

CARRUTHERS, William (1869). On the structure of the stems of the arborescent Lycopodiaceae of the coal measures. *Monthly Microscopical Journal* 2: 177–81 + t. 27. *Geological Magazine* 4: 199–201 + t. 9. 8vo. Original paper wrappers printed with title. Pamphlet at RBGE, ex Museum (CML). No Cleghorn annotations.

CARRUTHERS, William (1869). The cryptogamic forests of the coal period. *Geological Magazine* 6: 289–300 + 3 text figs. 8vo. Original paper wrappers printed with title. Pamphlet (reprint, paginated 2–12) at RBGE, ex Museum (CML). No Cleghorn annotations, but two extra illustrations inserted.

HEER, Oswald (1862). Uber die von Dr Lyall in Grönland entdeckten fossilen Pflanzen.

Vier. Nat. Ges. Zur. Pamphlet at RBGE, ex Museum (?CML). Not found.

KING, William & ROWNEY, Thomas Henry (1870). *On Eozoon canadense*. Dublin. 8vo. Pamphlet (reprint, paginated 4–48 from *Proceedings of the Royal Irish Academy* 10: 506–51 + tt 61–64. 1869) at RBGE, ex Museum (?CML). No Cleghorn annotations.

MORRIS, John (1863). Coal plants. *Proceedings of the Geologists' Association* 1: 289–301. 8vo. Original

wrappers, with title printed on front. Pamphlet (reprint, paginated 4–16) at RBGE, ex Museum (?CML). No Cleghorn annotations.

TREVELYAN, Sir Walter Calverley (1870). Note on the occurrence of the trunk of an oak in the boulder clay. *Natural History Transactions of Northumberland and Durham* 3: 382–4. 8vo. Original wrappers. Pamphlet (reprint, with new half-title) at RBGE, ex Museum (?CML). No Cleghorn annotations; front cover annotated 'with Sir W.C. Trevelyan's comp^{ts}.'

Botany

FLORAS

India & Ceylon

AITCHISON, James Edward Tierney (1869). *A Catalogue of the Plants of the Punjab and Sindh*. London. 8vo. EUL. Original boards. Flyleaf inscribed 'With the Author's Comp^{ts}', no notes.

BEDDOME, Richard Henry (1869–73). *The Flora Sylvatica of South India*. 2 vols. Madras. 4to. EUL. Original half-calf binding. No signature or annotations (in fact pristine and unused), but on front pastedown of vol. 1 a newspaper clipping review (from

Gardeners' Chronicle 2(n.s.): 491. 1874), anon but likely to be by Cleghorn as including the fascinating and otherwise un-knowable information that the plates 'have been executed by the same native draftsman [as Wight's *Icones*], Govindu, **or his son**' ... 'such facilities for publication as are to be found in this country do not exist in our great Eastern dominion, and we therefore withhold our criticism on the typography and style of the volume ... The volumes may be said to embody the notes and experience of eighteen years' research, the author having been appointed Dr Cleghorn's assistant in 1856, and having succeeded him as Conservator in 1868, while the analytical descriptions and the letterpress of the work have occupied Colonel Beddome's time for the last five years, to the exclusion of every other pursuit except his regular official work. It is indeed surprising that he should have accomplished so much while occupied with administrative and inspecting duties'. At start of vol. 2 a folded folio of India Office paper with an incomplete and shorter (but overlapping) review in Cleghorn's hand:

Beddome's Flora Sylvatica. The want of a work to enable Forest Officers, Civil Engineers and Settlers in Southern India to identify the trees in their respective ranges by short descriptions and correct delineation has long been felt and is now supplied. Major Beddome has completed the Flora Sylvatica of the Madras Presidency in 26 nos. Every important tree has been figured, including many new to science, and at least one species of every different genus. Most of the drawings have been executed from living specimens, and the labour of the definitions and the letterpress of the work have occupied ~~Major~~ Colonel Beddome's time for the last 3 5

years to the exclusion of every other pursuit except his regular official work, and it is indeed surprising that he has been able to accomplish so much, while occupied inspecting and administrative duties. Some of the plates in the earlier numbers are reproduced from Wight's figures, but there is a great improvement in the later delineations, and many of the analytic representations are highly instructive'.

BEDDOME, Richard Henry (1874). *Icones Plantarum Indiae Orientalis.* Vol. 1. Madras. 4to. CML. At RBGE. Original binding. No signature, but names corrected by Cleghorn on pp 3, 4, 8, 10, 14, 15, 20, 23, 25, 27, 35.

BIDIE, George (1874). *Report on Neilgherry Loranthaceous Parasitical Plants.* Madras. 4to. EUL. Original binding. Title-page inscribed 'Dr Cleghorn with Compliments G. Bidie'.

BURMANN, Johannes (1737). *Thesaurus Zeylanicus.* Amsterdam. 4to. CML. At RBGE. In old binding. With H Cleghorn bookplate on recto of portrait frontispiece, plates annotated by Cleghorn with Linnaean names.

BURMANN, Nicolaas Laurens (1768). *Flora Indica: cui accedit Series Zoophytorum Indicorum, necnon Prodromus*

Florae Capensis. **Leiden. 4to. CML.** At RBGE. Rebound. With H Cleghorn bookplate on inside front board, many plates annotated with modern names (e.g., t. 44, *Clerodendron calamitosum*, also with *Botanical Magazine* reference). Cleghorn paid 15 shillings for this from Pamplin in October 1854.

CATHCART, John Ferguson & HOOKER, Joseph Dalton (1855). *Illustrations of Himalayan Plants*. **London. Folio. CML.** At RBGE. In original binding. Signed 'H Cleghorn' in pencil on title-page. Cleghorn paid £5 11 shillings for this from Pamplin in 1856. Note. Cleghorn's name appears on the printed list of subscribers.

CLARKE, Charles Barron (1876). *Compositae Indicae*. Calcutta. 8vo. EUL. Original binding. Half-title inscribed 'From the Author', no annotations.

COLDSTREAM, William (1889). *Illustration of some of the Grasses of the Southern Punjab*. London. Folio. CML. At RBGE. Original printed boards. No signature or annotations.

COMMELIN, Caspar (1696). *Flora Malabarica*. **Leiden. 8vo. EUL.** Original vellum binding. With H Cleghorn bookplate on front pastedown (and '2/6' in pencil, presumably the price C paid for it), many marginal annotations of names but not in C's hands, but those on pp 92 (*Caesalpinia sappan*) and pp 108–9 (*Euphorbia* spp.) are his.

DALZELL, Nicholas A. (1858). *Catalogue of the Indigenous Flowering Plants of the Bombay Presidency*. **Surat. 8vo. CML.** At RBGE. In original paper wrapper. Signed in ink on outside 'H Cleghorn'; on inside cover attached a piece of paper with the dedication 'Dr Cleghorn Conservator of Forests Madras Presidency with the Author's kind regards'.

DALZELL, Nicholas A. & GIBSON, Alexander (1861). *The Bombay Flora*. **Bombay. 8vo. CML.** At RBGE. Rebound. Signed 'H Cleghorn' in ink on title-page and in pencil 'corrected copy', annotations pp 30 (Vide Coorg diary), 38 (record of *Chickrassia nimmonii* for Nuggur), 148 (correction: '5 of the folds'), many other marginal marks (especially crosses, ticks, lines).

DILLWYN, Lewis Weston (1839). *A Review of the References to the Hortus Malabaricus of H. van Rheede van Draakenstein*. **Swansea. 8vo. EUL.** A gift from Dillwyn to Pamplin, passed on to C and bound in Madras. 'American Mission Press Bindery Madras' label, title-page inscribed 'Dr H Cleghorn Madras from W.P.', interleaved, and almost every species has updated binomial, many with notes; at end inserted two folded folios with C's hand-written 'Index to Hortus Malabaricus arranged according to De Candolle's Prodromus'.

DRURY, Heber (1864–69).
Handbook of the Indian Flora.
3 vols. Travancore & London. 8vo. CML. At RBGE. Original binding. Vol. 1 front flyleaf inscribed 'With the authors best regards. Trevandrum June 27 1864' and in ink signed 'H Cleghorn'. Review clipping from unknown paper reproduced from *Times of India*. Front flyleaf of vol. 2. inscribed 'Hugh Cleghorn Esq with the authors kind regards. Trevandrum April 10 1866'. Front flyleaf of vol. 3 inscribed 'With the authors Kind regards', and attached is a letter:

> Victoria Place, Monmouth May 12 [?1869] My dear Cleghorn, I take the chance of this finding you to say I have sent you a copy of the 3d volume of the 'Indian Flora' which has been completed since I returned home. I did the best I could for the grasses – and gingers which might have been more complete had I access to more books. I waited in vain for De Candolle's last volume to assist me in the Peppers – All these shall have greater attention if ever in my lifetime a second editions (in one volume) should be called for. I suppose you are going to

return to India or are you home for good? We are coming to stay with some friends in Linlithgow in the Autumn. I wish I thought we could meet. Sanderson I find still a satellite attendant on the Marquess of Tweeddale. Goodbye – I shall be rather curious to know if this ever reaches you & more particularly glad to know that you are well and thriving. Believe me yours ever sincerely Heber Drury.

GRAHAM, John (1839).
Catalogue of the plants growing in Bombay and its Vicinity. **Bombay. 8vo. CML.** At RBGE. Rebound. No signature or annotations.

GRIFFITH, William (1847–54).
Notulae ad Plantas Asiaticas.
Pts 1, 2, 4. Calcutta. 8vo. EUL. Part 1, original binding, H Cleghorn bookplate on front pastedown, title-page stamped 'Honble Company's Botanic Garden Calcutta', no annotations. Part 2, original binding, H Cleghorn bookplate on front pastedown, pages uncut, no annotations. Part 4, rebound but enclosing original paper wrappers, the front one signed 'H Cleghorn' in pencil, with H Cleghorn bookplate on flyleaf; annotations on pp 35 *Ehretia* – correction, *Fagraea Malabarica*; 95 [*Lycium*] = '*Puneeria coagulans* (Stocks)'; 736 [*Naravelia*] '*laurifolia* Wall.'.

GRIFFITH, William (1847–54).

Notulae ad Plantas Asiaticas. Parts 1–4 (bound in 2). Calcutta. **8vo. CML.** At RBGE. No signature or annotations.

GRIFFITH, William (1847–54). *Icones Plantarum Asiaticarum. Parts 1–4.* **Calcutta, 1847–54. 4to. CML.** At RBGE. Original binding. No signature or annotations.

GRIFFITH, William (1848). *Itinerary Notes of Plants collected in the Khasyah and Bootan Mountains, 1837–38, in Affghanistan and Neighbouring Countries, 1839 to 1841.* **Calcutta. 8vo. CML.** At RBGE. Rebound. With H. Cleghorn bookplate on verso of flyleaf; title-page signed in pencil.

HAMILTON, Francis (*né* BUCHANAN) (1822–37). *Commentary on the Hortus Malabaricus.* **Articles from *Transactions of the Linnean Society* vols 13–15, 17. London. 4to. EUL.** Bound by Cleghorn. No signature or annotations.

HASSKARL, Justus Karl (1867). *Horti Malabarici Rheedeani Clavis Locupletissima.* **Dresden. 4to. CML.** At RBGE. Rebound. On inside board, reattached, is a label annotated 'This Clavis Rheedeana I send to you with my kindest regards Dr J K Haskarl cogn[omen]. Retzius. Cleve January 21ˢᵗ

1882. Annotated on title-page 'Dr Cleghorn I[ndia]. Office'.

HOOKER, Joseph Dalton (1875–94). *The Flora of British India.* 6 vols. London. 8vo. CML. At RBGE vols 1, 2, 3, 4, 5 [vol. 6 missing; vol. 7 not published until 1897]. Vol. 1 has a few marginal annotations – e.g. correction of spelling on p 2, added illustration ref p 9, 26, 29 (Bot. Mag.), 36 (Bot. Mag., Hort. Mal.), 51 (Hort. Mal.) etc.

HOOKER, Joseph D. & THOMSON, Thomas (1855). *Flora Indica.* **Vol. 1. London. 8vo. CML.** At RBGE. Rebound. Numerous annotations – of interest and probably made when C reviewed it (Cleghorn, 1856l) e.g. pp vii 'I trust the authors will continue their history of each Indian Genus & Species; in intro many marginal lines; 9 'read carefully from 9 to 12 incl. Describing species'; 20 where Hooker says 'it is more probable that species should have been created with a certain degree of variability, than that mutability should be part of the scheme of nature' Cleghorn has underlined 'more probable' and annotated the sentence 'certainly'; 21 concerning hybridization 'by Hooker to wch. he has paid a great deal of attention'; 30 H says variation may often be traced to physical causes C has annotated '<u>Not</u> often'; 32 'not so in Neilgherries' disputing H's statement on non-activity of *Digitalis* in Himalaya; p 32 on variability in habit 'Habit to be kept in view in describing sp vide p 34'; 37 – absence of oaks in Peninsula 'remarkable fact', absence of Cycadeae in Ceylon 'mistake'; 45 on flora of Malabar being well known 'doubtful' – 'e.g. Isonandra lately found at these places – 3 new plants found in my …'; 69 – collector of Hohenacker's Nilgiri plants corrected from Schmid to 'Metz'; 100 on species that are diverse in Himalaya, Cleghorn has added 'Pedicularis at least 5 sp. in Lahul'; 119 – correction that 'There is a Phoenix & a Nipa in Ceylon – fide Thwaites'; 128 to the statement 'Dr Wight has further published a few plants of the Bababuden hills' he has added 'received chiefly from H. Cleghorn'; 131 45 inch rainfall at Madras marked 'too high'; 133 – Carnatic flora ' Cassia auriculata Dodonaea viscosa' added to list for plains, 'roxburghii' given as species of Calamus, and '2 species' added to the generic name Phoenix; 137 – on vegetation of Mysore 'The greater part of the [?bush] consists chiefly of Cassia auriculata Dodonaea viscosa wch. are the most common bushes throughout this part of the country'; 159 added reference to Jacquemont; Lauraceae in Punjab 'only one fide Stewart' [showing that he

added notes in the 1860s as seen also in next note:]; 203 on Simla plants additional records for Benthamia fragifera 'Suraj', Cupressus torulosa 'junction of Ravi & Budhil', Sieversia elata 'abundant on Rotang Pass' and Cerasus Puddum 'In Kullu'; 211 additional record from Jacquemont (Cerasus prostrata); 233 addition refs for Griffith's work; 257 on Griffith specs 'many of wch. are deposited in the Herbarium of Kew'. In taxonomic section numerous marginal ticks and crosses, the odd locality and ref.; 93 long taxonomic note on Sageraea; 216 on affinities of Berberideae 'Good criterion in Lindley, who ... wild in affinities'; 221 Berberis vulgaris 'Naturalised in N England'; 231 Epimedium 'see Th[omsons] tr[avels] found Chenab Valley'; 232 on circumscription of Nymphaeaceae, also on p 236 (but trimmed, as are many of the notes'. This was clearly what he used, with Wight & Arnott, as his major Flora, adding notes to it into the 1860s.

L'ECLUSE, Charles de (1582). *Aliquot Notae in Garciae Aromatum Historiam.* **Antwerp. 8vo. CML.** At RBGE. Rebound. With H Cleghorn bookplate on front pastedown.

PIDDINGTON, Henry (1832). *An English Index to the Plants of India.* **Calcutta. 8vo. EUL.** Original binding. Signed 'H

Cleghorn' in pencil on title-page, no annotations.

RHEEDE, Hendrik van (1678–86). *Hortus Indicus Malabaricus.* **Vols 1–6 (bound in 4). Amsterdam. Folio. CML.** At RBGE. Rebound. With H Cleghorn bookplate on front pastedown. On flyleaf of Vol. 1 letter from R.K. Greville '33 George Square July 14 1851. My dear Cleghorn We have got into the library again – that is we have ventured to open the door & I now send you the fraction of a copy of the Hort. Malab. I promised. I forget whether it was the earlier or the later volumes which you said were the most difficult to procure– I find mine are the first four, & I shall be delighted if they are those least attainable. They are of no use <u>whatsoever</u> to me – & consequently shall consider any Mosses, Ferns & Land & fresh water shells you may chance to fall in with a very <u>profitable exchange</u>– Believe me ever Most truly yours R.K. Greville'. Many plates annotated with Linnaean names by C.

RHEEDE, Hendrik van (1774). *Horti Malabarici Pars Prima.* **Ed. John Hill. London. 4to. CML.** At RBGE. Rebound. No signature or annotations.

ROTH, Albrecht Wilhelm (1821). *Novae Plantarum Species Praesertim Indiae Orientalis.* **Halberstadt. 8vo. EUL.** In original paper wrappers. On inside cover bookplates of H Cleghorn, and Dr J.M.W. Baumann, doubtless obtained second-hand by C (but where/when?): '4/6' written in pencil on inside front cover.

ROXBURGH, William (1820, 1824). *Flora Indica.* **Edited by W. Carey. 2 vols. Serampore. 8vo. CML.** Rebound. No signature, and surprisingly with no annotations.

ROYLE, John Forbes (1833–40). *Illustrations of the Botany ... of the Himalayan Mountains.* **London. 2 vols. Folio. CML.** At RBGE. Original binding. Recto of flyleaf annotated in pencil 'LCS p 4 2 vols 70 Rs [showing that C bought it in India, and that it was second hand]. H Cleghorn bookplate on inside front board. Many corrections to Latin bird names on pp lxxvii–viii [by previous owner?]. Significant C annotations on pp 176 (illeg, about damage to timber by white ants); 277 (marginal line against chiretta); 314–6 (many lines against account of *Rheum*); 342 (marginal line against Amentiferae being common in N European forests).

SMITH, Henry (1857). *Specimens of Nature Printing from Unprepared Plants.* **Madras. Folio. CML.** At RBGE. Original binding. With H Cleghorn bookplate on front pastedown; one plate annotated 'Cynosurus' (actually *Eleusine*).

STEWART, John Lindsay (1869). *Punjab Plants.* **Lahore. 8vo. EUL.** Original binding. With H Cleghorn bookplate on front paste-down, on which also an annotation by C 'Reviewed by HC in Gard. Chronicle Nov 29 1869. p. 1211.', with marginal lines and pp 22 [*Gossypium*] 'What is Stocks Gossypium see Trop. Afr. Flora'; 23 [*Malva*] also verticillata & borealis; 183 [Polygonaceae] 'see Babington & Royle's Polyg.'.

THWAITES, George Henry Kendrick (1864). *Enumeratio Plantarum Zeylanicae.* **London. 8vo. CML.** Not at RBGE (another copy kept).

WALLICH, Nathaniel (1830–32). *Plantae Asiaticae Rariores.* **3 vols. London. Folio. CML.** At RBGE. In original binding (bound as one volume), with bookseller's label on inside front board 'A. Bielefeld's Hofbuchandlung Carlsruhe'. No signature or annotations, the colouring of the plates is rather harsh.

WIGHT, Robert (1834). *Contributions to the Botany of India.* **London. 8vo. EUL.** Original binding (but must be post-1839, as W.H. Allen publisher's catalogue from February 1839 at back). HUGH CLEGHORN bookplate on front pastedown, and opposite it a H Cleghorn one; many annotations with cross-references to plates in Wight's Icones. Also pp 17 [for both *Siegesbeckia* and *Xanthium*] 'Shemoga'; 25 [*Centaurea cyanus*] 'cultivated in gardens Bangalore'; 27 [after *Sonchus wightianus*] 'occurs near Shemoga – leaves lyrate, pinnatifid, the terminal lobe acutely angled (hastate) and longest – on being wounded – much milky juice exudes'; 35 [*Hoya coronaria*] Bot. Mag. reference added; 51 [*Tylophora asthmatica*] 'also Plukt. 96 t 7'; 53 [*Calotropis*] 'Madras Journal of Lit & Science vol II p. 69. t. 1'; 81 [*Cyperus bulbosus*] 'Madras common'; 99 [*Fimbrisylis royleana*] 'F brizoides var D Royleana Kew Misc 6: 28'; 109 [*Isolepis barbata*] 'St Thome'; on back flyleaf 'RW 13th Aug 1839'. [This date is mysterious, Wight was in India at the time, but Cleghorn had not yet arrived, but from the Shimoga annotations C clearly had it with him in Mysore].

WIGHT, Robert (1838–53). *Icones Plantarum Indiae Orientalis.* **6 vols. Madras. 8vo. CML.** Not at RBGE (another set kept).

WIGHT, Robert (1838–50). *Illustrations of Indian Botany.* **2 vols. Madras. 4to. CML.** Not at RBGE (another set kept).

WIGHT, Robert (1845–51).

Spicilegium Neilgherrense. **2 vols. Madras. 4to. CML.** Not at RBGE (another set kept).

WIGHT, Robert. & WALKER-ARNOTT, George A.W. (1834). *Prodromus Florae Peninsulae Indiae Orientalis.* **London. 8vo.** Not apparently in CML, but must have come from Museum (ink stamp 'Royal Scottish Museum') later. Cleghorn's interleaved and heavily annotated copy, presented to him by Wight. Numerous manuscript additions by Cleghorn, and many cuttings from a variety of printed sources. Also contains additional manuscript material by 1. William Henry Sykes, 2. Charles Drew and 3. Sir Walter Elliot.

1. fragment (two-sided) of letter from Sykes (inserted before half-title):

> a clump of fifty. Since his time Mr Robertson [?perhaps Henry Dundas Robertson (1790–1845) who became Collector of Poona up till 1834] & subsequent Collectors have done much to improve the physical aspect of the country by the plantation of numerous topes. (*Bassia latifolia* & avenues of Banyan & other trees).
>
> (1) Towards the centre of the district, the surface of the plain presents a monotonous & almost treeless extent, of … waste bounded by the Horizon, & unbroken … by a … rocky

> elevations that stand
>
> Madras Journal Oct 1840 – last number recd. by Roy Socy.
>
> nothing can exceed the magnificence & beauty of the vegetation of the Ghauts. The brilliancy of the Erythrinas – the Cassia (Cass: fistulosa) – the lofty Bombax & Cochlospermum the Convolvulaceae – Malvaceae, Zingiberaceae surprise & delight the European Botanist [Col: Sykes]

[This appears to be part of a letter written after Sykes returned to Britain, probably in the 1850s, in response to an enquiry from Cleghorn – about aspects of vegetation in the Deccan [possibly around Poona] and asking which copies of the *Madras Journal* had reached the Royal Society library, in which Sykes was active].

2. Note on *Naragemia* by Charles Drew inserted after p. 116 (after p. 323 another note by Drew, but transcribed in Cleghorn's hand).

3. Letter (after p 278) from Walter Elliot on mourning paper 'Guindy Thursday'

> My dear Cleghorn,
>
> A Yanadi [a group who lived primarily on Sriharikota Island] brought me this specimen yesterday but I had not time to look at till this morng. I dont recollect seeing it before.

Is it [C has filled in name *Acacia cineraria* Willd. in pencil] The two pair of pinnae with 6 to 8 or 10 pairs of leafflets, the numerous prickles & the large stipules look something like it.

The root with that of Flacourtia sepiaria (a piece of wh. he also brought & wh. is in the box) & another not to be procured hereafter, are ... to form a decoction used by females of the wild tribes after confinements

Yrs W. Elliot

You can tell me this evg.

(before p. 313) fragment of letter (two-sided)

Did you know that Terminalia Catappa was not indigenous? Wallich says it is introduced! Whence? I suppose the Tamarind is also for like Catappa I have never found it except near the abodes of man.

(the verso has the termination of the letter, the signature 'Walter Elliot')

WILLDENOW, Carl Ludwig (1794). *Phytographia. Fasc. 1.* **Erlangen. Folio. CML.** At RBGE. Rebound, but enclosing original front board. Blurred ink stamp of Madras Medical College, and an annotation by J.P. Rottler on p 4.

Britain

CHILDS, Archibald Prentice (1857). *The British Botanist's Field-Book*. London. 8vo. CML. At RBGE. Original binding. No signature or annotations, but with bookseller's label, Maclachlan & Stewart, South Bridge, Edinburgh.

COWELL, Henry Matthew (1839). *Floral Guide for East Kent*. Faversham. 8vo. CML. At RBGE. Rebound. No signature or annotations. Note: A strange purchase, but curiously it is dedicated to Lady Harris, i.e. Cleghorn's future boss's mother. Among subscribers are J.H. Balfour, Greville and Prof Graham (also Charles Lush,

Bombay), so perhaps bought under their influence while C an undergraduate.

DILLWYN, Lewis Weston (1848). *Materials for a Flora and Fauna of Swansea and the Neighbourhood*. Swansea. 8vo. CML. Not at RBGE.

GREVILLE, Robert Kaye (1824). *Flora Edinensis*. Edinburgh. 8vo. EUL. Original binding. HUGH CLEGHORN bookplate on front pastedown. Pages uncut and no annotations.

HOOKER, Joseph Dalton (1870). *The Student's Flora of the British Islands*. London. 8vo. CML. Not at RBGE.

HOOKER, William Jackson (1838). *The British Flora*. Ed. 4. Vol. 1. London. 8vo. EUL. Original binding. Bookseller's label 'Henry Ormston 18 South College Street Edinburgh' on front pastedown. Signed 'Hugh F.C. Cleghorn 1840' on flyleaf, no annotations, with a Longman's catalogue bound in at end.

HOPKIRK, Thomas (1813). *Flora Glottiana: a Catalogue of the Indigenous Plants in the Neighbourhood of Glasgow*. Glasgow. 8vo. CML. Not at RBGE.

IRVINE, Alexander (1858). *Illustrated Handbook of the British Plants*. London. 8vo. CML. Not at RBGE (J.H. Balfour's copy kept).

JOHNS, the Rev. Charles Alexander (undated). *Flowers of the Field*. Ed 6. London. 8vo. CML. At RBGE. Original binding. Signed 'H Cleghorn' on title-page, no annotations.

KEYS, Isaiah W.N. (1867). *Flora of Devon and Cornwall: Balsamineae–Umbelliferae*. Plymouth. 8vo. CML. Not at RBGE (a complete copy of the work kept, of which this formed only a single part).

KNAPP, Frances Holliday (1846). *Botanical Chart of British Flowering Plants and Ferns*. Bath. 8vo. CML. Not at RBGE.

LINDLEY, John (1841). *Synopsis of the British Flora*. London. 12mo. CML. At RBGE. Rebound. Inscribed on flyleaf 'T.C. Archer Esq. from his Friend Wm. Johnson July 22nd 1851' and annotated by C 'Purchased H. Cleghorn 26 Feb. 1884'.

MACREIGHT, Daniel Chambers (1837). *Manual of British Botany*. London. 8vo. CML. At RBGE. Rebound. No signatures, no annotations.

McALPINE, Archibald Nichol (1890). *How to Know Grasses by the Leaves*. Edinburgh. 8vo. EUL. Original binding. Inscribed on flyleaf 'To Dr Cleghorn with the Author's Compts–'; newspaper clipping with review stuck in.

PAGET, Charles J. & Sir James (1834). *Sketch of the Natural History of Yarmouth and its Neighbourhood*. London. 8vo. CML. Not at RBGE (another copy kept).

[PAMPLIN, William & IRVINE, Alexander] (1857). *A Botanical Tour in the Highlands of Perthshire, by 'W.P. and A.I.'* London. 8vo. CML. Not at RBGE (another copy kept).

PRIOR, Richard Chandler Alexander (1863). *On the Popular Names of British Plants*. London. 8vo. CML. Not at RBGE (another copy kept).

PURTON, Thomas (1817–21). *A Botanical Description of British Plants in the Midland Counties*. 3 vols. Stratford upon-Avon & London. 8vo. CML. At RBGE, bound in 2 vols. Rebound. Vol. 2 with H Cleghorn bookplate on flyleaf, no annotations.

SOWERBY, James & SMITH, James Edward (1795–1804). *English Botany*. 5 vols. London. 8vo. CML. Not at RBGE (another copy kept).

WITHERING, William (1830). *An Arrangement of British Plants*. 4 vols. Ed 7. London. 8vo. CML. Not at RBGE (another copy kept).

Europe

BENTHAM, George (1826). *Catalogue des plantes indigènes des Pyrénées et du Bas Languedoc*. Paris. 8vo. CML. Not at RBGE (the copy kept is inscribed to the Wernerian Society by Walker-Arnott on Bentham's behalf).

BIASOLETTO, Bartolomeo (1846). *Excursion botaniche sullo Schneeberg*. Trieste. 8vo. EUL. Pamphlet bound by Cleghorn with works by Cleghorn, & J. Shier. No signature or annotations.

BOCCONE, Paolo (1674). *Icones et Descriptiones Rariorum Plantarum Siciliae, Melitae, Galliae et Italiae*. Oxford. 8vo. CML. At RBGE. Rebound. No signature or annotations.

CLAIRVILLE, Joseph Philippe de (1819). *Manuel d'herborisation en Suisse*. Genève. 8vo. EUL. Original binding. Armorial bookplate of Robert James

Shuttleworth on front paste-down, no annotations.

DUTHIE, John Firminger (1876). *Botanical Excursions … Baths of Lucca in 1873* (reprinted from *Transactions of the Botanical Society of Edinburgh* 12: 66–84). Edinburgh. 8vo. EUL. Pamphlet, bound with works by G.A. Hight & J.H. Balfour. Cover inscribed 'With J.F. Duthie's compliments'.

GRÉNIER, Jean Charles Marie & GODRON, Dominique-Alexandre (1848). *Flore de France*. Vol. 1. Paris. 8vo. CML. Not at RBGE (a whole set kept).

HELDREICH, Theodor von (1862). *Die Nutzpflanzen Griechlands*. Athens. 8vo. EUL. Rebound, but enclosing original paper wrappers. Front wrapper inscribed 'Mr Al[exander] Irvine, hommage de l'Auteur'.

HENFREY, Arthur (1852). *The Vegetation of Europe*. London. 8vo. CML. Not at RBGE (another copy kept).

LINNAEUS, Carolus (1792). Flora Lapponica (ed. J.E. Smith). London. 8vo. EUL. Original boards. With Heriot of Ramornie armorial bookplate on front pastedown, and modern EUL label concealing an inscription probably referring to its presentation to 'Cleghorn'

(includes dried plant specimens of *Bromus mollis* and leaves of *Salix cf cinerea, S. viminalis*).

MAGNOL, Pierre (1686). *Botanicum Monspeliense*. Montpelier. 12mo. CML. At RBGE. Rebound. No signature (and only pre-Cleghorn annotations).

POTONIÉ, Henry (1886). *Flora von Nord- und Mittel Deutschland*. Berlin. 8vo. EUL.

Rest of world

AMMAN, Johann. (1739). *Stirpium Rariorum in Imperio Rutheno Icones et Descriptiones*. St Petersburg. 4to. At RBGE. Inscribed in blue pencil on title-page by C 'Royal Bot. Garden Library March 10. 1892 from H. Cleghorn'. This handsomely bound volume (half-calf with gold tooling on spine) appears to have been picked up as a bargain by Cleghorn in a second-hand bookseller and passed on to RBGE: the verso of the flyleaf has the price of 5/6 deleted and replaced by 3/-.

[ALPINUS, Prosper. *De Plantis Aegypti Liber*. Copy of an unknown edition (?Venice, 1592) bought for 1½ francs by Cleghorn in Florence in 1868 (letter of HC to JHB 1 iv 1868

RBGE f. 226), but in neither EUL nor CML collection]

BENTHAM, George (1861). *Flora Hongkongensis*. London. 8vo. CML. At RBGE. Rebound. Cleghorn's signature on title-page, no annotations.

BLANCO, Manuel (1837). *Flora de Filipinas*. Manila. 8vo. CML. Not at RBGE.

BURMANN, Johannes (1738–39). *Rariorum Africanarum Plantarum, Decades I–X*. Amsterdam. 4to. CML. At RBGE. Rebound. No signature, plates 61 & 62 annotated.

BUXBAUM, Johann Christian (1728–40). *Plantarum minus cognitarum Centurim I–V, complectens Plantas circa*

Byzantium et in Oriente observatas. 5 vols. St Petersburg. 4to. CML. At RBGE. Rebound. No signature or annotations.

DESFONTAINES, René Louiche (1798). *Flora Atlantica.* 2 vols. Paris. 4to. CML. Vol. 2 (only) at RBGE. Original binding. No signature or annotations.

GRAY, Asa (1849). *Genera Florae Americae Boreali-Orientalis Illustrata.* Vol. 2. New York. 8vo. EUL. Original binding. Flyleaf signed in pencil 'H Cleghorn', no notes.

GRAY, Asa (1868). *Manual of Botany of the Northern United States.* Ed 5. New York. 8vo. CML. Not at RBGE.

HARVEY, William Henry (1838). *Genera of South African Plants.* Cape Town. 8vo. EUL. Original binding (very fine cloth with inscribed diamond pattern, alternately hatched and plain). With H Cleghorn bookplate on front pastedown; annotations on pp 64, 86, 87, 89, 90 (on Legumes – was C taking an interest in these while at the Cape?).

HARVEY, William H. & SONDER, Otto Wilhelm (1859–60). *Flora Capensis. Vol. 1.* Dublin. 8vo. EUL. Original binding. Half-title signed 'H Cleghorn' in pencil, title-page signed in pencil 'H Cleghorn 1861'; notes on pp 8 (marginal mark against

Annonaceae), 61 (correction from Addenda), 24 (see Errata).

HARVEY, William H., & SONDER, Otto Wilhelm (1859–65). *Flora Capensis.* 3 vols. Dublin & Cape Town. 8vo. CML. Vols 2 & 3 at RBGE (3 is rebound), Vol. 1 replaced by another copy. No signature or annotations.

HASSKARL, Justus Karl (1844). *Tweede Catalogus der in's Lands Plantentuin te Buitenzorg Gekweekte gewassen.* Batavia. 8vo. CML. At RBGE. Rebound. Signed on title-page, no annotations.

HOOKER, Joseph Dalton (1853). *Introductory Essay to the Flora of New Zealand.* London. 4to. CML. At RBGE a copy lacking its wrapper or title page (and therefore the Memorial Library stamp) is presumably Cleghorn's copy, but bears no annotations.

HOOKER, Joseph Dalton (1860). *Flora Tasmaniae.* 2 vols. London. 4to. CML. Not at RBGE (another copy kept). (Note: These were exceptionally expensive volumes when published – the *Flora of New Zealand* cost £12/12 coloured or £8/15 plain, *Flora Antarctica* £10/15 coloured or £7/10 plain – L. Reeve catalogue).

HOOKER, William Jackson, & WALKER-ARNOTT, G.A. (1830–41). *The Botany of Captain Beechey's Voyage.*

London. 4to. CML. At RBGE. Rebound. No signature.

HORSFIELD, Thomas, BENNETT, John J. & BROWN, Robert (1838–40). *Plantae Javanicae Rariores Parts 1 and 2*. London. Folio. CML. At RBGE. Rebound, but with original boards included. With H. Cleghorn bookplate on front pastedown of both parts, with bookseller's label H. Baillère on first part.

JAMESON, William (1865). *Synopsis Plantarum Æquatoriensium*. Vol. 1. Quito. 8vo. CML. At RBGE. Rebound. Interleaved copy with annotations presumably by Isaac Anderson Henry, to whom inscribed by the author. Presumably given by Henry to Cleghorn.

LEDEBOUR, Karl Friedrich (1829–33). *Flora Altaica*. 4 vols. Berlin. 8vo. CML. Vols 1 & 2 bound as one at RBGE (second part presumably lost, a full set of Ball's kept). In original binding. Inscribed 'J.L. Stewart MD. Feby /62', doubtless given to Cleghorn by Stewart, or purchased by Cleghorn after Stewart's death.

LOWE, Richard Thomas (1868). *A Manual Flora of Madeira*. Vols 1 and 2(1). Londo. 12mo. CML. At RBGE. Rebound (the two parts in one). No signature or annotations.

MUELLER, Ferdinand von (1858–59). *Fragmenta Phytographia Australiae*. Vol. 1. Melbourne. 8vo. CML. AT RBGE. Rebound. With no signature or annotations. Cleghorn must have been given it by an official body (such as the Calcutta/Madras Government or the India Office) as it is stamped 'Received 8 May 1860'.

NUTTALL, Thomas (1818). *Genera of North American Plants and Catalogue of Species, to the year 1817*. Philadelphia. 8vo. At RBGE. Rebound. With H Cleghorn bookplate in both volumes, no annotations.

PLUMIER Charles (1703). *Nova Plantarum Americanarum Genera*. Paris. 4to. CML. At RBGE. In original vellum binding. No signature, C has added some Linnaean names e.g. on pp 20–26 and on plates 33–39.

RÖMER, Johann Jakob (1796). *Scriptores de Plantis Hispanicis, Lusitanicis, Brasiliensibus*. Nuremberg. 8vo. EUL. Pamphlet bound by Cleghorn with Swartz, *Genera et Species Filicum*. On front pastedown H Cleghorn bookplate, and titles of the two works in C's hand.

[ROUPELL, Arabella & HARVEY, William H.] (1849). *Specimens of the Flora of South Africa by a Lady*. London. Folio. CML. At RBGE. In original leather binding (by Rowbotham, India Rubber Binder, Castle Street East, Oxford Street), rebacked, gold tooling on front 'Cape Flowers by a Lady'. Inscribed on front board by Cleghorn 'These were drawn by Mrs Roupell'. Signed on verso of flyleaf in pencil 'H Cleghorn'. H Cleghorn bookplate on back pastedown. Note: Published too early for Cleghorn to have been a subscriber, though two Madras friends, Mrs Walter Elliot and Mrs [Margaret Reade] Brown, were.

THUNBERG, Carl Peter (1784). *Flora Japonica*. Leipzig. 8vo. CML. Not at RBGE (another copy kept).

Monographs

Flowering plants/Conifers

AGARDH, Jacob Georg (1835). *Synopsis Generis Lupini*. Lund. 8vo. Pamphlet at RBGE, ex-Museum (?CML). Original marbled card binding. Presentation copy to Robert Brown. No marks to show Cleghorn's ownership.

ANDERSON, Thomas (1864). On the identification of the Acanthaceae of the Linnean Herbarium. *Journal of the Linnean Society* 7: 111–8. 8vo. Pamphlet at RBGE, ex-Museum (?CML). No marks to show Cleghorn's ownership.

ANDERSSON, Nils Johan (1860). On East Indian Salices. *Journal of the Linnean Society* 4: 39–58. 8vo. Original paper wrappers. Pamphlet at RBGE, ex-Museum (?CML). No marks to show Cleghorn's ownership.

BABINGTON, Charles Cardale (1844). Monograph of the British Atripliceae. *Transactions of the Botanical Society [of Edinburgh]* 1: 2–14 + tt 1, 2. 8vo. Pamphlet at RBGE, ex-Museum (?CML). No marks to show Cleghorn's ownership.

BAILLON, Henri Ernest (1858). *Etude générale du groupe euphorbiacées*. Paris. 8vo. CML. At RBGE. No signature or annotations.

BAKER, John Gilbert (1871). *Revision of the Genera and Species of Herbaceous Capsular Gamophyllous Liliaceae* (reprinted from *Journal of the Linnean Society (Botany)* 11: 349–436). London. 8vo. CML. At RBGE. In early paper covers. No signature or annotations.

BAKER, John Gilbert (1875). *Revision of the Genera and Species of Asparagaceae* (reprinted from *Journal of the Linnean Society (Botany)* 14: 508–632). London. 8vo. CML. At RBGE. Original (rebacked) binding. No signature or annotations.

BAKER, John Gilbert (1888). *Handbook of the Amaryllideae.* London. 8vo. CML. Not at RBGE.

BATKA, Wenceslas (1835). Lauri Malabathri Lamarckii Adumbratio. *Nova Acta Physico-Medica Academiae Caeasrea Leopolina-Carolinae Naturae Curiorsorum* **17: 615–22 + t. 45. 4to. Original wrappers. Pamphlet at RBGE ex-Museum (CML).** On front wrapper a cutting from an unknown Indian publication on 'Malabathrum' clearly attached by Cleghorn, and on a label giving the price and title from a secondhand bookseller, C has added in pencil the name 'Cinnamomum iners'.

BENTHAM, George (1832–36). *Labiatarum Genera et Species.* London. 8vo. CML. At RBGE. Rebound. No signature or annotations.

BERWICK, Thomas (1891). Observations on glands in the cotyledons, and on the mineral secretions of *Galium aparine* L. *Transaction of the Botanical Society of Edinburgh* 18: 436–44 + t. 3. 8vo. Original paper covers. Pamphlet at RBGE, ex-Museum (?CML). Front endpaper inscribed 'With the Writers respects': given the St Andrews connection, this is likely to be to C, but no other annotations.

BIRDWOOD, George (1870). *On the Genus* Boswellia *with description and figures of three new species.* London. 4to. Pamphlet at RBGE, (not accessioned, but ex-Museum and probably CML). Cleghorn's copy of a proof with mss corrections by Birdwood of the preface (only) to the reprint of this article from the *Transactions of the Linnean Society* 27: 111 – 48, 1870; annotated on title page by Cleghorn 'From Lin. Soc. Trans. xxvii.' Note: The final printed version had a preface of iv pages, but the pagination of this item is [i–]iv–v; it is of interest for the background information contained on the Victoria and Albert Museum, Bombay. At RBGE is a copy of another (later?) reprint of this article, printed by Eyre and Spottiswoode and with the plates redrawn.

BLUME, Carl Ludwig (1823). *Bijdrage tot de Kennis onzer Javaansche Eiken* (reprinted from *Verhandelingen van het Bataviaasch Genootschap van Kunsten en Wetenschappen,* vol. 9). [Batavia]. 8vo. CML. Not at RBGE.

BLUME, Carl Ludwig (1826). *Monographie der Oost-Indische Pepersoorten* (reprinted from *Verhandelingen van het Bataviaasch Genootschap van Kunsten en Wetenschappen*). [Batavia]. 8vo. CML. At RBGE. Rebound. No signature or annotations.

BRONGNIART, Adolphe (1833). Description des deux nouveaux genres Becquerelia et Pleurostachys de la famille des Cypéracées. *Annales des Sciences Naturelles* 28: 419–28. 8vo. Original printed wrappers. Pamphlet (reprint, paginated 2–11) at RBGE, (not accessioned, but ex-Museum and probably CML). No C annotations; cover with author's dedication to Robert Brown.

BROWN, the Rev. John Croumbie (1864). *Letter from the Rev. J.C. Brown, LL.D., Colonial Botanist, and Professor of Botany in the South African College, Cape Town, to Jas. Chapman, Esq., on the* Welwitschia mirabilis. Wynberg. 4to. Pamphlet (paginated 2–4) at RBGE, ex-Museum (?CML). No marks to show C's ownership.

BROWN, Robert (1827). Character and description of *Kingia*. 'Ex King's Narrative [vol.] 2'. Pamphlet at RBGE, ex-Museum (?CML). Not found.

BROWN, Robert (1868). A monograph of the coniferous genus Thuja, Linn., and of the North American species of the genus Libocedrus. *Transactions of the Botanical Society of Edinburgh* 9: 358–78. 8vo. Original paper wrappers. Pamphlet at RBGE, ex-Museum (CML). Front cover inscribed 'With The Author's Comp^ts.' Editorial correction by C and two inserted clippings, one with C's annotations.

BUCHENAU, Franz (1869). Übersicht der in den Jahren 1855–57 in Hochasien von den Brüdern Schlagintweit gesammelten Butomaceen, Alismaceen, Juncaginaceen und Juncaceen. *Göttingen Nachrichten* 13: 237–58. 8vo. Pamphlet at RBGE, ex-Museum (?CML). No marks to show C's ownership.

BUIST, George (1857). The Lotus or sacred bean of India. *Transactions of the Geographical Society of Bombay* 13: 1–10 + tt 1 – 4. 8vo. Original paper wrappers. Pamphlet (reprint, paginated 2–8) at RBGE, ex-Museum (CML). Front cover inscribed 'Dr Cleghorn from the Author "For Auld Lang Syne"; two clippings inserted by C.

CANNART D'HAMALE, Frédéric de (1870). Monographe historique et littéraire des Lis. Malines. Pamphlet at RBGE, ex-Museum (?CML). Not found.

CASSINI, Henri (1829). Tableau synoptique des Synanthérées. *Annales des Sciences Naturelles* 17: 387–423. 8vo. Original paper wrappers printed with title. Pamphlet (reprint, paginated 2–38) at RBGE, ex-Museum (?CML). Inscribed by author to Robert Brown and with many ms corrections by author. No C annotations.

CAVANILLES, Antonio José (1790). *Monadelphiae Classis Dissertationes Decem* [part]. Madrid. 4to. EUL. Rebound. With H Cleghorn bookplate transferred to new front pastedown, title-page signed in blue pencil 'H Cleghorn', no annotations (but he had the *Passiflora* plates copied). Note: Contains ninth (genera *Banisteria, Triopteris, Tetrapteris, Molina* & *Flabellaria*, tt 243–264) and tenth (*Passiflora*, tt 265–296) parts, and title-page and preface (with analytical key) of whole work.

CHOISY, Jacques-Denys (1841). De Convolvulaceis dissertatio tertia. *Genève Mémoires Societé Physique* 9: 262–88 + tt 1–5. 4to. Pamphlet at RBGE, ex-Museum (?CML). No Cleghorn annotations.

COLDSTREAM, William. (1886). Notes on the grasses of the Southern Punjab. *Transactions of the Botanical Society of Edinburgh* 16: 277–9. 8vo. Original paper wrappers. Pamphlet at RBGE, ex-Museum (?CML). No C annotations.

COLLA, Luigi (1826). Mémoire sur le Melanopsidium nigrum des jardiniers, et formation d'un genre nouveau dans la famille des Rubiacées. *Mémoires de la Société Linnéenne de Paris* 4: 15–27 + t. 22. 8vo. Original paper wrappers. Pamphlet (1825 preprint, paginated 4–16) at RBGE, ex-Museum (?CML). Front cover inscribed by author to Robert Brown, and with the annotation 'Billiottia D.C.' in C's hand, the plate annotated by him with the same name and authority. This shows that the Brown reprints were owned by C and from him reached the Museum collection.

COSSON, Ernest (1854). Classification des espèces du genre Avena de groupe de l'Avena sativa (Avena, sect. Avenotypus), et considérations sur la composition et la structure de l'épillet dans la famille des graminées. *Bulletin de la Société Botanique de France* 1: 11–18. 8vo. Original wrappers. Pamphlet (reprint, paginated 2–8) at RBGE, (not accessioned, but ex-Museum and probably CML). No C annotations; front cover with dedication from author to Robert Brown.

DICKSON, Alexander (1866, read 1864). Note on the position of the carpellary groups in *Malope* and *Kitaibelia*. *Transactions of the Botanical Society [of Edinburgh]* 8: 228–30. 8vo. Pamphlet at RBGE, ex-Museum (?CML). No annotations by C.

DON, David (1823). An illustration of the natural family of plants called "Melastomaceae". *Memoirs of the Wernerian Society* 4: 276–329. 8vo. Pamphlet at RBGE, ex-Museum (?CML). Not found.

DON, David (1824). Memoir on the classification of *Gnaphalium* and *Xeranthemum* of Linnaeus. *Memoirs of the Wernerian Society* 5: 533–63. 8vo. Pamphlet at RBGE, ex-Museum (?CML). Not found.

DON, David (1832). Description of some new species of *Malesherbia, Kageneckia, Quillaja*, and of a new genus of the order Salicariae. *Edinburgh New Philosophical Journal* 12: 100–3. 8vo. Pamphlet at RBGE, ex-Museum (?CML). Not found.

DON, David (1834). An attempt at a new arrangement of the Ericaceae. *Edinburgh New Philosophical Journal* 17: 150–60. 8vo. Pamphlet at RBGE, ex-Museum (?CML). Not found.

DON, David (1837). Descriptions of Indian Gentianae. *Transactions of the Linnean Society.* 17: 503–32. 4to. Original paper wrappers.

Pamphlet at RBGE, ex-Museum (?CML). No annotations by C, but attached to front wrapper a cutting from a bookseller's catalogue showing the reprint was bought secondhand for '7s 6d', perhaps by C.

DUVAU, Auguste (1826). Considérations générales sur le genre *Veronica. Annales des Sciences Naturelles* 8: 163–86 + t. 26. 8vo. Original wrappers with printed title. Pamphlet (reprint, paginated 2–24) at RBGE ex-Museum (?CML). Front cover inscribed by author to Robert Brown, and with author's corrections. No C annotations.

ENDLICHER, Stephan (1847). *Synopsis Coniferarum*. Sangalli. 8vo. EUL. Original binding. No signature, but many annotations in ink and pencil, mainly synonyms e.g. p 101 [*Pinus bifida*] 'like webbia…', p 93 'religiosa'.

FRANCHET, Adrien (1888). Les Mutisiacées du Yun-nan. *Journal de Botanique* 2: 65–71 + tt 2, 3. 8vo. Original wrappers. Pamphlet (reprint, paginated 2–7) at RBGE, ex-Museum (?CML). No C annotations.

GODRON, Dominique Alexandre (1842). *Quelques Observations sur la famille des alsinées.* Nancy. 8vo. Original wrappers. Pamphlet (reprint from

Mémoires de Société des Sciences Nancy, paginated 2–21) at RBGE ex-Museum (?CML). No C annotations.

GRAY, Asa (1837). *Melianthacearum Americae Septentrionalis Revisio*. Novi-Eboraci. 8vo. Original card wrappers. Pamphlet (reprint from *Annals of the New York Lyceum of Natural History*, vol. 4) at RBGE, (not accessioned, but ex-Museum and probably CML). No C annotations; flyleaf with dedication from author to Robert Brown.

GRIFFITH, William (1836). On the family of Rhizophoreae. 8vo. Pamphlet at RBGE, ex Museum (?CML). First published in *Transactions of the Medical and Physical Society of Calcutta* 8: 1–12 + t. 2, but this is a reprint from an unknown Indian publication, paginated 440–2. No C annotations.

GRIFFITH, William (1836). Description of some grasses which form part of the vegetation in the jheels of the district of Sylhet. *Journal of the Asiatic Society of Bengal* **5: 570–5 + tt 23, 24. 8vo. Pamphlet (t. 24 missing) at RBGE ex-Museum (?CML).** No C annotations.

GRIFFITH, William (1836). On a new genus of Scrophularineae. *Madras Journal of Literature and Science* **4: 373–7 + t. 11.**

8vo. Pamphlet at RBGE (reprint, paginated 2–5). Annotated on front cover by C 'Madras Journal of Science IV, 1836'.

GRIFFITH, William (1850). *Palms of British East India.* **Calcutta. Folio. CML.** At RBGE. Original printed boards. With H Cleghorn bookplate on front pastedown.

HAWORTH, Adrian Hardy (1829). A description of the subgenus *Epiphyllum*. *Philosophical Magazine and Annals* 6: 107–10. 8vo. Pamphlet (reprint, not paginated) at RBGE, ex-Museum (?CML). No C annotations.

HAWORTH, Adrian Hardy (1831). A botanical description of *Hermione cypri*. *Philosophical Magazine and Annals* 9: 183–5. 8vo. Pamphlet (reprint, not paginated) at RBGE, ex-Museum (?CML). No Cleghorn annotations, but title page annotated by the author 'No 30. To Mr Hunneman, with Authors respects', and perhaps passed on to C by Pamplin, who was John Hunneman's son-in-law.

HERBERT, William, the Rev & Hon (1821). *An Appendix* [to *Edwards's Botanical Register* vol. 7]: *Preliminary Treatise* [on Amaryllidaceae pp 1–52 + 4 plates]. London. 8vo. Pamphlet at RBGE, ex-Museum (?CML). Note: The bound copy at RBGE might be this, but the paper cover that might have had the accession number is missing.

HOOKER, Joseph Dalton (1855). On some remarkable exostoses developed on the roots of various species of Coniferae. *Proceedings of the Linnean Society* 2: 335–6. 8vo. Pamphlet at RBGE, ex-Museum (?CML). No C annotations.

HOOKER, Joseph Dalton (1865). On the identity of the *Pinus peuce* Griseb., of Macedonia, with the *P. excelsa* of the Himalaya Mountains. *Journal of the Linnean Society* 8: 145–6. 8vo. Original wrappers. Pamphlet at RBGE, ex-Museum (?CML). No C annotations.

HORT, the Rev. Fenton John Anthony (1851). On a supposed new species of *Rubus*. *Transactions of the Botanical Society [of Edinburgh]* 4: 113–6. 8vo. Pamphlet at RBGE, ex-Museum (?CML). No C annotations.

KER, John Bellenden (1817). *On the genus Pancratium*. London: W. Bulmer and Co. 8vo. Pamphlet (reprint, paginated [1–]2–22 from *Quarterly Journal of Science and the Arts* 3: 316–37 + t. 3) at RBGE, ex-Museum (?CML). No C annotations, but probably his as it has an Indian

provenance: on verso of title-page in an early hand is a list of 'Names of Pancratium in the Calcutta Garden'.

KLOTZSCH, Johann Friedrich (1851). *Studien über die naturliche Klasse Bicornes Linné* (reprinted from *Linnaea* 51: 1–88). [Halle]. 8vo. CML. At RBGE. In original binding. Annotated on flyleaf 'Dr Robert Brown London – the Author Linnaea 1851, vol XXIV [and with a few author's corrections]'. Stamped with Prussian export book-stamp 'Vertrag vom 13 Mai 1846'.

KORTHALS, Pieter Willem (1839). *Verhandeling over de op Java, Sumatra, en Borneo verzamelde Loranthaceae* (reprinted from *Verhandelingen van het Bataviaasch Genootschap van Kunsten en Wetenschappen*). [Batavia]. 8vo. CML. At RBGE. In original binding. No signature, or annotations.

KUNTH, Karl Sigismund (1833). *Enumeratio Plantarum*. Vol. 1, Gramineae. Stuttgart & Tübingen. 8vo. CML. Not at RBGE (Ball's complete set kept).

LEEFE, the Rev. John Ewbank (1841). Remarks on some curious metamorphoses of the pistil of *Salix caprea*. *Transactions of the Botanical Society [of Edinburgh]* 1: 113–4 + t. 8vo. Pamphlet at RBGE, ex-Museum (?CML). No C annotations.

LEES, Edwin (1844). Remarks on the mode of growth of the British Fruticose Rubi; and the forms derivable from *Rubus Caesius*. *Transactions of the Botanical Society [of Edinburgh]* 1: 172–8 + t. 8. 8vo. Pamphlet at RBGE, ex-Museum (?CML). No C annotations but stitching of text to plate suggests his ownership.

LINDLEY, John (1839–40). *The Genera and Species of Orchidaceous Plants*. Parts 5 and 7. London. 8vo. CML. At RBGE. Pt 8 in original paper wrappers. No signature or annotations.

LINDLEY, John (1846). *Orchidaceae Lindenianae: or Notes upon a Collection of Orchids formed in Colombia and Cuba by Mr J. Linden*. London. 8vo. CML. At RBGE. In original boards. No signature or annotations.

LINDLEY, John (1852–55). *Folia Orchidacea*. Vol. 1. London. 8vo. CML. Not at RBGE (a complete set kept).

LINDLEY, John (1857, 1859). Contributions to the Orchidology of India I & II. *Journal of the Linnean Society* 1: 170–90; 3: 1–63. 8vo. Original wrappers. Pamphlet at RBGE, ex-Museum (CML). On verso of title-page a journal clipping attached in Cleghorn's manner, referring to reading of this paper; in text annotations 'G' and 'W' in pencil beside species collected by Griffith and Wight respectively but not in C's hand.

LINDLEY, John (1859). *Folia Orchidacea*. Parts 7 and 8. London. 8vo. CML. Not at RBGE (a complete set kept).

LINDLEY, John (1862). West African tropical orchids. *Journal of the Linnean Society* 6: 3: 123–40. 8vo. Pamphlet at RBGE, ex Museum (CML). Title-page annotated in ink by C with source of article.

LOWE, the Rev. Richard Thomas (1860). Some account of the "Chaparro" of Fuerteventura, a new species of *Convolvulus*. *Annals & Magazine of Natural History* 6: 153–6. 8vo. Pamphlet (reprint, paginated 2–4) at RBGE, ex-Museum (CML). C has annotated the paper title with the epithet of the new species.

MACFARLANE, John Muirhead (1889). Observations on pitchered insectivorous plants 1. *Annals of Botany* 3: 253–6 + t. 17. 8vo. Original wrappers. Pamphlet at RBGE, ex-Museum (?CML). No C annotations.

MASTERS, Maxwell Tylden (1869). Synopsis of South-African Restiaceae. *Journal of the Linnean Society* 10: 209–79 + t 7, 8. 8vo. Original wrappers. Pamphlet at RBGE, ex-Museum (?CML). No C annotations.

MASTERS, Maxwell Tylden (1893) Notes on the genera of Taxaceae and Coniferae. *Journal of the Linnean Society* 30: 1–42. 8vo. Pamphlet at RBGE, ex-Museum (CML). No C annotations (but with CML printed stamp).

MIERS, John (1855). On the structure of the seed and peculiar form of the embryo in the Clusiaceae. *Proceedings of the Linnean Society* **2: 333–9; 343–7. 8vo. Pamphlet at RBGE, ex-Museum (CML).** On title-page is stuck a clipping annotated by C with reference to another paper on the same family by Spruce.

MORETTI, Giuseppe (1841). *Prodromo di una monografia del genere Morus.* **Milan. 8vo. Original wrappers. Pamphlet (reprint, paginated 2–18, from** *Giornale dell'I.R. Instituto Lombardo di Scienze, Lettere ed Arti e Biblioteca Italiana***) at RBGE, ex-Museum (?CML).** Front wrapper with author's dedication to Robert Brown; no C annotations.

MURRAY, Andrew (1855). New Californian conifers. *Edinburgh New Philosophical Journal* 1(n.s.): 284–95 + tt 6–11. 8vo. Pamphlet at RBGE, ex-Museum (?CML). No C annotations.

MURRAY, Andrew (1866). On the homologies of the male and female flowers of conifers. *Annals and Magazine of Natural History* 18: 212–21; 304–6 +

t. 10. 8vo. Original wrappers. Pamphlet (reprint, paginated 2–10) at RBGE, ex-Museum (?CML). No C annotations.

NEES VON ESENBECK, Chrisitan Gottfried Daniel (1837, read 1832). Monograph of the East Indian Solaneae. *Transactions of the Linnean Society* **17: 37–82. 4to. Original wrappers. Pamphlet at RBGE, ex-Museum (CML).** Front wrapper inscribed by Robert Wight 'Dr Cleghorn from RW'.

NEES VON ESENBECK, Chrisitan Gottfried Daniel (1830). Beitrag zur Kenntniss der Familien der Restiaceen in Rücksicht auf Gattungen und Arten. *Linnaea* 5: 627–66. 12mo. Original wrappers. Pamphlet at RBGE, ex-Museum (?CML). Front wrapper inscribed by author to Robert Brown; no C annotations.

NEES VON ESENBECK, Chrisitan Gottfried Daniel (1834). Uebersicht der Cyperaceengatungen. *Linnaea* 9: 273–306 + t. 4. 12mo. Original wrappers. Pamphlet at RBGE, ex-Museum (?CML). Front wrapper inscribed by author to Robert Brown; no C annotations.

OLIVER, Francis Wall (1888). On the structure, development and affinities of *Trapella*, Oliv., a new genus of Pedalineae. *Annals of Botany* 2: 75–115 + tt 5–9. 8vo.

Original wrappers. Pamphlet at RBGE, ex-Museum (?CML). No C annotations.

PARLATORE, Filippo (1855). Note sur le *Vallisneria spiralis*. *Bulletin de la Societé Botanique de France*. 2: 299–303. 8vo. Pamphlet (reprint, paginated 2–6) at RBGE, ex-Museum (?CML). No C annotations.

PASQUALE, Giuseppe Antonio (1863). *Osservazione sui canali resiniferi o serbatoi della resina degli strobili de' coniferi*. Napoli: Antonio Cons. 8vo. Original wrappers. Pamphlet (reprint with new title-page from *Annali dell'Accademia degli Aspiranti Naturalisti di Napoli*) at RBGE, ex-Museum (CML). Inscribed on title-page 'Dr H.F. Cleghorn by the author'.

PLANCHON, Jules Emile (1847). *Mémoire sur la famille des simaroubées.* **Orleans. 8vo. Pamphlet (reprint with new title-page from** *Mémoires de la Societé Royale des Sciences, Belles-lettres et Arts d'Orléans,* **vol. 7) at RBGE, ex-Museum (?CML).** No C annotations; title-page inscribed by author to Robert Brown.

PLANCHON, Jules Emile (1850). Prodromus monographiae ordinis Connaracearum. *Linnaea* **23: 411–42. 8vo. Pamphlet at RBGE, ex-Museum (?CML).** No C annotations; title-page inscribed by author to Robert Brown.

PLANCHON, Jules Emile (1850). *Quelques mots sur les inflorescences épiphylles a l'occasion d'une espèce nouvelle d'*Erythrochiton. Nancy. 8vo. Original wrappers. Pamphlet (reprint, with new title-page, paginated 4–8, from *Memoires de l'Académie de Stanislas*) at RBGE, ex-Museum (?CML). No C annotations; front wrapper inscribed by author to Robert Brown.

RALPH, Thomas Shearman (1849). *Icones-Carpologicae. Part 1. Leguminosae.* London. 4to. CML. At RBGE. Original binding (printed boards). With H Cleghorn bookplate on front pastedown, signed 'H Cleghorn' in pencil on title-page, with numerous marginal markings.

ST HILAIRE, Auguste de (1831). Observations sur le genre *Anacardium* **et les nouvelles espèces qu'on doit y faire entrer.** *Annales des Sciences Naturelles* **33: 268–74. 8vo. Original printed wrappers. Pamphlet (reprint, paginated 2–8) at RBGE, ex-Museum (?CML).** Title-page inscribed by author to Robert Brown; no C annotations.

ST HILAIRE, Auguste de & Moquin-Tandon, C.H.B. Alfred (1830). Mémoire sur la symmétrie des capparidées et des familles qui ont le plus de rapports avec elles. *Annales des Sciences Naturelles* 20: 318–26. 8vo. Original printed wrappers.

Pamphlet (reprint, paginated 2–8) at RBGE, ex-Museum (?CML). Title-page inscribed by authors to Robert Brown; no C annotations.

SANDERSON, John Scott (1850). On the embryogeny of *Hippuris vulgaris*. *Transactions of the Botanical Society [of Edinburgh]* 4: 51–7. 8vo. Pamphlet at RBGE, ex-Museum (?CML). No C annotations.

SAVI, Gaetano (1822). *Osservazioni sopra i generi Phaseolus et Dolichos. Memoria I.* Pisa. 8vo. Original printed wrappers. Pamphlet (reprint, paginated 4–20, from *Nouvo Giornale*, vol. 3) at RBGE, ex-Museum (CML). Plate annotated by C with names beside three fruits of three different species.

SCOTT, John (1864). Remarks on the sexual changes in the inflorescences of *Zea mays*. *Edinburgh New Philosophical Journal* 19 (n.s.): 55–62. 8vo. Pamphlet at RBGE, ex-Museum (?CML). No C annotations.

SPACH, Edouard (1834). Generum et specierum Hippocastanearum revisio. *Annales des Sciences Naturelles* 2: 50–64. 8vo. Pamphlet (reprint, paginated 2–15) at RBGE, ex-Museum (?CML). No C annotations.

SPACH, Edouard (1834). Revisio generis Acerum. *Annales des Sciences Naturelles* 2: 160–80.

8vo. Pamphlet (reprint, paginated 2–21) at RBGE, ex-Museum (?CML). No C annotations, but stitched with thread in his manner.

SPACH, Edouard (1834). Revisio generis Tiliarum. *Annales des Sciences Naturelles* 2: 331–47 + t. 15. 8vo. Pamphlet (reprint, paginated 2–16) at RBGE, ex-Museum (?CML). No C annotations.

SPACH, Edouard (1835). Revisio Grossulariearum. *Annales des Sciences Naturelles* 4: 16–31 + t. 1. 8vo. Pamphlet (reprint, paginated 2–16) at RBGE, ex-Museum (?CML). No C annotations.

TORREY, John (1867). On *Ammobroma*, a new genus of plants, allied to *Corallophyllum* and *Pholisma*. *Annals of the New York Lyceum of Natural History* 8: 51–6 + t. 8vo. Original wrappers. Pamphlet at RBGE, ex-Museum (CML). Front cover annotated by C in ink 'xcvii. Lennoaceae Ammobroma'.

TULASNE, Louis-René (1855). Diagnoses nonnullas e Monimiacearum recencione tentata excerptas praemitit. *Annales des Sciences Naturelles* 3 (ser 4): 29–46. 8vo. Original printed wrapper. Pamphlet at RBGE, ex-Museum (CML). Front cover annotated by C '170. Monimiaceae'.

WEBB, Philip Barker (1840). Notice sur le *Parolinia*, nouveau genre de la famille des Crucifères, et sur des espèces à ajouter à la flore des Canaries. *Annales des Sciences Naturelles* 13: 129–39 + t. 3. 8vo. Original wrappers. Pamphlet (reprint, paginated 2–11) at RBGE, ex-Museum (CML). Front cover with dedication by author to Robert Brown; annotated by C 'Parolinia'.

WEBB, Philip Barker (1843). Sur le genre *Retama*. *Annales des Sciences Naturelles* 20: 269–83. 8vo. Original wrappers. Pamphlet (reprint, paginated 2–15) at RBGE, ex-Museum (CML). Front cover with dedication by author to Robert Brown; annotated by C 'Retama. (Genista sectio)'.

WEBB, Philip Barker (1846). De Dicherantho Paronychiearum genere novo. *Annales des Sciences Naturelles* 5 (ser 3): 27–30 + t. 2. 8vo. Original wrappers. Pamphlet at RBGE, ex-Museum (CML). Front cover with dedication by author to Robert Brown; annotated by C 'Dicheranthus'.

WEBB, Philip Barker (1851). *Hemicrambe*, Cruciferarum genus novum. *Annales des Sciences Naturelles* 16 (ser 3): 246–9 + t. 19. 8vo. Original wrappers. Pamphlet (reprint, paginated 2–4) at RBGE, ex-Museum (CML). Front cover with dedication by author to Robert Brown; annotated by C 'Hemicrambe'.

WEBB, Philip Barker (1852). Observations sur le groupe des Ulicinées et énumération de ses espèces. *Annales des Sciences Naturelles* 17 (ser 3): 280–91 + t. 2. 8vo. Original wrappers. Pamphlet (reprint, paginated 2–13) at RBGE, ex-Museum (?CML). Front cover with dedication by author to Robert Brown; no C annotations.

WEDDELL, Hugh Algernon (1848). Revue du genre *Cinchona*. *Annales des Sciences Naturelles* 10 (ser 3): 5–14. 8vo. Original wrappers. Pamphlet at RBGE, ex-Museum (?CML). Front cover with dedication by author to Robert Brown; no C annotations.

WIGHT, Robert (1840). Remarks on the fruit of the Natural Order Cucurbitaceae. *Madras Journal of Literature and Science* 12: 43–54 + t. 4. 8vo. Pamphlet (reprint, paginated 2–12) at RBGE, ex-Museum (CML). Title-page annotated 'Dr Arnott from the Author'; and by C 'Madras Jour, of Science'.

WIKSTROM, Johan Emanuel (1818). Granskning af de till Thymelaearum Växtordning hörande Slägten och

Arter. *Kungliga Svenska Vetenskapsakademiens Handlingar* **39: 263–355 + t. 10. 8vo. Original wrappers. Pamphlet at RBGE, ex-Museum (?CML).** No C annotations; front cover with dedication to Robert Brown from the author.

WILSON, John Hardie (1890). The mucilage- and other glands of the Plumbagineae. *Annals of Botany* 4: 231–58 + tt 10–3. 8vo. Original wrappers. Pamphlet at RBGE, ex-Museum (CML). No C annotations; on front cover 'To Dr Cleghorn with Dr Wilson's kind regards'.

WILSON, John Hardie (1891). Observations on the fertilisation and hybridisation of some species of *Albuca*. *Botanisch Jaarboek (Gent)* 3: 233–259 + t. 8. 8vo. Original wrappers. Pamphlet (reprint with additional pagination 4–29) at RBGE, ex-Museum (CML). No C annotations; on flyleaf 'Dr Cleghorn with the author's compliments'.

Cryptogams (including diatoms and fungi)

BEDDOME, Richard Henry (1866–68). *The Ferns of British India*. Madras. 4to. CML. Not at RBGE (a later edition kept).

BERKELEY, the Rev Miles Joseph (1838). On the fructification of the Pileate and Clavate Hymenomycetous fungi. *Annals and Magazine of Natural History* 1: 81–101 + tt 4, 5. 8vo. Original paper covers. Pamphlet at RBGE, ex-Museum (?CML). No marks to show C's ownership, and dedication on title-page 'R.T. Lowe from M.J.B.'

BERKELEY, the Rev Miles Joseph (1843). Notice of fungi in the herbarium of the British Museum. *Annals and Magazine of Natural History* 10 (supp): 369–85 + tt 9–12. 8vo. Original paper covers. Pamphlet at RBGE, ex-Museum (?CML). No marks to show C's ownership; dedication on title-page 'To Mr. R. Brown with the authors best respects'.

BERKELEY, the Rev Miles Joseph (1848). On a peculiar form of mildew in onions. *Journal of the Royal Horticultural Society* 3: 91–8. 8vo. Original paper covers. Pamphlet (reprint, paginated 4–10) at RBGE, ex-Museum (?CML). 'Mucor' on cover possibly in C's hand.

BLUME, Carl Ludwig (1836–48). *Rumphia sive Commentationes Botanicae*. Vols 2 (tt 87–173), 3 (tt 138–73), 4 (tt 174–200B). Leiden. Folio. EUL. Vol. 2 unbound, vols 3, 4 in original board portfolios. No ownership or annotations.

[BOSANQUET, Edwin] 'E.B.' (1854). *A Plain and Easy Account of the British Ferns*. London. 8vo. CML. At RBGE. Original binding. No signature or annotations.

BRÉBISSON, Alphonse de (1867). *Note sur quelques diatomées marines rare ou peu connues du littoral de Cherbourg* (ed 2, reprinted from *Mémoires de la Société impériale des Sciences naturelles de Cherbourg*, vol. 2, 1854). Paris. 8vo. Original paper covers. Pamphlet at RBGE, ex-Museum (?CML). No marks to show C's ownership [perhaps significant that he visited the publisher in 1868].

COOKE, Mordecai Cubitt (1865). *Hardwicke's Science Gossip Easy Guide to the study of British Hepaticae*. London: Robert Hardwicke. 4to. Original paper wrappers, printed with title. Pamphlet at RBGE, ex-Museum (?CML). No annotations by C.

DICKIE, George (1844, read 1841). Remarks on the structure and morphology of *Marchantia*. *Transactions of the Botanical Society [of Edinburgh]* 1: 107–12 + t. 6. 8vo. Pamphlet at RBGE, ex-Museum (?CML). No annotations by C.

FRANCIS, George W. (1837). *Analysis of the British Ferns and their Allies*. London. 8vo. CML. At RBGE. Rebound. No signature or annotations.

GREVILLE, Robert Kaye & HOOKER, William Jackson (1831). Enumeratio filicum. Part I. Lycopodineae Sw. *Botanical Miscellany* 2: 360–403. 8vo. Original wrappers. Pamphlet (reprint, paginated 2–44) at RBGE, (not accessioned, but ex-Museum and probably CML). No C annotations; flyleaf with dedication from Hooker to Robert Brown.

GRIFFITH, William (1845). On *Azolla* and *Salvinia*. *Calcutta Journal of Natural History* 5: 227–73 + tt 15–20. 8vo. Pamphlet at RBGE, ex-Museum (?CML). No C annotations.

HARVEY, William Henry (1840). Musci Indici; or list of mosses collected in the East Indies by Dr Wallich. *Hooker's Journal of Botany* 2: 1–21 + tt 17–24. 8vo. Pamphlet at RBGE, ex-Museum (CML). Front page annotated by C 'Hook.' in front of journal title.

HOOKER, William Jackson (1818–20). *Musci Exotici*. 2 vols. London. 8vo. CML. At RBGE. Original binding. No annotations, with H Cleghorn bookplate on both front pastedowns. Flyleaf of vol. 1 has two second-hand-bookseller's prices, crossed out '53/-' (itself a considerable reduction on the original price of the book, 4 guineas given on the printed paper spine label), and '5 Rs', which shows that C bought the volumes in India.

HOOKER, William Jackson (1818–20). *Musci Exotici* (Large paper edition, with coloured plates). 2 vols. London. 4to. CML. At RBGE. With bookplates of George Warren Walker, and H Cleghorn on front pastedown.

HOOKER, William Jackson (1838[–?42]), *Genera Filicum*. London. 8vo. CML. At RBGE. Rebound. Annotated on title-page by Anna Maria Walker 'A.W[arren] Walker from Sir W.J. Hooker' and on dedication page 'Dr Hugh Cleghorn with kind regards from George Warren Walker 1853'. Note: Incomplete, the last part (with 20 plates) is missing.

HOOKER, William Jackson (1846–64). *Species Filicum*. 5 vols. London. 8vo. CML. Not at RBGE (another set kept).

HOOKER, William Jackson & GREVILLE, Robert Kaye (1824). Sketch of the characters of the species of mosses belonging to the genus *Orthotrichum*, (including *Schlotheimia*, *Micromitrion* and *Ulota*), *Glyphomitiron*, and *Zygodon*. *Edinburgh Journal of Science* 1: 110–33 + tt 4, 5. 8vo. Pamphlet at RBGE, ex-Museum (CML). Annotated by C on first page with the source of the article, and on page 132 with a completion of missing text from p 133.

HOWIE, Charles (1889). *The Moss Flora of Fife and Kinross*. Cupar. 8vo. CML. Not at RBGE (other copy kept).

JOHNSTON, Christopher (1860). Descriptions of Diatomaceae, chiefly of those found in "Elide" (Lower California) guano. *Quarterly Journal of Microscopical Science* 8: 11–21 + t. 4. 8vo. Original wrappers. Pamphlet (reprint, paginated 2–11) at RBGE, ex-Museum (?CML). No C annotations.

KITTON, Frederic (1867). Remarks on the publication of new genera and species from insufficient material. *Quarterly Journal of Microscopical Science* 7: 118–21. 8vo. Original wrappers. Pamphlet (reprint, paginated 2–4) at RBGE, ex-Museum (?CML). No C annotations; front cover annotated 'with the Authors compts' and text with his minor corrections.

KITTON, Frederic (1868). Remarks on some of the new species of Diatomaceae recently published by the Rev. E. O'Meara. *Quarterly Journal of Microscopical Science* 8: 13,

16, 17. 8vo. Original wrappers. Pamphlet (reprint, paginated 2–5) at RBGE, ex-Museum (?CML). No C annotations.

LEIGHTON, the Rev. William Allport (1872). *The Lichen Flora of Great Britain, Ireland, and the Channel Islands*. Ed 2. Shrewsbury. 12mo. CML. At RBGE. Original binding. Inscribed on front flyleaf 'Presented by the author to J. Smith ex curator Royal Gardens, Kew'.

LÉVEILLÉ, Joseph-Henri (1843). Mémoire sur le genre *Sclerotium*. *Annales des Sciences Naturelles* 20: 219–48 + tt 6, 7. 8vo. Original wrappers. Pamphlet at RBGE, ex-Museum (?CML). Front wrapper annotated 'Mr Robt. Brown' and by C 'Sclerotium'.

MONTAGNE, Camille (1838). De l'organisation et du mode de reproduction des caulerpées et en particulier du *Caulerpa Webbiana*, espèce nouvelle des iles Canaries. *Annales des Sciences Naturelles* 9 (ser. 2): 129–50 + t. 6. 8vo. Original wrappers. Pamphlet (reprint, paginated 2–22) at RBGE, ex-Museum (CML). Front wrapper with author's dedication to Robert Brown, and annotated by C 'Caulerpa'.

MONTAGNE, Camille (1842). Du genre *Xiphophora*. *Annales des Sciences Naturelles* 18 (ser. 2):

200–6. 8vo. Pamphlet (reprint, paginated 2–7) at RBGE, ex-Museum (?CML). No C annotations.

MOORE, David (1873). *Synopsis of all the Mosses Known to Inhabit Ireland*. Dublin. 8vo. CML. Not at RBGE (presentation copy to Alexander Dickson kept).

MOORE, Thomas (1863). *British Ferns and their Allies*. London. 8vo. CML. At RBGE. Rebound. The signature 'Griffiths' on title-page, and some annotations presumably by that owner (and press clipping about the death of Joseph Woods, aged 88, at The Crescent, Southover, Lewes).

NEES VON ESENBECK, Chrisitan Gottfried Daniel (1830). *Enumeratio Plantarum Cryptogamicarum Javae et Insularum Adiacentium, quas a Blumio er Reinwardtio Collectas. Fasc. 1. Hepaticas Complectens*. Vratislavia. 8vo. Original printed wrappers. Pamphlet at RBGE, ex-Museum (?CML). Front cover inscribed by Nees to Robert Brown; no C annotations. Note: Has a pencil price '2/6' – suggesting that these were sold by a bookseller after Brown's death.

NEWMAN, Edward (1840). *History of British Ferns*. London. 8vo. CML. Not at RBGE (Thomas Kipling's copy kept).

NEWMAN, Edward (undated). *History of British Ferns.* Ed 5. London. 8vo. CML. At RBGE. Original binding. No signature or annotations.

PERSOON, Christiaan Hendrik (1801). *Synopsis Methodica Fungorum. Pars Prima.* Göttingen. 8vo. CML. At RBGE. Rebound. No signature or annotations.

PLOWRIGHT, Charles Bagge (1889). *Monograph of the British Uredineae and Ustilagineae.* London. 8vo. CML. Not at RBGE (two other copies kept, one being the mycologist Malcolm Wilson's).

POOLEY, Charles (1863). *The Diatomaceae of Weston-super-Mare.* London. 12mo. Pamphlet at RBGE, ex-Museum (?CML). No C annotations.

RALFS, John (1853, read 1849). On the Nostochineae. *Transactions of the Botanical Society [of Edinburgh]* 4: 1–23 + tt 1, 2. 8vo. Pamphlet at RBGE, ex-Museum (?CML). No C annotations.

RALFS, John (1853, read 1850). Remarks on *Dickiea. Transactions of the Botanical Society [of Edinburgh]* 4: 121–2. 8vo. Pamphlet at RBGE, ex-Museum (?CML). No C annotations.

RALFS, John (1853, read 1851). On *Chantransia*, Desv. *Transactions of the Botanical Society [of Edinburgh]* 4: 123–6. 8vo. Pamphlet at RBGE, ex-Museum (CML). With newspaper cutting referring to reading of paper stuck (in C's manner) to title-page.

RATTRAY, John (1885). Observations on the oil bodies of the Jungermanniae. *Transactions of the Botanical Society [of Edinburgh]* 16: 123–8. 8vo. Pamphlet at RBGE, ex-Museum (CML). Annotated by C in pencil, on title-page, with source of publication.

ROPER, Freeman Clarke Samuel (1863). On the genus *Licmophora* (Agardh). *Journal of the Microscopical Society* 3: 36–53. 8vo. Original wrappers. Pamphlet (reprint, paginated 2–10) at RBGE, ex-Museum (?CML). No C annotations.

SCHAARSCHMIDT, Julius (1884). Notes on Afghanistan algae. *Journal of the Linnean Society* 21: 241–50 + t. 5. 8vo. Pamphlet at RBGE, ex-Museum (?CML). No C annotations.

SCHMID, the Rev. Bernhard (1857–8). A list of Neilgherry ferns. *Madras Journal of Literature and Science* 3: 79–83 and A list of Neilgherry mosses, l.c. pp 83–87. 8vo. Pamphlet (reprint, paginated 2–10) at

RBGE, ex-Museum (?CML). No C annotations.

SMITH, John (1866). *Ferns: British and Foreign*. London. 8vo. CML. At RBGE. Previously (1869) owned by someone with an illegible signature who has added some localities.

SMITH, the Rev. William (1859). *List of British Diatomaceae in the British Museum*. London. 12mo. Pamphlet at RBGE, ex-Museum (?CML). Not found.

STARK, Robert Mackenzie (1854). *A Popular History of British Mosses*. London. 8vo. CML. At RBGE. Original binding. Note. This cost 10/6 when new (L. Reeve catalogue).

SWARTZ, Olof (1790). *Genera et Species Filicum*. [Stockholm]. 8vo. EUL. Pamphlet, bound with Römer *Scriptores de Plantis Hispanicis*. On front pastedown H Cleghorn bookplate and the titles of the two works in C's hand; titlepage inscribed 'diario botanico a Cl. Schrader edito Gottingae 1800', and on first page the ink stamp of Madras Medical College 1852 (Note. Perhaps one of Rottler's books, cf. the copy of Willdenow, 1794).

TAYLOR, Thomas (1844, read 1841). Descriptions of *Jungermannia ulicina*, (Taylor) and of *J. Lyoni*, (Taylor). *Transactions of the Botanical Society [of Edinburgh]* 1: 115–7 + t. 7. 8vo. Pamphlet at RBGE, ex-Museum (?CML). No C annotations.

THURET, Gustave Adolphe (1853). *Note sur la fécondation des fucacées*. Cherbourg: A. Lecauf. 8vo. Original wrappers. Pamphlet (reprint, with new title-page, paginated 2–9 from *Mémoires de la Société des Sciences Naturelles de Cherbourg*, vol. 1) at RBGE, ex-Museum (?CML). No C annotations; front wrapper inscribed 'Hommage de l'auteur' (probaby to Robert Brown).

TRAILL, George William (1886). *The Marine Algae of Joppa*. Edinburgh. 8vo. CML. Not at RBGE.

TRAILL, George William (1888). *The Marine Algae of Elie*. Edinburgh. 4to. CML. Not at RBGE.

TURNER, Dawson (1804). *Muscologiae Hiberniae Spicelegium*. Yarmouth. 8vo. CML. Not at RBGE (another copy kept).

WALLICH, George Charles (1860). The markings of the Diatomaceae in common use as test-objects. *Annals and Magazine of Natural History* 5: 122–30. 8vo. Pamphlet (reprint, paginated 2–9) at RBGE, ex-Museum (?CML). No C annotations.

WOODWARD, Joseph Janvier
(1876). Notes on the markings
of *Navicula Rhomboides. Monthly
Microscopical Journal* 15:

209–11 + tt 135, 136. 8vo.
Original wrappers. Pamphlet at
RBGE, ex-Museum (?CML).
No C annotations.

BAILLON, Henri Ernst (1876–92).
Dictionnaire de Botanique.
4 vols. Paris. 4to. CML. At
RBGE. Original binding, by
Fletcher & Son, binder to St
Andrews University (Plate 8.v).
No signature, frontispiece of
vol. 3 annotated with plant
name by C.

**CANDOLLE, Augustin Pyramus
de & Alphonse de (1824–
73).** *Prodromus Systematis
Naturalis Regni Vegetabilis.*
**Vols 1–17 (in 20). Paris. 8vo.
CML.** At RBGE. Some in
original binding, some rebound.
Some with H Cleghorn
bookplate. No annotations
(those present are by later RBGE
taxonomists). C has stuck a
notice from *Gardeners' Chronicle*
on flyleaf of vol. 12. Publishers
catalogues bound in at end of
vol. 8 (J-B Baillère, Nov 1843),
9 (Fortin, Masson & Cie, Nov
1844), 10 (J-B Baillère, n.d.), 12
(Victor Masson, n.d.) and 13(2)
(J-B Baillère, May 1849).

CLUSIUS, Carolus (1605).
Exoticorum Libri Decem.
[Leiden]. Folio. CML. At
RBGE. Rebound. No signature,
verso of title-page stamped

'Museum Britannicum 1831
duplicate for sale'.

DURAND, Théophile
(1888). *Index Generum
Phanerogamorum.* Bruxelles.
8vo. CML. Not at RBGE (two
other copies 'Supplied for Public
Service' kept).

**ENDLICHER, Stephan (1836–
40).** *Genera Plantarum
secundum Ordines Naturales
disposita.* **Vienna. 4to. CML.**
At RBGE. Original binding.
Signed 'H Cleghorn' in pencil
on title-page, inside front board
with price £2.18.0. Annotations
pp 224, 572 etc., but probably
not C's.

FIELDING, Henry Barron &
GARDNER, George (1844).
Sertum Plantarum. London.
8vo. EUL. Original boards. No
signature or annotations. (Note:
This work is closely modelled on
Hooker's *Icones Plantarum*, and
although published in London
by Baillière, the plates are by
Allan & Ferguson of Glasgow,
lithographed after drawings by
Mrs Fielding – doubtless due
to Gardner's connection with
Hooker).

GAERTNER, Joseph (1788–91). *De Fructibus et Seminibus Plantarum.* 2 vols. Stuttgart & Tübingen. 4to. CML. At RBGE. Original binding. No signature or annotations.

GAERTNER, Karl Frederick (1805). *Supplementum Carpologiae seu Continuatio Operis Josephi Gaertner de Fructibus et Seminibus Plantarum.* Leipzig. 4to. CML. At RBGE. Rebound. With H Cleghorn bookplate on verso of flyleaf. On title-page a Prussian book-export stamp 'Vertrag vom 13 Mai 1846'.

[GISEKE, Paul Dietrich (1779). *Index Linnaeanus in Leonhardi Plukenetii, M.D., Opera Botanica.* Hamburg: for the author and C.E. Bohn. Not in EUL or CML**, but C appears to have had a copy when in Madras (see Kew Director's Correspondence 55/65 C to W.J. Hooker 9 Jun 1855)].

JACQUIN, Nicholas Joseph (1764–71). *Observationum Botanicarum. Partes I–IV.* Vienna. 4to. CML. At RBGE. Original binding. No signature or annotations.

LAMARCK, Jean-Antoine-Pierre-Antoine de Monet, Chevalier de [& POIRET, J.L.M.] (1783–1808). *Encyclopédie Méthodique: Botanique.* 8 vols. Paris. 4to. CML. At

RBGE. Vols 5 & 6 in original bindings, others rebound. Some with H Cleghorn bookplate, no annotations.

LAMARCK, Jean-Antoine-Pierre-Antoine de Monet, Chevalier de [& POIRET, J.L.M.] (1810–17). *Supplement to Encyclopédie Méthodique: Botanique.* 5 vols. Paris. 4to. CML. At RBGE. Rebound. All volumes with H Cleghorn bookplate, no annotations.

LAMARCK, Jean-Antoine-Pierre-Antoine de Monet, Chevalier de (1791–1819). *Tableau Encyclopédique et Méthodique des Trois Règnes de la Nature: Botanique.* Bound as 2 vols of text and 3 of plates. Paris. 4to. CML. At RBGE. Rebound. No bookplates or signatures, some of plates (of Indian species) annotated by C with names. Note. Lacks the third volume and the last 50 plates. The plates are possibly of the 1823 reprinting.

MIERS, John (1851–71). *Contributions to Botany.* Vols 1 & 3. London. 4to. CML. Not at RBGE (complete set presented by Miss Miers in 1896 kept).

PHILIBERT, J.C. [Jean Baptiste Charles Legendre de Luçay] (1806). *Dictionnaire abrégé de Botanique.* Paris. 8vo. CML. At RBGE, rebound. No signature or annotations.

PLUKENET, Leonard (1691–1769). *Opera.* 4 vols. London. 4to. **CML.** At RBGE. Rebound. All volumes with H Cleghorn bookplate, vol. 1 inscribed on flyleaf by Robert Wight 'Dr Cleghorn with the kind regards & wishes of his friend RW', to which C has added 'Dr. R Wight' and 'see Trimen Jour. Linn. Soc. XXIV'; the plates of Indian plants in vols 1 and 3 are annotated with Linnaean names by C. The volumes were sent to Madras by Pamplin in 1853. Note. Vol. 1, 1691; vol. 3, 1700; vols 2 and 4, ed. 2, 1769.

SALISBURY, Richard Anthony (1866). *The Genera of Plants: a Fragment Containing Part of Liriogamae.* London. 8vo. CML. At RBGE. Rebound. Title-page inscribed 'Mr Morson with J.E. Gray's [the editor] Kindest Regards' Note: Probably Thomas Newborn Robert Morson (1799–1874), pharmacist; Gray (1800–1875) was Keeper of Zoology at the British Museum.

SALISBURY, Richard Anthony & HOOKER, William (1806). *The Paradisus Londinensis.* Vol. 1 Part 1. London. 4to. CML. Not at RBGE (another copy kept).

SCHNIZLEIN, Adalbert (1843–70). *Iconographia Familiarum Naturalium Regni Vegetabilis.* 4 vols of plates, 1 of text. Bonn. 4to. EUL. Loose plates in original board portfolios. No signatures or annotations (except a few pencil re-numberings). Note: These are exquisite lithographs, largely uncoloured, each plate with only a few details coloured. Did C start to subscribe to this uncommon work when it began in 1843? – it would have been useful in teaching in Madras, but perhaps more likely to have been bought when complete.

STEUDEL, Ernest Theophilus (1840–41). *Nomenclator Botanicus.* 2 vols. Stuttgart & Tübingen. 8vo. CML. Not at RBGE (University Library copy kept).

TOURNEFORT, Joseph Pitton de (1719). *Institutiones Rei Herbariae.* Ed 3. 3 vols. Paris. 4to. CML. At RBGE. Rebound. Bookplate of William Morehead on inside front boards.

VAHL, Martin (1790). *Symbolae Botanicae. Partes I–III.* Copenhagen. Folio. CML. At RBGE. In original boards (bound as one). With H Cleghorn bookplate on front pastedown, plates annotated with names by C. On front pastedown in pencil 25/- (presumably what C paid for it).

WALPERS, Wilhelm Gerhard (1842–47). *Repertorium Botanices Systematicae.* 6 vols. Leipzig. 8vo. CML. Not at RBGE (Ball's set kept).

WARD, Harry Marshall (1889). *Diseases of Plants*. London. 8vo. EUL. Original binding. Title-page signed in blue pencil 'H Cleghorn', no annotations.

ZANONI, Giacomo (1675). *Istoria Botanica*. Bologna. 4to. CML. At RBGE. Rebound, signed in pencil 'H Cleghorn' on title-page.

TEXTBOOKS

CANDOLLE, Augustin Pyramus de & SPRENGEL, Kurt (1821). *Elements of the Philosophy of Plants*. Translated from the German. Edinburgh. 8vo. CML. At RBGE. Rebound. No signature. Marginal lines on pp 99, 108, 109, 163, 166 etc on natural classification, nature of genera etc.

[COX, Emily M.] (1855). *Popular Geography of Plants*. Edited by Charles Daubeny. London. 12mo. CML. At RBGE. Original binding (rebacked). Signed 'H Cleghorn' in pencil title-page and with H Cleghorn bookplate on front pastedown, no annotations.

DUNCAN, John Shute (1826). *Botanical Theology: evidences of the existence and attributes of the Deity, collected from the appearances of Nature*. Ed 2. Oxford. 8vo. CML. At RBGE. Original binding. No signature or annotations.

EICHLER, August Wilhelm (1886). *Syllabus der Vorlesungen über ... Botanik*. 4te Aufl. Berlin. 8vo. EUL. Pamphlet bound by

Cleghorn with works by C.A. Chardon, P. Lawson, R.H. Greg, Scott & Redgrave. No signature or annotations.

GRAHAM, Thomas (1841). *Outlines of Botany*. London. 8vo. EUL. Original binding. Signed in pencil 'H Cleghorn' on title-page, an illegible annotation on back paste-down. Note: Graham was a London undergraduate who became a naval surgeon.

GRAY, Asa (1842). *The Botanical Text-Book*. New York. 12mo. CML. Not at RBGE.

GRAY, Asa (1881). *The Botanical Text-Book*. Ed 6. Part I. Structural Botany. London. 8vo. CML. At RBGE. Rebound. Pencil signature on title-page, no annotations.

HOOKER, William Jackson (1837). *Botanical Illustrations*. Glasgow. 4to. CML. At RBGE. Rebound. No signature. On plate 15 are manuscript additions in Hooker's hand, the captions for figs 13–16 (which are also printed on a tipped in erratum slip) – perhaps Hooker gave Cleghorn this copy?

HOOKER, William Jackson (1859). The article '*Botany*' (from *Admiralty Manual*, ed. 3, edited by J.F.W. Herschel). London. 8vo. EUL. A pamphlet in original wrappers. No signature or annotations.

JACKSON, Benjamin Daydon (1882). *Vegetable Technology*. London. 8vo. CML. At RBGE. Original binding. Correction on p 62 about an attribution 'not Falconer'; marginal crosses on pp 224, 225 about references to *Hydrocotyle asiatica*. An interesting book published by the Index Society – references to economic botany. Six of C's papers/books are listed on p 38, against which C has corrected the spelling of 'Pauontee'.

JOHNSTONE, Alexander (1891). *Botany: a Concise Manual for Students of Medicine and Science*. Edinburgh & London. 8vo. CML. Not at RBGE.

KNIGHT, William (1832). *Outlines of Botany*. Aberdeen. 12mo. CML. At RBGE. Rebound. Annotated on title-page 'To Doctor Dauney with best Complts. from Dr. K'. Interleaved copy, but with no notes. Note: Alexander Dauney (1749–1833) was professor of Civil Law, King's College, Aberdeen.

LEE, James (1788). *An Introduction to Botany*. Ed 4. London. 8vo. CML. At RBGE. Original

leather binding (rebacked). HUGH CLEGHORN bookplate on inside front board.

LEES, Edwin (1834). *The Affinities of Plants with Man and Animals*. London. 8vo. CML. At RBGE. In old binding. No signature or annotations.

LINDLEY, John (1849). *School Botany*. New edition. London. 8vo. CML. At RBGE. Rebound. No signature, a few marginal marks – e.g. pp 48, 58, 142.

MEYEN, Franz Julius Ferdinand (1846). *Outlines of the Geography of Plants* (translated M. Johnston). London. 8vo. EUL. Original binding. Flyleaf signed 'Adam White' in ink and H Cleghorn in pencil, on front paste-down pencil notes presumably about purchase from second-hand bookseller ('Ed Rev with Index 12 . 5 …' and a bookplate has been removed. Title page – beside the printed Translated by Margaret Johnston is written in pencil 'The late … now Mrs Philip Maclagan'. (Note: T.C. Jerdon is in printed list of Ray Society subscribers under 'Madras Literary Society'. Adam White, zoologist at BM, born Edinburgh and one of C's proposers for the Linnean Society in November 1851).

PHILIBERT, J.C. [Jean Baptiste Charles Legendre de Luçay] (1806). *Exercises de botanique*. Ed 2. 2 vols. Paris. 8vo. EUL.

RALPH, Thomas Shearman (1849). *Elementary Botany*. London. 12mo. CML. At RBGE. Rebound. No signature or annotations.

RATTRAY, James [1830, or later ed]. *Botanical Chart*. Glasgow. Folding. CML. At RBGE. Rebound. No signature or annotations.

RENNIE, James (1834). *Alphabet of Botany*. London. 12mo. EUL. Original binding. No signature or annotations; old shelfmark A 11-13 on front pastedown.

RICHARD, Achille (1837). *Nouveaux Eléménts de Botanique*. Nouvelle édition, par Drapiez. Bruxelles. 8mo. CML. At RBGE. Original binding. No signature or annotations, duplicate stamped on flyleaf Zoological Society of London.

THOMÉ, Otto W. (1877). *Text-Book of Structural and Physiological Botany*. Translated and edited by A.W. Bennett. London. 8vo. CML. Not at RBGE.

[WILLIAMS, Joseph] (1855). *The Botanist's Vade-Mecum*. London & Glasgow. 8vo. CML. Not at RBGE (Balfour's copy kept).

Economic botany

India

AITCHISON, James Edward Tierney (1889). The source of badsha or royal salep. *Transactions of the Botanical Society of Edinburgh* 17: 434–40 + t. 7. 8vo. Original paper wrappers. Pamphlet at RBGE, ex-Museum (CML). Front cover inscribed by author 'J.G. Baker Esq. with kind regards JA'; and in C's hand 'Allium Macleanii'.

ANON (1855). *Papers Regarding the Cultivation of Hemp in India*. Agra. 8vo. CML.

At RBGE. In early binding (rebacked). No signature or annotations.

ANON (1874). *The Cultivation and Curing of Tobacco in Bengal*. Calcutta. 8vo. CML. At RBGE. In original card boards. No signature; marginal lines on pp 1, 2.

[BALFOUR, Edward Green (1862). *Second Supplement to Cyclopedia of India*. Madras. 8vo]. EUL. Original binding. No signature or annotations.

[BENGAL (1860). *Papers Relating to the Cultivation of Indigo.* Calcutta. 8vo]. EUL. Original paper wrappers. No signature or annotations.

BIDIE, George (1869). *Report on the Ravages of the Borer in Coffee Estates.* Madras. 8vo. CML. Not at RBGE.

BIRDWOOD, George Christopher Molesworth (1862). *Economic Products of Bombay.* Bombay. 8vo. EUL. Original binding. Front pastedown signed 'H Cleghorn Lahore 1863', also signed in pencil on title-page; pp 97–106 [names of drugs] annotated from the works of Royle, Honigberger, W. Jameson and J.L. Stewart.

CAMPBELL-WALKER, Inches (1884). The sandal wood oil stills of South Canara. *Indian Forester* 10: 262–4 + tt 1, 2. 8vo. Original printed wrappers. Pamphlet (reprint, paginated 2–3) at RBGE, ex-Museum (?CML). No C annotations; front cover signed 'With Major I. Campbell Walker's compliments'.

CHAPMAN, John (1851). *Cotton and Commerce of India.* London. 8vo. EUL. Original binding. Half-title signed 'H Cleghorn' in blue pencil – prices on front paste-down suggest it was bought second-hand by C, and the numerous annotations

are not in his hand (publisher's catalogue of Chapman, dated 1 Jan 1851, bound in at end).

CHRISTISON, Robert (1846). Observations on a new variety of gamboge from Mysore. 8vo. Pamphlet at RBGE, ex Museum (CML). Paper originally published in *Pharmaceutical Journal* 6: 60–9, but this is a reprint from an untraced Indian periodical, paginated 667–74. Inserted are copies of two letters from C to Christison from Shimoga date 3 March and 7 September 1846, and a ms description of *Garcinia pictoria* as found in Wynaad in an unknown hand.

CLEGHORN, H.F.C. (1855). *Memorandum on Indian Grasses, and the Mode of Cultivating and Improving Pasture Lands.* Madras. Folio. Pamphlet (paginated 2–3) at RBGE, ex-Museum (?CML); with it a *Memorandum on Indian Grasses, and their Cultivation, for Cavalry Purposes* (Madras, folio, pp [1 –]2–4) by C.G. Ottley & Thos. Pritchard.

CLEGHORN, H.F.C. (1856). Notes on the sand-binding plants of the Madras beach. *Journal of the Agricultural and Horticultural Society of India* 9: 174–7 + 1 plate. 8vo. Pamphlet (reprint, paginated 2–4) at RBGE, ex-Museum (?CML). No C annotations.

CLEGHORN, H.F.C. (1858). *Memorandum on Pauchontee*. Madras. Folio. EUL. Original paper wrappers. Title-page inscribed in pencil by Cleghorn 'Bassia elliptica (Dalzell) see Kew Miscellany'.

CLEGHORN, H.F.C. (1854). *Note on the Aegle marmelos* (reprinted from *Indian Annals Med. Sci.* 2: 222–4). Calcutta. 8vo. EUL. Pamphlet bound by Cleghorn with works by L. Pappe, W.B. O'Shaughnessey, E.J. Waring, J.H. Balfour, T.W.C. Martius, & R. Lyell. With H Cleghorn bookplate on front paste-down, with C's manuscript contents list on flyleaf.

CLEGHORN, H.F.C. (1861). *Notes upon the Coconut Tree* (reprinted from *Edinburgh New Philosophical Journal* 14 (n.s.): 173–83). Edinburgh. 8vo. EUL. Pamphlet bound by Cleghorn with works by J. Shier & Biasoletto.

CLEGHORN, H.F.C. (1851). *Remarks on Calysaccion longifolium* (reprinted from *Pharmaceutical Journal* 10: 597–8). London. 8vo. EUL. Pamphlet bound by Cleghorn with works by L. Pappe, W.B. O'Shaughnessey, E.J. Waring, J.H. Balfour, T.W.C. Martius, & R. Lyell. With H Cleghorn bookplate on front paste-down, and his contents list on flyleaf.

COOKE, Mordecai Cubitt (1874). *Report on Gums, Resins etc. in Indian Museum*. London. Folio. EUL. Original paper wrappers. Signed on front cover 'H Cleghorn' in ink, no notes.

COOKE, Mordecai Cubitt (1871). *Report on Oil Seeds and Oils in Indian Museum*. London. Folio. EUL.

COPE, Henry. (1841). A connected view of the species of lichens, with their botanical relationship existing between them and the Indian productions. *Journal of the Asiatic Society of Bengal* **10: 888–94. 8vo. Pamphlet (reprint, paginated 2–8) at RBGE, ex-Museum (?CML).** No Cleghorn annotations, but stitched together with it (and suggesting C's ownership) a further pamphlet, a letter from Cope on the same subject (paginated 2–6), doubtless reprinted from the same periodical.

DAVIES, Robert Henry (ed.) (1862). *Report on Trade and Resources of the Countries on the North-Western Boundary of British India.* **Lahore. 8vo. CML.** At RBGE. Interleaved copy, rebound. Signed in ink 'H Cleghorn' on title-page, marginal corrections pp v, 20, 21, annotations facing pp 6, 14; a major one on Asafoetida facing App VII p xli. Also the set of 6 accompanying maps in original binding.

DRURY, Heber (1858). *Useful Plants of India.* **Madras. 8vo. EUL.** Interleaved and annotated proof copy, heavily annotated and grangerised. Title-page signed 'H Cleghorn' in ink and annotated by Drury 'Another proof please H D'. On Front pastedown a letter from Drury: 'I really feel greatly indebted to you for the trouble you took while at Madras about this & the useful plants: Altho' from what you say Francis Appavoo will be well up to the work [presumably proof-reading], still he will not be able to replace you in the occasional annotations & additions which so much enhance the value of the book. – I am on my way back to Trevandrum and thence probably to Courtallum – but I shall be within hail if you come that way – which I sincerely hope you will manage. Believe me Yours very sincerely Heber Drury'. Opposite this, on the flyleaf, is an anonymous review of the book from 'The Indian Field' March 26, conceivably written by Cleghorn himself.

Too many additions to list, and Cleghorn continued to add to it until the end of his Indian sojourn and later (e.g. cutting from Agri-Horticultural Society of India 21 May 1874 p 128).

Additions include clippings (e.g., p 17 one for 'Specific for Diarrhoaea and Dysentery Pogson's Compound Bael Powder ... Apply to Lieutenant Pogson, Simla ... [he] can only guarantee the Medicine, made under his personal superintendence'; ms literature references for particular species (e.g., from Waring, and Tennant's Ceylon, Bennett's Gatherings of a Nat. in Australasia), and from experience – e.g. *Acacia catechu* opposite p 6 'Abundant in the Terai of N.W. Himalaya near Hardwar, a shabby looking thorny tree the dry legumes hang in April. Fl: in rainy season'.

p 19 – note on *Aeschynomene aspera* 'It has been employed by Entomologists for lining the drawers of their cabinets & in its texture very much resembles "Ricepaper" the produce of *Aralia papyrifera*. HC.

p 37 opposite *Andropogon citratum* 'The lower ranges of Hills (Mysore, Wynad) are covered with the tall Lemon Grass, whose oppressive perfume and coarse texture, when full grown, renders it distasteful to cattle, wch. will only crop the delicate [?braid] that springs up after the surface has been annually burnt'.

p 61 – specially many cuttings and ms notes on *Bambusa* and p 153 on coffee, p 287 *Linum*, 434 on tea (which is added, not in Drury originally).

p 93 – newspaper cuttings about prickly pear.

p 109 notes on use of cannabis 'Cultivated near villages in N.W. Himalaya for 3 purposes. 1. To make coarse thick cloth, worn by the poorer classes. 2. To make ropes. 3. To make churrus – intoxicating drug much used for smoking with tobacco, article of traffic.'

p 126 – title of paper on *Castanospermum* by HC in *J.A.H.S. India* vol. X 116.

p 128 – an addition 'Cedrus Deodara', with newspaper cutting dated 28 ix 1861 giving prices of timber at Umballa 'A few hundred Deodar one-inch plants, for flooring or roofing; also beams 18 feet long, 6 inches by 5, price 4 Rs. each. The planks are seasoned, and will be sold at Rs. 45 per 100'.

p 153 – cuttings about coffee, and ms note by C dated May 1876 [showing continued interest after leaving India] of value of coffee estates form 'Ch. of Commerce, Madras. Coffee. Madras Presidency. Estates 430. Acreage 150,000. Value £2 ½ millions. Laborers 40,000'.

p 255 – *Humulus lupulus* 'Introduced at Dehra – 16 pounds sent to Mussoorie Brewery. In Kunawar, the hop has failed from the same cause wch. destroyed the grape. The rains descend at the very season when fruit is ripening so destroys it'.

p 393 – on sandalwood quotes Darwin Researches in Geol. and Nat. Hist. pp 552, 583.

p 405 – folded folio of 'Memo No 26' on Sal by Brandis (including growth rates), signed 'D.B. Calcutta 8/4 64', with addition by HC ('This treatment (pollarding) cannot be recommended – one of the special advantages of sal timber is the fine straight bole – wch. renders it valuable for many purposes').

p 416 on *Sterculia foetida* 'objectionable for avenues from the fetor of the flowers & the deciduous foliage'.

p 445 – newspaper cutting with report to Govt. on Neilgherry nettle by McIvor, 12 April 1862.

Another book review on back pastedown (anonymous and source not given).

DUTHIE, John Firminger (1893). *Field and Garden Crops of NW Provinces and Oudh*. Part 3. Roorkee. 4to. EUL. Original binding. No signature or annotations.

DUTHIE, John Firminger, & FULLER, Joseph Bampfylde (1882–83). *Field and Garden Crops of the N.W. Provinces and Oudh*. Parts 1, 2. Roorkee. 4to. CML. Not at RBGE.

FERGUSON, William (1850). *Description of the Palmyra Palm of Ceylon*. Colombo: Observer Press. 8vo. Original

wrappers with printed (and illustrated) front cover. **Pamphlet at RBGE, ex-Museum (?CML).** No annotations by C; title-page inscribed 'James Loos Esqre. with the author's kind regards'. Note: Loos was the first Principal of the Ceylon Medical College.

GRAHAM, Robert (1836). **Remarks on the gamboge tree of Ceylon, and character of *Hebradendron* a new genus of Guttiferae, and that to which the tree belongs.** *Companion to the Botanical Magazine* **2: 193–200 + t. 27. 8vo. Pamphlet at RBGE, ex-Museum (CML).** Plate is annotated by C 'Hooker Comp. Bot. Mag.'.

HANNAY, Simon Fraser (1850). **On the rheeas or nettle grasses, and other textile-fibres of Assam.** *Journal of the Agricultural and Horticultural Society of India* **7: 215–25. 8vo. Pamphlet at RBGE, ex-Museum (CML).** Front page annotated by C 'A.H.S.I. vol. vii. 1850'.

KERR, Hem Chunder (1874). *Report of Cultivation of Jute in Bengal*. Calcutta. Folio. EUL.

LYELL, Robert (1857). *Notes on the Patna Opium Agency* (Records of the Bengal Govt. No XXV). Calcutta. 8vo. EUL. Pamphlet bound by C

with works by L. Pappe, W.B. O'Shaughnessey, E.J. Waring, T.W.C. Martius, Cleghorn & J.H. Balfour. Bookplate on front paste-down, with C's manuscript contents list on flyleaf.

MARSHALL, Henry (1836). *Contribution to a Natural History of the Coco-nut Tree.* **Edinburgh. 8vo. Pamphlet (reprint from *Memoirs of the Wernerian Natural History Society* 5: 107 – 48, 1824) at RBGE, ex-Museum (CML).** Inserted is a newspaper clipping about C's paper on the coconut delivered to BSE in 1861.

MARTIUS, Theodor Wilhelm Christian (1853). *Die ostindische Rohwarensammlung [raw materials] der Friedrich-Alexanders Universität zu Erlangen.* Erlangen. 8vo. EUL. Pamphlet bound by C with works by L. Pappe, W.B. O'Shaughnessey, E.J. Waring, J.H. Balfour, Cleghorn & R. Lyell. Bookplate on front paste-down, with C's manuscript contents list on flyleaf.

McCANN, Hugh W. (1883). *Report on Dyes and Tans of Bengal.* Calcutta. 8vo. EUL.

O'CONNOR, J.E. (1873). *Report on Production of Tobacco in India.* Calcutta. Folio. EUL. Original binding. No signature or annotations.

PARLATORE, Filippo (1864). Sul Kamala [*Rottlera tinctoria*]. *Lo Sperimentale* 14: 59–64. **8vo. Original wrappers. Pamphlet (reprint, pagination 4–8) at RBGE, ex-Museum (?CML).** No C annotations, title-page inscribed by author to H.F. Hance.

PHIPPS, John (1832). *A Series of Treatises on the Principal Products of Bengal. No 1. Indigo.* **Calcutta. 8vo. EUL.**

ROYLE, John Forbes (1851). *On the Culture and Commerce of Cotton in India etc.* **London. 8vo. EUL.** Original binding. With H Cleghorn bookplate on front paste-down. Short pencil index on back flyleaf; inserted at p 264 is a folded folio with 1½ sides of manuscript notes by C 'Culture of Cotton in America', presumably copied from an unidentified source.

ROYLE, John Forbes (1855). *The Fibrous Plants of India.* **London. 8vo. EUL.** Original binding. Title page stamped 'Govt. of India Library', no annotations, pages uncut.

ST HILAIRE, Auguste de (1837). **Histoire de l'indigo depuis l'origine des temps historiques jusqu'a l'année 1833. 8vo. Original wrappers. Pamphlet (reprint paginated 2–16 from 'Des Nouvelles Annales des Voyages') at RBGE, ex-Museum (?CML).** Title page

inscribed 'Mr R. Brown'; no C annotations.

SHORTT, John (1888). *Monograph on the Cocoanut Palm.* Madras. 8vo. CML. At RBGE. In original boards. No signature or annotations. Note: With fascinating illustrations, two photo-etched plates, lithographs – transfer by T. Thagarajoo, lith. J. Suares 1887, showing pests, and artefacts (teapot, sugar pot, etc.) made of coconut shell.

STRETTELL, George W. (1874). *Note on Caoutchouc obtained from the* Chavannesia esculenta. Rangoon. 8vo. Original printed wrapper. Pamphlet at RBGE, ex-Museum (CML). Front cover annotated by C with generic name *Urceola* (twice, one in pencil, one in ink). Inserted a ms note, not in C's hand, copied from Ribbentrop's Pegu Forest Report.

TRELOAR, William Purdie (1884). *The Prince of Palms* [*Cocos nucifera*]. London. Oblong 8vo. Original printed wrappers. Pamphlet at RBGE, ex-Museum (?CML). No C annotations.

WATSON, John Forbes (1872). *List of Indian Products*. Part 2. London. 8vo. EUL. Original wrappers. No signature or annotations.

WATSON, John Forbes (1871). *Report on Cultivation of Tobacco in India*. London. Folio. EUL.

[WATSON, John Forbes (1879).
Report on Indian Wheat.
London. Folio]. EUL.

GENERAL

**ANON (1851). *Gutta percha
its Discovery, History and
Manifold Uses*. London. 12mo.
Original wrappers, front one
printed with illustration and
title. Pamphlet at RBGE,
ex-Museum (?CML).** No C
annotations.

ANON (1887). *Flax Growing: its
Cultivation, Preparation, and
Profits*. Dundee. 12mo. Original
paper wrappers, front one
printed with title. Pamphlet at
RBGE, ex-Museum (?CML).
No C annotations.

ARCHER, Thomas Croxen (1853).
Popular Economic Botany.
London. 8vo. EUL. Original
gilt-stamped cloth binding.
With H Cleghorn bookplate
on flyleaf, and signed in ink on
title-page. Annotation on
p 24 (grapes), p 27 (quote
from Milton about figs), 38–41
(citrus), p 52 about S American
Indians throwing stones at
monkeys to get them to throw
back brazil nuts 'We cannot
but doubt this "on dit" of the
S. American monkeys', p 55
(Cashew nut) reference to Penny
Cyclopedia, p 84 (*Tacca*), 85
(salep from 'tuberous roots of
Satyrium ...'), p 86 (semolina)

'generally considered to be the
seeds of Festuca fluitans', pp 90,
94, 113, 163 (corrections),
p 134 (cocoa pods) '7–8– even
9 Inches long at "Burleer" Mr
Thomas Garden in the Coonoor
Ghat', pp 198/9, corrections to
Myrobalans, p 206 (red sandal),
p 211 (manjit), 217 (saffron),
226 (oak galls) etc.

BROWN, Samuel (1809). *Essay on
Iron Rigging*. London. 8vo. EUL.

BULLIARD, Pierre (1784). *Histoire
des plantes vénéneuses et suspectes
de la France*. Paris. Folio. CML.
At RBGE. Original binding.
No signature, only older
annotations.

BURNETT, Mary Ann (1842–
45). *Plantae Utiliores*. 2 vols.
London. 4to. CML. At RBGE.
Rebound, no signature or
annotations. Note: A little
known work with hand-
coloured plates, the author
was sister of Gilbert Thomas
Burnett.

CANDOLLE, Alphonse L.P.P. de.
(1852). Note sur une pomme
de terre du Mexique. *Révue
Horticole* 1 (ser. 4): 211–7. 8vo.
Pamphlet (reprint, paginated
2–7) at RBGE, ex-Museum

(?CML). Inscribed in pencil on title-page 'Mr Robert Brown'. No signs of C's ownership.

[COLLINS, James (1872). *Report on the Caoutchouc of Commerce*. London. 8vo]. EUL. Original binding. No signature or annotations.

COOKE, Mordecai Cubitt (1876). *Report on Diseased Leaves of Coffee etc*. London. Folio. EUL.

[CROSS, Robert (1877). *Report on India-rubber Trees*. Edinburgh. Folio]. EUL.

DECAISNE, Joseph (1854). Histoire et culture de l'igname de Chine (*Dioscorea Batatas, Dne.*). *Révue Horticole* 3 (ser 4): 243–53; 443–52. 8vo. Original wrappers. Pamphlet (reprint, paginated 2–24) at RBGE, (not accessioned, but ex-Museum, ?CML). No C annotations; flyleaf with Robert Brown's name doubtless inscribed by the author.

DICKSON, Robert (1837). *A Lecture on the Dry Rot*. London. 8vo. EUL.

DUCHESNE, Edouard Adolphe (1836). *Répertoires des plantes utiles et des plantes vénéneuses du globe*. Paris. 8vo. CML. At RBGE. Rebound. No signature; many species marked in margin with a dot, some with a line up to p 33, also on p 99.

GUÉRIN-MÉNEVILLE, Félix Edouard & PERROTTET, George Samuel (1842). *Mémoire sur un insecte et un champignon qui ravagent les cafiers aux Antilles*. Paris. 8vo. Original paper wrappers, front one printed with title. Pamphlet at RBGE, ex-Museum (CML). Front cover signed 'H. Cleghorn' in ink.

HANBURY, Daniel (1869). Historical notes on manna. *Pharmaceutical Journal* 11: 326–30. 8vo. Original wrappers, front one printed with title. Pamphlet (reprint, paginated 2–5) at RBGE, ex-Museum (?CML). No C annotations.

HANCOCK, Thomas (1857). *Personal Narrative of the Origin of Caoutchouc*. London. 8vo. EUL. Original binding. With H Cleghorn bookplate on front paste-down; flyleaf inscribed 'G. Wellington's'.

KOOPS, Matthias (1801). *Historical Account of the Substances which have been used to Describe Events, and to Convey Ideas, from the Earliest Date to the Invention of Paper*. Ed 2. London. 8vo. EUL. Rebound. Signed 'H Cleghorn' in pencil on title-page, no annotations.

LAWSON, Peter & Co. (1860). *On the Kohl-rabi*. London. Pamphlet at RBGE, ex Museum (?CML). Not found.

[MÉDECINS, SOCIÉTÉ DE] (1802). *Dictionnaire botanique et pharmaceutique*. Part 1 (A–IMP). Paris. 8vo. At RBGE. Rebound. No signature, someone (a Scottish child, possibly C, has added some English names (e.g. Blae-Berry p 15).

MONTAGNE, Camille (1850). A micrographic study of the disease of Saffron known under the name of Tacon. *Journal of the Horticultural Society* 5: 21–26. 8vo. Original wrappers. Pamphlet (reprinted from *Mémoires Société Biologique de Paris*, with new title-page and paginated 4–8) at RBGE, ex-Museum (CML). Front wrapper annotated with author's dedication to Robert Brown, and by C 'Rhizoctonia'.

MUELLER, Ferdinand von (1880). *Select Extra-Tropical Plants Readily Eligible for Industrial Culture or Naturalisation*. Indian edition. Calcutta. 8vo. CML. At RBGE. Original binding. No signature or annotations.

PARLATORE, Filippo (1866). *Le Specie dei Cotoni*. Firenze. Folio. CML. Not at RBGE (another copy of plates kept).

POUCHET, Félix Archimède (1835–36). *Traité élémentaire de botanique appliqué*. 2 vols. Paris. 8vo. EUL. Original bindings. With H Cleghorn bookplate on front pastedowns, no annotations.

PRÉVET, Jules (1864). *Du karouba [Ceratonia siliqua], sa description botanique et ses usages*. Paris. 4to. Original Wrappers. Pamphlet at RBGE, ex-Museum (CML). Front wrapper signed 'H. Cleghorn' in ink.

RISSO, Joseph Antoine (1853). *Extracts translated* [by Lady Reid, née Sarah Bolland] *from the Natural History of Orange Trees by A. Risso* (ed. 3). Malta. 8vo. Original printed wrapper. Pamphlet at RBGE, ex-Museum (?CML). No C annotations; inscribed on front cover 'Dr Thos. Thomson from Sir Wm. Reid' [Governor of Malta, and husband of the translator].

Biographical & bibliographical

[BALFOUR, John Hutton] (1884). *In Memoriam Prof. J.H. Balfour*. Edinburgh (reprinted from *Edinburgh Medical Journal*, March 1884). 8vo. Pamphlet bound by C with works by J.A. Guillemin, G. Inzenga, B. Holditch, Cleghorn & J.H. Balfour.

BRITTEN, James & BOULGER, George S. (1893). *A Biographical Index of British and Irish Botanists*. London. 8vo. CML. Not at RBGE.

EVELYN, John (1857). *Diary and Correspondence*. Edited by William Bray. 4 vols. London. 8vo. CML. At RBGE. Rebound. With H Cleghorn bookplate in all four volumes, no annotations.

HARVEY, William Henry (1869). *Memoir*. London. 8vo. CML. At RBGE. Rebound. With signature on title-page, no annotations.

JACKSON, Benjamin Daydon (1881). *Guide to the Literature of Botany*. London. 8vo. CML. At RBGE, rebound. Signed 'H Cleghorn' on title-page, with a few annotations by C.

JONES, Sir William *et al.* (1792). *Dissertations and Miscellaneous Pieces relating to the History and Antiquities ... of Asia*. 2 vols. London. 8vo. Author's collection. Original binding (rebacked). With H Cleghorn bookplate on front pastedowns, vol. 1 pp 398–400 annotated by C with Linnaean names. Vol. 2 signed on title-page by C.M. Wade (Sir Claude Martin Wade, 1794–1861), probably purchased second-hand by C in Madras.

LASÈGUE, Antoine (1845). *Musée botanique de M. Benjamin Delessert*. Paris. 8vo. CML. Not at RBGE (Ball's and another copy kept).

[LINNEAN SOCIETY of LONDON (1866–7). *Catalogue of the Natural History Library*. 2 pts. London. 8vo]. EUL. Original binding. No signature or annotations.

PRITZEL, George Augustus (1855). *Iconum Botanicarum Index Locupletissimus*. Berlin and London. 8vo. CML. At RBGE, rebound. Signature on title-page, no annotations.

PRITZEL, George Augustus (1866). *Iconum Botanicarum Index Locupletissimus*. Part 2. Berlin. 4to. CML. Not at RBGE (Ball's copy kept).

PRITZEL, George Augustus. *Thesaurus Literaturae Botanicae Omnium Gentium*. Ed 2. Leipzig, 1872. 4to. CML. At. RBGE. Rebound. No signature or annotations.

PULTENEY, Richard (1805). *General View of the Writings of Linnaeus*. Ed 2, edited by W.G. Maton. London. 4to. CML. Not at RBGE.

SOUTHEY, Robert & SOUTHEY, the Rev. Charles Cuthbert. (1844). *The Life of the Rev. Andrew Bell*. 3 vols. 8vo. London & Edinburgh. Private collection, Stravithie House. Original buckram binding. Title-page inscribed 'Presented by the Trustees' [presumably to Peter Cleghorn as the heir of Hugh Cleghorn, some of whose letters were used by Southey in the compilation this, his last work]; signed in pencil on title-page 'H. Cleghorn'.

WIKSTRÖM, Johan Emanuel (1831). *Conspectus Litteraturae Botanicae in Suecia*. Stockholm. 8vo. EUL. In old binding. No signature or annotations.

Exhibitions and museums

ANON [1864]. *Rough List of Live Stock, Machinery and Implements, and Agricultural Produce to be Exhibited at the Bengal Agricultural Show, 1864.* **[?Calcutta]. 8vo. CML.** At RBGE. In original boards. No signature or annotations.

[BIRDWOOD, George Christopher Molesworth (1864). *Report on the Government Central Museum* **(Selections from Records of Bombay Government, No. 83, n.s.). Bombay. 8vo]. EUL.** Original binding. No signature or annotations.

BRANDIS, Dietrich (1878). *Catalogue of Specimens of Timber, Bamboo, Canes &c, from the Government Forests, India, sent to the Paris Exhibition, 1878.* Calcutta. 8vo. EUL. Original boards. Signed on front board 'H Cleghorn' in ink.

DELEUZE, Joseph Phillipe François (1823). *History of Royal Museum of Natural History [in Paris]*. Paris. 8vo. EUL. Rebound. With H Cleghorn bookplate on half-title, signed in pencil on title-page. Note: Includes a description of the Jardin des Plantes, as well as the Muséum d'Histoire Naturelle – a substantial work, translated (by whom?) into English.

EDINBURGH INTERNATIONAL FORESTY EXHIBITION (1884). *Official Catalogue*. Edinburgh. 8vo. EUL. Original paper wrappers. No signature or annotations.

HOLTZAPFFEL, Charles [& ROYLE, John Forbes] (1852). *Descriptive Catalogue of Woods.* **London. 8vo. EUL.** Bought by Cleghorn from Pamplin in 1856. Original binding. Front pastedown and title-page both signed in pencil 'H Cleghorn', marginal marks p 69; p 89 beside Kingwood 'Homalia'.

PARIS, EXPOSITION UNIVERSELLE 1855 (1856). *Proceedings of the Madras Central Committee.* **Madras. Folio. EUL.** Original paper wrappers. Front wrapper signed 'H Cleghorn' in ink, on title-page is stuck a newspaper clipping about the exhibition from the *Hurkaru* of 8 March 1856.

ROSE, William Kinnaird (1884). *Handguide to the International Forestry Exhibition.* Edinburgh. 12mo. EUL. Original paper wrappers. No signature or annotations.

[VIENNA WELT-ANSTELLUNG 1873 (1873). *Catalogue of Indian Department* (by J.F. Watson). London. 8vo]. EUL. Original boards. No signature or annotations.

WATSON, John Forbes (1874). *On the Measures for Working the India Museum etc.* London. Folio. EUL.

Indian official reports
(other than forest dept)

ASSAM & BURMA (1873). *Selection of Papers Regarding the Hill Tracts.* [Calcutta]. 8vo. EUL.

ASSAM (1884–93). *Report of the Administration, 1882/3–1892/3.* Shillong. Folio. EUL.

ASSAM (1881–82). *Report on Administration, 1880/1, 1881/2.* Shillong. 8vo. EUL.

BANGALORE (1883–95). *Report on Administration, etc. 1881/2–1894/5.* 14 vols. Bangalore. Folio. EUL.

BARODA STATE (1883–89). *Report on Administration, 1880–88.* 8 vols. Calcutta. 8vo. EUL.

BENGAL (1881–91). *Report on Administration of Bengal 1880/1–1890/1.* 11 vols. Calcutta. 8vo and Folio. EUL.

BOMBAY PRESIDENCY (1865). *Selections from the Records. Papers Relating to Pearl Fisheries in Ceylon.* Bombay. 8vo. EUL. Original boards. No signature or annotations.

BOMBAY (1881–95). *Report on Administration of Bombay Presidency 1880/1–1894/5.*

14 vols. Bombay. 8vo and Folio. EUL.

[CENTRAL PROVINCES (1891–92). *Report on Administration 1880/1–1891–9*. Vols 1–11. Nagpur. 8vo & Folio]. EUL.

HYDERABAD ASSIGNED DISTRICTS (1881–92). *Administration Reports 1880–92*. 12 vols. Hyderabad. Folio. EUL.

INDIA, FOREIGN DEPARTMENT (1853–56). *Selections from the Records. Nos 2, 4, 6, 18.* **Calcutta. 8vo. EUL.**

INDIA, FOREIGN DEPARTMENT (1856–58). *Selections from the Records. Nos 20* **[concerning Pegu, and Punjab silk experiment], 24 [about Guicowar's Hospital, thugee and Andamans]. Calcutta. 8vo. EUL.** Original binding. No signature or annotations.

[INDIA, FOREIGN DEPARTMENT (1856). *Report on the Census … 1855.* **Calcutta. 8vo]. EUL.** Original binding. No signature or annotations.

INDIA, HOME DEPARTMENT (1855–59). *Selections from the Records, Nos 8 (suppl), 25.* **Calcutta. 8vo. EUL.**

INDIA, HOME DEPARTMENT (1854). *History of the Rise & Progress of the Operations for the Suppression of Human Sacrifice & Female Infanticide in the Hill Tracts of Orissa.* **Selections from the Records, No 5. Calcutta. 8vo. EUL.** Original binding. No signature or notes.

INDIA, PUBLIC WORKS DEPARTMENT (1864). *Selections from the Records, No. 42. Correspondence Relating to the Deterioration of Lands from the Presence in the Soil of Reh.* **Calcutta. 8vo. EUL.** Original boards. Lithographed bookplate 'Mr Dietrich Brandis' on front pastedown, no annotations.

INDIA, PUBLIC WORKS DEPARTMENT (1866). *Classified List [of staff] etc.* **Calcutta. 8vo. EUL.** Original binding. Title-page inscribed by C 'Forest Branch'. Note. An example of a book from his Simla office – a list of staff of PWD for whole of India; gives Brandis as Inspector General (appt April 64, on leave for 18 months from 25 April 1865; Cleghorn as Officiating I.G. until May 1866.

MADRAS (1873). *Annual Volume of Trade etc. 1871/2*. Madras. 4to. EUL.

[MADRAS (1877). *Annual Report of the Civil Dispensaries, 1875–76*. Calcutta. 8vo]. EUL. Original binding. No signature or annotations.

MADRAS (1883–92). *Report on Administration of Madras Presidency 1880/1, 1881/2, 1882/3–1891/2.* 12 vols. Madras. Folio. EUL.

MADRAS (1881–82). *Report on Administration of the Madras Presidency 1880–82.* Madras. 8vo. EUL.

[MADRAS (1876). *Selections from the Records, No 52. Report on Treatment of Leprosy.* Madras. 8vo]. EUL. Original boards. No signature or annotations.

MYSORE (1864). *Selections from the Records of the Mysore Commissioner's Office.* Bangalore. 8vo. EUL. Original binding. Signed in pencil 'H Cleghorn' on title-page, no annotations. Note: Includes papers by Benjamin Heyne and Hudlestone Stokes.

NEISON, Francis Gustavius Pavius (1856). *Reports on Madras Medical Fund.* London. 4to. EUL. Original binding. No signature or annotations, but it must be C's as it has a Madras provenance – in it is a printed insert by John Mayer (C's Medical College colleague) dated Madras 9 June 1857.

PUNJAB (1881–94). *Report on the Administration, 1880/1–1891/2, 1893/4.* 13 vols. Lahore. 8vo & Folio. EUL.

SAUNDERS, Leslie Seymour (1873). *Report on the Revised Land Revenue Settlement in Lahore ... 1865–69.* Lahore. 8vo. EUL. Original boards. No signature or annotations.

Journals/periodicals

India

ASIATIC RESEARCHES (1820). **Vol. 13. Calcutta. 4to. CML.** At RBGE. Rebound. Title-page annotated 'Presented to Dr Mackenzie by his friend H.H. Wilson Esq. Calcutta 1825'. Note: Perhaps Dr William Mackenzie (1785–1866), husband of C's maternal aunt Margaret, a Madras surgeon who retired to Edinburgh 1830.

INDIAN FORESTER (1883). Vol. 9. Roorkee. 8vo. EUL. (Note: The rest of C's set is at RBGE – see below).

INDIAN FORESTER (1876–96). Vols 1–8, 10–22. Calcutta, Roorkee etc. 8vo; Index to vols 1–17. Mussoorie, 1892. 8vo. CML. All except index (replaced by later version) at RBGE. In original binding. First volume signed 'H. Cleghorn' in pencil on title-page.

JOURNAL of the **AGRICULTURAL and HORTICULTURAL SOCIETY of INDIA (1845–66). Vol. 4 pt 4, 6 pts 2–4, 7 pts 1–2, 8 pt 5, 13 pt 4, 14 pts 1–3. Calcutta. 8vo. EUL.** In original paper wrappers. Some parts signed on front covers 'H Cleghorn' in pencil, no notes. Note: Bound into back of one is a flier for the Calcutta Society for the Prevention of Cruelty to Animals, of which Colesworthy Grant (3 Hare St.) was Secretary.

JOURNAL of the ASIATIC **SOCIETY of BENGAL (1832–66). Vols 1–21, and 32, 33 and 34. Calcutta. 8vo. Index to, vols 1–23. Calcutta, 1856. 8vo. CML.** At RBGE vols 1–20 + index; vols 17–19 in original binding. With H Cleghorn bookplate on front pastedown.

MADRAS JOURNAL of **LITERATURE and SCIENCE (1833–61). Vols 1–22. Madras. 8vo.** At St Andrews University Library. Original bindings. With H Cleghorn bookplate on inside front board of vols 1–20, title-page of vol. 2 signed in pencil.

PROCEEDINGS of the **AGRICULTURAL and HORTICULTURAL SOCIETY of BOMBAY (1838). Bombay. 8vo.** Bound with Ingledew (1837) and Proceedings of Agri-Horticultural Society of Madras. With H Cleghorn bookplate on flyleaf. Not in CML, acquired by RBGE from Cleghorn's library c. 2008 (ex Stravithie Sale).

PROCEEDINGS of the **AGRICULTURAL and HORTICULTURAL SOCIETY OF BOMBAY (1843). Nos I and II. Bombay. 8vo.** Bound with Ingledew (1837) and *Proceedings of Agri-Horticultural Society of Madras*. With H Cleghorn bookplate on flyleaf. Not in CML, acquired by RBGE from Cleghorn's library c. 2008 (ex Stravithie Sale).

PROCEEDINGS of the **AGRICULTURAL and HORTICULTURAL SOCIETY OF MADRAS (ed. R. Wight) (1839). Madras. 8vo.** Bound with Ingledew (1837) and *Proceedings of Agri-Horticultural Society of Bombay*. With H Cleghorn bookplate on flyleaf. Not in CML, acquired by RBGE from Cleghorn's library c. 2008 (ex Stravithie Sale).

TRANSACTIONS of the AGRI- **HORTICULTURAL SOCIETY [of WESTERN INDIA] (1852). Vol. 1. Bombay. 8vo.** At RBGE. In old binding. This must have been given to Cleghorn by Alexander Gibson, as it contains Gibson's own corrections to his (badly printed) Bombay forest reports.

PROCEEDINGS *of the* **ASIATIC SOCIETY** *of* **BENGAL** *for* *1866* **(1866). Calcutta. 8vo. CML.** Not at RBGE.

BRITAIN AND REST OF WORLD

ALMANACH du CULTIVATEUR: 1874 (1874). Paris. 16mo. CML. At RBGE. In original paper wrappers, no signature or annotations.

ALMANACH du JARDINIER: 1873 & 1874 (1873–4). 2 vols. Paris. 16mo. CML. At RBGE. In original paper wrappers. Both parts signed 'H Cleghorn' in ink, on front cover.

BOTANIC GARDEN, THE (1825–35). 8 vols in 4 (ed Benjamin Maund). London. 4to. CML. At RBGE. Flyleaf of vol. 1 inscribed 'Sarah Sophia Tongue From her dear Mamma Jany 1826'. '8 vols in 4, 32/-' written on front pastedown.

BOTANICAL GAZETTE (1850–51). Nos. 22 and 23 (vol. 2) and vol. 3. London. 8vo. CML. At RBGE. In Cleghorn's boards. With H Cleghorn bookplate, and binder's label 'American Mission Press Bindery Madras'.

COMPANION to the BOTANICAL MAGAZINE (1835–36). Vols 1–2. London. 8vo. CML. At RBGE.

CURTIS'S BOTANICAL MAGAZINE (1793–1822). 1st Series. 49 vols. London. 8vo. CML. At RBGE (missing vol. 1).

CURTIS'S BOTANICAL MAGAZINE (1827–32). 2nd Series. 6 vols. London. 8vo. CML. Vols 1–5 at RBGE. Title-page annotated 'Richard Chambers F.L.S. Castle Street, Leicester Square, London'.

CURTIS'S BOTANICAL MAGAZINE (1817, 1828, 1883). Indexes to vols 1–42; to vols 1–53; to vols 1–107. London. 8vo. CML. Not at RBGE.

EDWARDS'S BOTANICAL REGISTER (1815–31). Vols. 1–9 and 12–17. London. 8vo. CML. At RBGE vols 1–9, 14–16.

EDWARDS'S BOTANICAL REGISTER (1838–47). New Series. Vols. 1–5 and 7–10. London. 8vo. CML. At RBGE.

FLORAL CABINET. 6 vols. 8vo. CML. Not at RBGE. (Note: Title unknown; presumably

different to Knowles &
Westcott, which ran only
to three volumes).

FLORE des SERRES et des JARDINS
de L'EUROPE (1852–55).
Vols 8–10. Ghent. 4to. CML.
At RBGE. Original binding.
No ownership notes.

FLORIST'S JOURNAL (1840–42).
Vols 1–3. London. 8vo. CML.
At RBGE. In original binding.
No ownership notes.

GARDEN and FOREST (1888–93).
Vols 1–6. New York. 4to. CML.
At RBGE. Original binding
(Fletcher and Son, Binders to
the University, St Andrews).
With occasional marginal lines,
e.g., vol. 3: 460 against the 9
Forestry Schools in Germany.

GARDENER'S MAGAZINE, THE
(ed. J.C. Loudon). (1826–43).
Vols 1–19. London. 8vo. CML.
Vols 1, 4, 5, 8–19 at RBGE.

HOOKER'S JOURNAL of BOTANY
(1834–41). Vols 1–3. London.
8vo. CML. Not at RBGE
(another set kept).

HOOKER'S JOURNAL of
BOTANY and KEW GARDEN
MISCELLANY (1849–57). Vols
1–9. London. 8vo. CML. Not at
RBGE (another set kept).

ICONES PLANTARUM (ed. W.J.
Hooker) (1837–89. First Series,
vols. 1–4. Second Series, vols
1–6. Third Series, vols 1–9.
London. 8vo. CML. Not at
RBGE (another set kept).

JOURNAL of BOTANY, BRITISH
and FOREIGN (1865–95).
Vols 1, 3–17, 19–33. London.
8vo. EUL.

JOURNAL OF FORESTRY
(1878–86). Vols 1–11. London.
8vo. CML. At RBGE. Original
binding. No signature or
annotations.

**JOURNAL of the INDIAN
ARCHIPELAGO (1847–49).
3 vols. Singapore. 8vo. EUL.**
With H Cleghorn bookplate
on front pastedowns of all
three volumes, no annotations.
Note: This includes J.R. Logan's
paper 'The probable effects on
the climate of Pinang of the
continued destruction of its hill
jungles' in vol. 2: 534–5, 1848.

LANDWIRTHSCHAFTLICHEN
VERSUCHS-STATIONEN
(1874). Vol. 17. Chemnitz.
8vo. CML. At RBGE. In old
binding. No signature, no
annotations.

PAXTON'S MAGAZINE of
BOTANY (1834–40). Vols 1, 2,
6, 7. London. 4to. CML. Not
at RBGE.

QUARTERLY JOURNAL of
SCIENCE (1868–70). Vols 5–7.
London. 8vo. CML. Not at
RBGE.

SCOTTISH NATURALIST, THE
(ed. F.B. White) (1883–90).
Vols 1–6 (in 3). Perth, 1871–82;
series 3. Nos 1–4. Perth, 1891;
new series. 4 vols (in 2). Perth.
8vo. EUL.

TECHNOLOGIST, THE (ed. P.L. Simmonds) (1861). Vols I–II, 1, 14. London. 8vo. EUL. With H Cleghorn bookplate on front paste-down, pages uncut, no annotations.

TIMBER TRADES JOURNAL (1894). *19th Annual Special Issue.* London. 8vo. CML. Not at RBGE.

Note: Cleghorn also received copies of *Transactions of the Botanical Society of Edinburgh*, and *Edinburgh New Philosophical Journal* in India, but these were not included in the bequests.

Medical

AINSLIE, Whitelaw (1826). *Materia Medica of Hindoostan.* 2 vols. London. 8vo. EUL.

Vol. 1 – original binding (half-calf). With HUGH CLEGHORN bookplate on front pastedown; flyleaf inscribed Geo. B[eane] Macdonell, Rajahmundry 1829' and by Cleghorn 'To H. Cleghorn 1846'; numerous marginal marks, and with interleaved sheets of notes – opp p 75 (Caryophylli), 84 (Colocynth), 124 (Soymida febrifuga), 254 (Castor oil), 368 (Salep Misree), 383 (Sarsaparilla).

Vol. 2 – original boards. Front flyleaf inscribed 'Geo Ballingall From the Author' – this has no notes by C.

BENTLEY, Robert (1864). On a new kind of matico, with some remarks on official matico.

Pharmaceutical Journal 5(n.s.): 290–6. 8vo. Original paper covers. Pamphlet (reprint, paginated 2–7) at RBGE, ex Museum (?CML). No marks to show C's ownership.

BOOTT, Francis (1827). *Two Introductory Lectures on Materia Medica.* London. 8vo. CML. At RBGE. In original boards. Annotated on outer board 'Geo. White Esq. 19 Buccleuch Place fr. the Author'.

BURDETT, Henry Charles (1877). *The Cottage Hospital, its Origin, Progress, Management and Work, with an alphabetical list of every Cottage Hospital at present opened & a Chapter on Hospitalism in Cottage Hospital Practice.* London. 8vo. EUL. Original binding. Title-page signed 'H Cleghorn', no annotations.

CALCARA, Pietro (1851). *Florula Medica Siciliana*. Palermo. 8vo. EUL. Rebound, but enclosing original wrappers. No signature or annotations.

CLEGHORN, H.F.C. (1855). Note on the varieties of "chiretta" used in the hospitals of Southern India. *Indian Annals of Medical Science* 2: 270–2 + tt 1–3. 8vo. Pamphlet at RBGE, (not accessioned, but ex Museum and probably CML). Cleghorn's own copy of a reprint (paginated 2–3), with the original drawings (two by Govindoo, one possibly by Rungasawmy) and a proof page pp 19/20 of Drury's *Useful Plants of India*.

CLEGHORN, H.F.C. *Note on the varieties of "Chiretta"* ... another copy at EUL, bound by C with works by L. Pappe, W.B. O'Shaughnessey, E.J. Waring, T.W.C. Martius & R. Lyell. With H Cleghorn bookplate on front paste-down, with C's ms contents list on flyleaf.

EDINBURGH, ROYAL BOTANIC GARDEN (1846). *List of Medicinal Plants Cultivated in the Open Air etc*. Edinburgh: P. Neill. 8vo. EUL. Pamphlet bound by C with works by L. Pappe, W.B. O'Shaughnessey, E.J. Waring, J.H. Balfour, T.W.C. Martius, Cleghorn & R. Lyell. With H Cleghorn bookplate on front paste-down, C's ms contents list on flyleaf.

FERGUSON, William (1887). *Notice of the late Sir W. Elliot, K.C.S.I., F.L.S., &c. of a Bazaar Drug called Gunta Barnigi, Bhooi Jamb, Siritekky, &c &c., identified for the first time as Premna herbacea, Rox.; with notice of Mr Bentham & Completion of Genera Plantarum*. Colombo. 8vo. Original printed wrappers. Pamphlet at RBGE, (not accessioned, but ex-Museum and probably CML). Front cover inscribed 'Hugh Francis Clarke Cleghorn M.D. L.L.D. By request of the late author'; with several ms corrections in text by C.

FLEMING, John (1810). *Catalogue of Indian Medicinal Plants* (reprinted from *Asiatic Researches* 11: 153–96). Calcutta. 4to. EUL. Original binding. On front paste-down printed label 'Vepery Mission Library', and H Cleghorn bookplate, title-page inscribed 'D̶r̶ ̶B̶e̶r̶r̶y̶ ̶w̶i̶t̶h̶ ̶D̶r̶ ̶F̶l̶e̶m̶i̶n̶g̶'s̶ ̶b̶e̶s̶t̶ ̶c̶o̶m̶p̶l̶i̶m̶e̶n̶t̶s̶', with added Tamil names and Roman transliterations by J.P. Rottler.

FRASER, Thomas Richard (1867). *A preliminary notice of the Akazga Ordeal of West Africa and of its Active Principle*. London. 8vo. Pamphlet (reprint, paginated 2–8, from the *British and Foreign Medico-Chiurgical Review*, 1867) at RBGE, ex-Museum (?CML). No C annotations, title-page annotated 'With Dr. Fraser's compliments'.

GERARDE, John (1633). *The Herball, or Generall Historie of Plantes*. London. Folio. CML. Not at RBGE.

GORKOM, Karel Wessel van (1883). *Handbook of Cinchona Culture*. Translated from the Dutch by B.D. Jackson. London. 8vo. CML. At RBGE. In original binding. Signed on title-page by C, no annotations.

HANBURY, Daniel (1862). *Notes on Chinese Materia Medica* (reprinted from *Pharmaceutical Journal*, 1860). London. 8vo. CML. At RBGE. In original binding. Verso of flyleaf inscribed 'Dr Cleghorn Madras with the Author's kind regards. London 7 April 1862'.

HANCOCK, John (1829). Observations on sarsaparilla and its preparations, with incidental remarks on certain other remedial agents in the cure of obstinate chronical disorders. *Transactions of the Medico-Botanical Society of London* 1: 61–78. 8vo. Pamphlet at RBGE, ex-Museum (?CML). No C annotations, but tied with thread in his characteristic manner.

HONIGBERGER, John Martin (1852). *Materia Medica* (from *Thirty-five Years in the East*). London. 8vo. CML. At RBGE.

Rebound. Heavily annotated in an unknown hand.

IRVINE, Robert Hamilton (1848). *The Native Materia Medica of Patna*. Calcutta. 8vo. CML. At RBGE. Rebound. No signature (though upper part of title-page trimmed), marginal marks on pp 19, 80, 81, 85, 88 and against *Andropogon martinii* (p 91) 'I paid 6 Rs for 3 quarts at Howsingabad HC'.

IRVING, James (1860). Report on a species of palsy prevalent in Pergunnah Khyraghur, in Zillah Allahabad from the use of *Lathyrus sativus* or kessaree dal, as an article of food. *Indian Annals of Medical Science* 7: 127–37. 8vo. Pamphlet (reprint, paginated 2–11) at RBGE, ex-Museum (CML). Annotated by C on title-page 'From "Indian Annalls (sic) of Medical Science" Calcutta 1859'.

IRVING, James (1859). *Notice of a Form of Paralysis of the Lower Extremities, extensively prevailing in Part of the District of Allahabad, produced by the use of 'Lathyrus sativus' as an article of food*. Calcutta: R.C. Lepage & Co. 8vo. Pamphlet (pp [1–]2–11, reprinted from *Indian Annals of Medical Science*) at RBGE, ex-Museum (?CML). No C annotations, but extensively marked with pencil as if for reproduction as an extract.

KING, George (1880). *Manual of Cinchona Cultivation in India*. Ed 2. Calcutta. 8vo. EUL. Original boards. Signed on front board 'H Cleghorn' in ink.

LINDLEY, John (1849). *Medical and Oeconomical Botany*. London. 8vo. EUL. Original binding. With H Cleghorn bookplate on front pastedown, signed 'H Cleghorn' in pencil on title-page, no annotations.

McIVOR, William Graham (1867). *Notes on the Propagation and Cultivation of the Medicinal Cinchonas*. Madras. 8vo. CML. At RBGE. Rebound. No signature or annotations.

MACKENZIE, Patrick (1820). *Practical Observations on the Medical Powers of Mineral Waters*. Ed 2. London. 8vo. EUL.

MANNERS, Thomas (1867). *Cases of Poisoning by Susumber Berries*. Edinburgh: Oliver & Boyd. 8vo. Pamphlet (reprint, with title on cover, paginated 2–8, from *Edinburgh Medical Journal*), at RBGE ex-Museum (?CML). No C annotations.

MARKHAM, Clements Robert (1867). *The Chinchona Species of New Granada*. London. 8vo. CML. At RBGE. In original paper wrappers. No signature or annotations.

MATTIOLI, Pietro Andrea (1560). *Commentarii in Libros sex P. Dioscoridis de Medica Materia*.

Venetiis. Folio. CML. At RBGE. Original binding (rebacked). No signature, annotations by C on pp 19 (*Acorus calamus* added), 261 (*Menyanthes*), 262 (*Ervum lens*), 273 (*Lavatera arborea*) etc.

O'SHAUGHNESSY, William Brooke (1838). *Memoranda on Indian Materia Medica*. [Calcutta]. 8vo. EUL. Pamphlet bound by C with works by L. Pappe, E.J. Waring, J.H. Balfour, T.W.C. Martius, Cleghorn & R. Lyell. After this, bound in an anonymous pamphlet 'Appendix' with native names of medicines in English, Tamool, Hindoostanie and Dukhanie signed L.C. Vanderpult (?), after which a 'Supplement' of 'Drugs exhibited by Dr Jesudasen', with a note at the end in Cleghorn's hand. With H Cleghorn bookplate on front paste-down, C's manuscript contents list on flyleaf.

PAPPE, Ludwig (1857). *Florae Capensis Medicae Prodromus*. Ed 2. Cape Town. 8vo. EUL. Pamphlet bound by C with works by W.B. O'Shaughnessey, E.J. Waring, J.H. Balfour, T.W.C. Martius, Cleghorn & R. Lyell. With bookplate on front paste-down, C's ms contents list on flyleaf.

STIVEN, William Sutherland [jr.] (1856). *Report on the Medical Uses of Berberry and its Preparations*. Agra. 8vo. CML. At RBGE in original paper wrappers. Signed in pencil on front cover; also on front cover in pencil 'from the Author'; no annotations but newspaper cutting about *Lycium* stuck on front flyleaf. Note. Stiven was an Edinburgh graduate (MD 1839); he also wrote on paper making.

TOURNEFORT, Joseph Pitton de (1719). *The Compleat Herbal*. Translated from the Latin. Vol. 1. London. 4to. CML. At RBGE. Rebound. No signature or annotations.

TRIANA, José Jerónima (1870). *Nouvelles études sur les quinquinas*. (Commission Chorographique des Etats-Unis et de la Colombie.). Paris. Folio. CML. At RBGE. Rebound. No signature or annotations.

WARING, Edward John [?1861]. *Notes on some of the Indigenous Medical Plants of India*. 8vo.

EUL. Pamphlet bound by C with works by L. Pappe, W.B. O'Shaughnessey, J.H. Balfour, T.W.C. Martius, Cleghorn & R. Lyell. With H Cleghorn bookplate on front paste-down, C's manuscript contents list on flyleaf.

WARING, Edward John [c. 1860]. *Notes on some of the Principal Indigenous Tonics of India*. 8vo. EUL. Pamphlet bound by C with works by L. Pappe, W.B. O'Shaughnessey, J.H. Balfour, T.W.C. Martius, Cleghorn & R. Lyell. With H Cleghorn bookplate on front paste-down, C's manuscript contents list on flyleaf.

WARING, Edward John (1868). *Pharmacopoeia of India*. London. 8vo. EUL. Original binding. Front flyleaf inscribed 'H. Cleghorn Received from S. Watson 22 Jany 1869', no annotations.

Miscellanea (including religion)

ANON (1863). *The Illustrated Madras Almanac for 1863*. Madras. 8vo. Front flyleaf inscribed 'C.A.S. Young 1863'. Lacking binding, this copy remained at Stravithie and was donated to RBGE by the Sprot family in 2017.

BALFOUR, John Hutton (1857). *Plants of the Bible. Trees & Shrubs*. Edinburgh. 8vo. Bonham's Sale. Inscribed 'Dr Cleghorn as a small mark of affectionate regard from Prof. & Mrs Balfour, 8 August 1861' – the date shows it to have been a wedding present.

HOSTIUS, Matthaeus (1582). *De Numeratione Emendata, Veteribus Latinis et Graecis Usitata.* Antverpiae, 8vo. CML. Not sent to RBGE.

PORTEUS, Beilby (1811). *The Works ... with his Life, by the Rev. Robert Hodgson.* A new edition. 6 vols. London. 8vo. Author's collection. Clearly bought second-hand by C in Madras, with bookseller's label on rear pastedown of vol. 1: 'J.R. Hogg Book Seller Madras. Books bought sold & exchanged. Prints, Stationery, Maps & Charts sold. Visiting Cards neatly Engraved & printed and Books neatly rebound'.

[SCHMID, Christoph von (1853). *Genouvefa.* Ed 8. Bound with *Rosa von Tannenberg.* Both Augsburg. 8vo. EUL. In old binding, with spine label 'German Tales', enclosing original paper wrappers. No signature or annotations, but from its location likely to be part of the Cleghorn Collection that got sent to EUL by mistake, and probably a relic of his sister Isabella.

SEEMANN, Berthold (1862–3). *Contributions to the Annals and Magazine of Natural History.* London. 8vo. Original wrappers. Pamphlet at RBGE, ex-Museum (?CML). No C annotations.

SETON-KARR, Walter Scott (1864). *Selections from Calcutta Gazettes of 1784–88.* Calcutta. 8vo. CML. At RBGE. Rebound. No Cleghorn signature, title-page inscribed 'R.N. Cust from WSSK April 1865'; a few marginal linings: pp 265 (borax), 268 (guinea grass). Note: Robert Needham Cust, senior civil servant, member of Viceroy's Council 1864–5, retired 1867, active in the British and Foreign Bible Society.

Other books at RBGE with a Cleghorn provenance

Presented by Cleghorn as an undergraduate to the Botanical Society of Edinburgh:

SALISBURY, William (1816). *The Botanist's Companion, or an introduction to the knowledge of Practical Botany and the uses of plants ...* 2 vols. London. 8vo. Flyleaf of vol. 1 inscribed in ink 'Presented by Hugh Cleghorn Esq 14 February 1839'.

And finally, a work donated to the
BSE by Cleghorn's aunt:

WESTON, Richard (1770).
   *The Universal Botanist and
   Nurseryman.* 4 vols. London.
   8vo. Inscribed on flyleaf 'Bot
   Soc, 11 Nov 1841, From Mrs
   Campbell, Society'.

Acknowledgements

Numerous individuals and organisations have provided invaluable help to the author over the long course of the Cleghorn project, to all of whom I am profoundly grateful. Among those who gave particular help on the library aspects of the work are:

Staff and colleagues at RBGE, especially Graham Hardy, and Caroline Muir for preparing the plates. In the libraries of the Royal Botanic Gardens Kew (Chris Mills), St Andrews University (Special Collections: Moira Mackenzie, Rachel Hart, Catriona Foote, Rachel Nordstrom), Edinburgh University Library (Centre for Research Collections: Tricia Boyd, Grant Buttars, Joseph Marshall, Elizabeth Quarmby-Lawrence, Denise Anderson), National Library of Scotland, British Library (Asian & African Studies).

Henry Baggott of Bonham's, Edinburgh, who shared as much information on the Cleghorn sale as permitted by auctioneer's etiquette; Graham Bradshaw (University of Toronto, Hannah Medical Collection); David and Renata Chalmers, current owners of Stravithie House, who showed me Cleghorn's original hand-written labels on the library shelves; Mark Glancy (National Museums of Scotland); Alan Grant; Cleghorn's descendants at Stravithie: the late Hugh and Elizabeth Sprot, and Geoffrey and Belinda Sprot

Many others have helped in less direct ways, and their names are listed in Noltie (2016a, pp. 285–6).

Illustrations of items in the collection of the University of Edinburgh are reproduced with the permission of the University's Centre for Research Collections.

Appendix:
a chronology of the
life of H.F.C. Clegorn

1820–4	infancy in Madras.
1824–42	youth and education, St Andrews & Edinburgh.
1842–8	second Indian period (mostly Mysore).
1848–51	first furlough – London and Scotland.
1851–60	third Indian period, Madras (Medical College and Forest Conservator).
1860–1	second furlough (one year).
1861–5	fourth Indian period – Western Himalaya and the Punjab.
1865	third furlough (six months).
1865–7	fifth and final Indian period – Madras, North India (Acting Inspector General of Forests), Madras.
1868–95	retirement in Scotland.

1819

20 JULY	marriage of Peter Cleghorn, Registrar of the Madras Court and Isabella Allan in Madras.

1820

9 AUGUST	Hugh Francis Clarke Cleghorn born in Madras.
19 SEPTEMBER	baptised in St George's Church, Madras.

1821

17 NOVEMBER   his brother, Allan Mackenzie Cleghorn, born in Madras.

1824

21 JANUARY   aged 3½, left Madras on ship *Britannia*, with his brother, in the care of Susan Foulis (*née* Low, wife of Fife neighbour Major General Sir David Foulis of Cairney Lodge) and an *ayah* Fatima, to be brought up at Wakefield (later renamed Stravithie), near St Andrews, Fife, by paternal grandfather (Hugh) and maiden aunts Rachel, Anne, Hughina ('Hugh') and Janet ('Jessie'), and Jane Dinwiddie, a nanny.

1 JUNE   death of his mother, Isabella Cleghorn, in Madras.

1827

MAY   return of Peter Cleghorn to London.

1831

SEPTEMBER   sent with brother to join the fourth-year class of the Classical Master, William Pyper, at Royal High School, Edinburgh, having already learned Latin to university-entrance level (and Greek to a lower standard), under a tutor, James Cruickshank.

1832

SEPTEMBER   entered class of the Rector, Dr Aglionby Ross Carson.

1833   Attends the new Madras College, St Andrews, founded the previous year; wins a prize in French and almost certainly also studied German.

1834

13 FEBRUARY   matriculates in faculty of 'Litterarum Graecarum et Humaniorum' at St Andrews University; takes classes in junior Latin and Greek in session 1833/4, and advanced Latin (with the Rev Thomas Gillespie, Professor of Humanity) and Greek (with Andrew Alexander, Professor of Greek) in session 1834/5.

1835

AUGUST   summer holiday to Loch Lomond, Glasgow, then to Manor Manse near Peebles.

SESSION 1835/6   continues advanced Latin and Greek; also takes the Second Mathematics class (with Thomas Duncan) and Chemistry (with Robert Briggs, Professor of Medicine).

1836

SESSION 1836/37   takes classes in Physics (with Thomas Jackson, Professor of Natural Philosophy), and Ethics (with the Rev. George Cook, Professor of Moral Philosophy).

1837

19 FEBRUARY   death of Cleghorn's beloved grandfather, Hugh.

5 APRIL   honorary member of Literary Society of St Andrews University, having been a member for sessions 1835/6 and 1836/7.

?SUMMER   apprenticed for five years to James Syme, Professor of Clinical Surgery, in Edinburgh.

OCTOBER   matriculates in Medical Faculty of Edinburgh University, takes Kenneth Treasurer Kemp's (extra-mural) Chemistry Course, Syme's on Clinical Surgery, Anatomy with Dr Peter David Handyside, and practical work in the Royal Infirmary.

10 NOVEMBER   signs 'obligation' to the Royal Medical Society.

1838

14 JUNE   admitted member of Botanical Society of Edinburgh.

SUMMER   attends Robert Graham's Botany course.

OCTOBER   matriculates in Medical Faculty, takes courses in Materia Medica (Robert Christison), Surgery (Sir Charles Bell), Natural History (Robert Jameson), Theory of Medicine (Dr William Pulteney Alison), Clinical Surgery (Syme), Anatomy (Handyside), and practical work in the Royal Infirmary.

1839	
SUMMER	takes Graham's Botany class again.
OCTOBER	matriculates in Medical Faculty, takes courses in Practice of Physic (James Home), Medical Jurisprudence (Thomas Stewart Traill), Pathology (Allen Thomson), Anatomy (Alexander Monro *tertius*), Practical Anatomy (Handyside), Clinical Surgery (Syme), Clinical Medicine (Alison) and practical at the Royal Infirmary
	Writes thesis on the healing of wounds for the Royal Medical Society.
DECEMBER– JANUARY	attends course of 12 lectures on systematic zoology given in St Andrews by Edward Forbes.
1840	Following death of Nicolson Bain, Cleghorn and Thomas Anderson appointed the first two honorary (as opposed to salaried) secretaries of the Royal Medical Society.
15 MAY	First medical examination: examiners Sir George Balingall, Monro, Alison, Jameson & Thomas Charles Hope. Cleghorn passed 'cum nota', but had to be re-examined by Hope on Chemistry in June and July.
OCTOBER	matriculates in Medical Faculty, takes courses in Military Surgery (Sir George Ballingall), Midwifery (James Young Simpson), Clinical Medicine, Clinical Surgery (Syme), and practicals in the Royal Infirmary.
	Elected one of the four Annual Presidents of the Royal Medical Society for their 104th session (1840/1); the others are G.E. Day, R.W. Mackenzie and Thomas Anderson (later Professor of Chemistry at Glasgow).
1841	
MAY–AUGUST	House-Surgeon in Edinburgh Infirmary.
23 JUNE	second Medical examination. Examiners: Traill, Simpson, Sir Charles Bell and Robert Christison. Cleghorn passed in Second division. Submitted doctoral thesis (no copy survives).

1842	Became Licentiate of Royal College of Surgeons of Edinburgh.
10 AUGUST	nominated for EIC service by John Loch.
15 AUGUST	set sail from Portsmouth on the ship *Wellington*.
26/7 AUGUST	at Madeira (makes notes on vegetation).
27 OCTOBER	at Cape of Good Hope, where he meets his brother Allan who is returning to Britain.
6 DECEMBER	arrives at Madras, and assigned to duty under the Surgeon of the General Hospital.
DECEMBER	Robert Wight gives him a copy of Wight & Arnott's *Prodromus*.

1843	
25 JULY	allowed to 'enter on the general duties of the Army, assigned to the General Hospital'.
28 JULY	appointed to be under Superintending Surgeon, Mysore Division.
4 AUGUST	appointed to medical charge of Her Majesty's 25th Regiment about to proceed to Bangalore, Cannanore, Bellary and Belgaum.
29 AUGUST	appointed to 2nd Regiment European Light Infantry (stationed at Bangalore).

1844	
MARCH	still at Bangalore with 2nd Regiment of European Light Infantry.
AUGUST	at Hurryhur (seconded to 35th Madras Native Infantry), still there in October.
4 NOVEMBER	his reprobate younger brother Allan dies in Hong Kong.

1845	
APRIL	back with 2nd Regiment European Light Infantry, stationed at Trichinopoly.
29 JULY	placed at disposal of the Commissioner of Mysore.
JULY	in medical charge of the Nugger Division of the Mysore Commission, under superintendence of Captain C.F. LeHardy of 14th Native Infantry.

AUGUST	appointed Magistrate, and learning Kannada.
6 OCTOBER	wrote a letter in 'Canarese' as a 'puzzler' for William Tennant, Professor of Hebrew and Oriental Languages at St Andrews.
NOVEMBER–DECEMBER	excursion to Baba Booden Hills, returning via Kadur and Tarikere.

1846

JANUARY	at Shimoga, excursion to Hurryhur.
FEBRUARY–JULY	long excursion to Sagar, then south through Western Ghats via Nagar, Mandagadde, Koppa, Ballalrayan Droog and Baba Booden hills. In March writes to Robert Christison about gamboge (*Garcinia* sp.), and to J.H. Balfour saying that he is employing a 'Mahratta draughtsman'.
JULY–DECEMBER	excursions to Mandagadde, Harihar, Tirthahalli and Channagiri.
DECEMBER–MARCH 1847	excursion via Ajjampur, Kadur, Santaveri, Vastara, Koppa, Agumbe and Mandagadde.

1847

22 MARCH–25 APRIL	to Kollur Ghat, Sagar, Gersoppa Falls, Sorab and Shikarpur.
5 MAY	William Campbell Onslow, Superintendent of Nuggur Division writes report to Mysore Government on damage being done by 'coomri' [shifting] cultivation, and decline in teak; *kumri* cultivation banned in greater part of Mysore and Coorg as a result.
21 JUNE–12 JULY	excursion to Kadur.
14 SEPTEMBER	Major-General Mark Cubbon (in Bangalore) grants Cleghorn three months sick leave in Madras, prior to applying for leave to return to Europe.
1 OCTOBER	returns to Madras suffering from 'Mysore fever'.

1848

18 FEBRUARY	left Madras for England on the *Sutlej*, on sick certificate.
1 APRIL	*Sutlej* caught in hurricane off the Cape of Good Hope and dismasted.
10 APRIL	arrives at Cape Town; waits until *Sutlej* repaired and sails from Cape via St Helena.
JULY (EARLY)	arrives in Britain.
4 DECEMBER	in Torquay recovering from dysentery (stays until April 1849).

1849

2 JULY	at Botanical Society of Edinburgh (BSE) meeting exhibits drawings of plants from Western Mysore.
AUGUST– SEPTEMBER	visit to Ireland with Dr John Merriman and his son, including Rathlin Island, Fair Head and the Giant's Causeway.
13 DECEMBER	at BSE meeting elected Vice-President, reads paper on the hedge-plants of India, and exhibits drawings.
IN 1849 OR 1850	rearranged Indian plants in the Edinburgh University herbarium, assisted by Thomas Anderson (then an undergraduate, later Superintendent of Calcutta Botanic Garden).

1850

9 JANUARY	at BSE meeting exhibits fruits of *Hydnocarpus* and *Sterculia*, reads Catherine Gage's list of Rathlin Island plants, and reports on Irish trip.
MARCH–APRIL	staying at Hearder's Hotel, Torquay.
11 JULY	talks to BSE about cotton cultivation in Mysore and exhibits cloth made of fibre of *Boehmeria nivea* from Singapore, which he had purchased in Trichinopoly.
1–6 AUGUST	attends British Association meeting in Edinburgh – requested, with J.F. Royle, R. Baird Smith and R. Strachey to prepare report 'On the probable effects, in an œconomical and physiological point of view, of the Destruction of Tropical Forests'.

17 SEPTEMBER	Cleghorn's sister, Rachel Jane, marries Alexander Sprot at Wakefield House.

1851

9 JANUARY	reads to BSE a memoir on J.P. Rottler (the Tranquebar missionary and botanist who had accompanied Cleghorn's grandfather to Ceylon in 1796).
13 FEBRUARY	reports to BSE on Wight's *Icones*, and exhibits specimens of *Osbeckia hispidissima* and *Mitreola paniculata*, recently published by Wight based on his Shimoga drawings, also specimens of *Dunbaria latifolia*, *Alysicarpus styracifolius* and *Hedysarum glumaceum*; also reports on the dye produced by *Rottlera tinctoria* 'used by the Mahommedans'.
26 FEBRUARY	on a Sub-committee for raising subscriptions to build a New Hall for the Royal Medical Society.
7 APRIL	in London. Has been staying in a noisy hotel with 'Sappers and Miners' working on the Great Exhibition, now staying with Richard Clarke, Secretary of the Royal Asiatic Society, at 17 Kensington Square. Has been working on records in India Office – doubtless the work for J.F. Royle, 'for ninety days', classifying Indian 'Raw Products' for the Great Exhibition.
19 JUNE	reads a paper to BSE on the 'Government teak plantations of Mysore and Malabar' and exhibits specimens of Mysore and Malabar teak. From this year (until 1865) many such specimens (fruits, wood, artefacts) donated to J.H. Balfour's Museum of Economic Botany.
7 JULY	reads summary of report on tropical deforestation to 'D Section' of the British Association meeting in Ipswich.
19 JULY	starts buying botanical books and prints from William Pamplin.
31 AUGUST	leaves Britain on the *Trafalgar*.
4 NOVEMBER	elected Fellow of the Linnean Society.
12 DECEMBER	arrives at Madras.

1852

APRIL   is Surgeon for 1st Division of Madras – having medical
             drawings made of the stages of leprosy; appointed
             acting secretary of Madras Agri-Horticultural
             Society for six months.

9 JULY   appointed acting Professor of Botany, Materia
             Medica and Therapeutics at Madras Medical College
             (appointment confirmed 1854).

16 JULY   'almost total loss' of Cleghorn's possessions in a fire
             at Oakes, Partridge & Co.

3 AUGUST   starts lecturing at Medical College – a two year course:
             Botany in the first and Materia Medica in the second.
             Has two artists at work in Horticultural Gardens,
             possibly T. and P. Rungasawmy.

8 OCTOBER   appointed acting Surgeon of 4th District of Madras
             (appointment confirmed 1854).

1853

25 JANUARY   appointed joint Secretary (with Colonel F.A. Reid) of
             Agri-Horticultural Society.

3 MARCH   Cleghorn and Reid deliver an address on Robert Wight's
             departure from Madras.

9 MARCH   writes to Balfour that he has kept on Wight's artist
             Govindoo and his 'Botanical Writer', and requests a
             pint of chloroform from the Edinburgh pharmacists
             Duncan & Flockhart.

12 APRIL   report on teaching for year 1852–3 – in Botany, 68
             lectures given, 20 examinations and 6 excursions; in
             Materia Medica, 100 lectures and 16 examinations

APRIL   Andrew T. Jaffrey arrives from Edinburgh as
             superintendent of Agri-Horticultural Society garden.

MAY   is one of editors of *Madras Christian Herald*.

13 JULY   writes preface to *Hortus Madraspatensis*, a catalogue
             of plants in the Agri-Horticultural Society garden.

1854

26 JANUARY   first of Cleghorn's numerous donations received by the
             Kew Museum of Economic Botany (dyes, fruits, resins,
             woods, etc.).

7 MARCH	appointed Surgeon of 4th District of Madras (until Dec 1856).
15 APRIL	report on teaching for year 1853–4 – in Botany, 78 lectures given, 15 examinations and 6 excursions; in Materia Medica, 88 lectures and 15 examinations; '2^d Dresser' Francis Appavoo helping to prepare specimens and diagrams for lectures.
MAY	starts correspondence with Alexander Grant, surgeon to the Governor-General in Calcutta, offering help (in Madras) with Grant's *Indian Annals of Medical Science*.
19 JUNE	since Wight's departure (1853) has been doing much applied botanical work (railway sleepers, sand-binding plants, etc.).
14 JULY	outlines of Lord Harris's proposal for Madras Exhibition published; committee includes Cleghorn, E.G. Balfour and Alexander Hunter.
22 SEPTEMBER	appointed Professor of Botany at Madras Medical College (until Dec 1856).

1855

20 FEBRUARY	opening of the first Madras Exhibition of 'the raw materials, machinery, manufactures, sculpture, models & the plastic art of the Madras Presidency & of the Neighbouring States'. Cleghorn removed from medical duties to act as secretary of subcommittee for Raw Products and 'Reporter' for 8 sections; Juror for 3 sections and 'Associate' on one section; also an exhibitor
13 MARCH	subscribes one guinea to Memorial for the zoologist Edward Forbes; working on *Ophelia elegans*, a gentian exported as a bitter from Vizagapatam.
11 APRIL	report on teaching for year 1854–5 – in Botany, 75 lectures given, 23 examinations and 6 excursions.
23 JULY	on the advice of Walter Elliot summoned for an initial private meeting with Lord Harris and Sir Arthur Cotton, about setting up a Madras forest conservancy; writing a report on 'Indian Pasturage', and on timber used for gun carriages.
15 AUGUST	appointed to committee for second Madras Exhibition to be held 2 February 1857.
17 SEPTEMBER	writing a report on Soldier's gardens.

27 SEPTEMBER	teaching, 'Police Duties, Coroners Inquests and [writing] Insurance Certificates' are keeping him busy (he was Medical Officer for the Indian Branch of the Medical, Invalid & General Life Assurance Society).
OCTOBER	writing a report on sand-binding plants of Madras beach for the Military Department.
10 DECEMBER	writes a memo on the 'vegetable tallow of Mysore & Canara' in response to request from Railway Company about lubricants for rolling stock.
DECEMBER	Appavoo appointed Cleghorn's official Assistant in the Medical College.
13 DECEMBER	leaves on P & O steamer *Bombay* for a 30-day visit to Calcutta to discuss forests matters and medical education with Thomas Thomson.

1856

26 FEBRUARY	elected to Managing Committee of Madras Literary Society.
4 MARCH	admitted Member of the Madras Literary Society 'of the 2nd Class'.
APRIL	report on teaching for 1855–6 – in Botany, 80 lectures, 21 examinations and 6 excursions.
9 JULY	asks Pamplin to supply him with books on forestry and arboriculture.
26 JULY	made honorary member of Pharmaceutical Society of Great Britain.
29 JULY	in Bangalore discussing upgrading of Lal Bagh with Cubbon and Andrew Jaffrey.
AUGUST	report to Madras Government on 'proposals for establishing Forest Conservancy'.
25 SEPTEMBER	exhibits photographs at Madras Photographic Society (including portraits of J.H. Balfour and Robert Wight).
14 OCTOBER	visited in Madras by Thomas Oldham, founder of the Geological Survey of India.
20 NOVEMBER	gale does great damage to trees in Madras, on which Cleghorn reports.
17 DECEMBER	writes preface to his Index to Wight's *Icones*.
19 DECEMBER	appointed Conservator of Forests, Madras (until 10 October 1867).

1857

JANUARY	visits Burma with Sir Patrick Grant (Commander-in-Chief, Madras Army) and Walter Elliot; meets Dietrich Brandis there; back in Madras by 13 February.
FEBRUARY	second Madras Exhibition of Raw Products, Arts and Manufactures of Southern India; Cleghorn on subcommittee for Raw Products, and on Juries for 8 sections.
24 MARCH	at Bangalore discussing Lal Bagh with Cubbon and Jaffrey.
18 APRIL	at Mangalore, on his first Forest Tour, looking at teak and the poon-spar tree.
18 MAY	at Dharwar, looking at cotton; Pamplin sends forestry books (including Patrick Matthew's *On Naval Timber & Arboriculture*) with *Heracleum giganteum* seeds for packing.
5 JUNE	at Toomkoor.
18 JULY	in Coimbatore, having just been in Nilgiris to report on the Ooty Garden.
16 AUGUST	at Calicut reporting on teak forests for the Collector of Malabar, visits Nilambur plantations.
8 SEPTEMBER	at Coimbatore, having been 'constantly travelling' for seven months.
2 OCTOBER	reply to E.B. Thomas on deforestation in the Nilgiris and its possible effect on recent erratic climate.
9 DECEMBER	in Madras (writes report on Pauchontee, *Palaquium ellipticum*).
29 DECEMBER	writes to Balfour about sending illustrations for his projected 'Plant Scenery of the World'; working on a 'Manual of South Indian Botany' (never completed); Robert Brown has replaced Jaffrey as Superintendent of the Agri-Horticultural Society garden.
	On committees of Madras Diocesan Committee of the Incorporated Society for the Propagation of the Gospel in Foreign Parts, Bishop Corrie's Grammar School, Madras School Book Society and Madras Sailors' Home (*Madras Almanac* for 1857).

1858

FEBRUARY	at Sriharikota (probably in connection with fuel supplies for Madras)
MARCH	with Austrian expedition to Pulicat; one of editors of *Madras Journal of Literature and Science*; about to start on 2nd Forest Tour.
8 APRIL	staying in Sir Mark Cubbon's house at Bangalore, where he welcomes William New as Superintendent of the Lal Bagh.
MID-APRIL	in the hills west of Vellore (Chittari, Yellagiri, Jawadi)
APRIL 26–30	in Coorg.
1 MAY	at Mangalore (1st Forest Report dated from there).
30 MAY	at Bellary (via Tumkur).
25 JUNE	at Madras.
8–19 JULY	around Salem district, including Shevaroy Hills with Lord Harris.
12 AUGUST	at Waliar (SW of Coimbatore).
15– 22 SEPTEMBER	expedition to Southern Range of Anamalai Hills. [Probably returns to Ooty to accompany Harris on his Travancore tour]
19 NOVEMBER	Lord Harris visits Nilambur plantations – Cleghorn almost certainly in attendance.
20 NOVEMBER	Governor's party reaches Calicut, where they stay at the Collector's Bungalow.
24 NOVEMBER	Harris's party met at Bolghatty, Cochin, by General William Cullen (British Resident to the Travancore and Cochin Courts) and his ADC Major Heber Drury.
26 NOVEMBER	Cleghorn with Dr Sanderson visits Cochin Circar Hospital at Ernakulum, then attends a Durbar in the Raja of Cochin's palace.
29 NOVEMBER	at Quilon, Cleghorn has narrowly escaped drowning on the steamer *Feroze*.
30 NOVEMBER– 4 DECEMBER	party at Trivandrum: Harris returns to Madras (Cleghorn remains on west coast).
20 DECEMBER	excursion from Calicut to Gundlupet, to investigate disputed territory between Malabar and Mysore of a tract of teak forest.

On committee of the East Indian Emigration Society (*Madras Almanac* for 1858). Joins the Calcutta-based Agricultural and Horticultural Society of India.

1859

17 JANUARY	a few weeks at Madras; sends photographs of the Nilgiris by Capt. Buchanan to Balfour for his 'Plant Scenery'; has bought 50 shares in the 'Great Southern Railway'.
31 JANUARY– MARCH	a trip to the Northern Division and Orissa on forest matters, especially sal for railway (and telegraph) use.
31 JANUARY	left Madras by ship on the *Dalhousie.*
1 FEBRUARY	touched at Eskapilly, 'to take in treasure'.
2 FEBRUARY	landed at Masulipatam.
6–7 FEBRUARY	at Vizagapatam.
10 FEBRUARY	at Chicacole.
12 FEBRUARY	at Behrampur, two-week excursion to sal forests around Russell Condah and Aska.
4 MARCH	visits garden of Surya Pracasa Row at Ankapilly, then area around Rajahmundry and Dowlaishwaram, returning to Madras by boat from Coconada.
5 APRIL	memorandum on management of 'minor jungles' of the Madras Presidency.
13 APRIL	in Madras, the new Governor Sir Charles Trevelyan, making financial cuts; Thomas Thomson has just visited *en route* to visit G.H.K. Thwaites at the Peradeniya Garden, Ceylon; continued communication with Balfour over Medical Missionaries and appeals for support in Edinburgh.
29 MAY–19 JUNE	in Nugger District and North Canara (for timber sales).
2 JUNE	travels from Sircee to Hurryhur to treat Lt Col James Grant Stewart.
1 JULY	at Mysore.
7 JULY– 26 AUGUST	in the Nilgiris, writing reports on 'Introduction of the Cinchona Trees' (30 August); Kunur Teak Plantation (27 August) and Mudumalai Forest (8 August).
1 SEPTEMBER	at Palghat, with his former assistant J.T. Maclagan who now works for Southern Railway (discussing timber requirements); has met the German missionary Johann

Friedrich Metz; then toured the Anamalais (15 October reported on Malsar Farm), Palni Hills, Cambum and Madura.

30 SEPTEMBER (–NOVEMBER)	in Nilgiris investigating coffee, Australian plantations and forests; writes report on 'Forests and Fuel of the Nilgiri Hills'.
20 NOVEMBER	in Bangalore, writing report on Lal Bagh; about to make a trip to Goa, to settle 'disputed boundaries between Madras & Bombay'; has first attack of 'Wynad Jungle Fever'.
9–27 DECEMBER	at Madras; writes reports on 'Suitability of Gali-Paravattam Hill [a new sanitarium inland from Vizagapatam] for coffee' and 'Australian Plantation near Wellington' (both dated 15 December – the latter concerning fuel supplies for Ooty), 2nd Forest Report (31 December); meets Sir Bartle Frere on his way to join the Legislative Council in Calcutta.

1860

4 JANUARY	embarked upon 3rd annual Forest Tour.
9 JANUARY	at Bangalore, another attack of Fever. Visits Nugger (sandal-wood) and Shimoga (railways); then to North Canara with Sebastien Müller; then to Sidashegur, where receives a summons to meet Trevelyan at Ooty; visits Nilambur en route.
FEBRUARY	must have reached Ooty, as Trevelyan only there 13–27.
4 MAY	from Ooty visits Wynad and Coimbatore.
23 MAY	order made by Madras Government banning *kumri* cultivation in Government forests without permission. Still in Ooty.
7 JULY	in Bangalore, prostrated by dysentery, about to return to Madras with sick certificate to England.
31 AUGUST	in Madras (3rd Forest Report dated from there).
27 SEPTEMBER	submits report on teak plantations and supply of teak timber from Malabar. Same day left Madras for twelve months furlough on sick certificate to Britain. Travels on the *Candia* via Galle, Aden, Suez; at Alexandria boarded the *Massilia*, then the *Vectis* to Marseilles; in Paris met the botanist Joseph Decaisne, and General George St

Patrick Lawrence to discuss the Lawrence Asylum at Ooty.

12 NOVEMBER	in London, staying with Dr Merriman at 45 Kensington Square; discussing timber supplies for Indian Navy and Railways with India Office.
1 DECEMBER	at Stravithie for his father's 77th birthday, about to spend two weeks in Edinburgh where Walter Elliot is also visiting (for Royal Society meetings, including one addressed by the Duke of Argyll, and to visit the Botanic Garden).
13 DECEMBER	on Council of BSE, has Francis Appavoo 'Native-Surgeon, Madras' elected Associate; read paper on tea.
	On committee for Madras People's Park (*Madras Almanac* for 1860).

1861

10 JANUARY	read paper on teak to BSE.
4 FEBRUARY	in Edinburgh, working on *Forests & Gardens of South India*. Expected to address (with his future brother-in-law John Cowan) AGM of Edinburgh Medical Missionary Society.
[1861, PROBABLY AT THIS POINT]	sends £5 to his former Madras medical pupil Dr Pulney Andy, who on 28 ix 1860 had received a St Andrews MD, but was now in difficulty in London.
20 FEBRUARY	attends banquet for the irrigation pioneer Sir Arthur Cotton, at Willis' Rooms, St James's Street, London.
21 FEBRUARY	promoted to Surgeon.
14 MARCH	reads paper by Trail at BSE.
23 MARCH	in London; meetings with Earl de Grey (later Marquess of Ripon) at India Office, and with W.H. Allen over the publication of *Forests & Gardens*.
29 APRIL	reads Anamalai paper to Royal Society of Edinburgh.
9 MAY	reads coconut paper to BSE.
13 JUNE	exhibits paintings made in the Agri-Horticultural Society garden at BSE meeting.
8 AUGUST	at Valleyfield, Penicuik, marries Marjory Isabella ('Mabel') Cowan, daughter of the papermaker and politician Charles Cowan of Logan House.

2 SEPTEMBER	staying with in-laws at 37 Royal Terrace, Edinburgh; has been entertaining the botanists Robert Wight, George Walker-Arnott and Robert Kaye Greville.
12 SEPTEMBER	Cleghorn and Mabel in London, staying with William Bonar; publication of *Forests & Gardens of South India*.
20 SEPTEMBER	the newlyweds leave Southampton on the *Indus*, with three Wardian Cases of plants from Kew, and a glass case of cinchona plants.
	On the same boat, either before or after Cairo, were William Muir (Bengal civil servant) and William Jameson (Superintendent of Saharunpur botanic garden).
7 OCTOBER	in Cairo, Egypt suffering from aftermath of a huge Nile flood.
26 OCTOBER	at Galle Cleghorn receives orders from the Government of India to go to Simla.
11 NOVEMBER	left Madras for Calcutta on steamer *Simla*; Mabel left with a colleague at Conoor.
NOVEMBER	ordered by Lord Canning to investigate timber resources of the Sutlej, Beas, Ravi and Chenab valleys; meetings in Calcutta with members of the Legislative Council about funding for the continuation of Hooker's *Flora Indica*.
3 DECEMBER	in Cawnpur (via Benares and Lucknow).
24 DECEMBER	in Simla.

1862

16 JANUARY	in Lahore (via Agra, Meerut, Roorkee, Saharunpur, Dehra Dun and Mussoorie).
27 JANUARY	to Mooltan to discuss timber needs of Indian Navy and Indus River Flotilla.
31 MARCH	leaves Simla with Capt. George A.F. Houchen (Superintendent of Hill Roads), to explore forests of Sutlej, Giri, Pabur and Tonse Rivers.
10 MAY	at Asrang in the Sutlej valley, investigating rhubarb; Mabel left at Chini.
C. 19 JUNE	at Dharamsala, preparing for 3 or 4 month tour of Ravi and Chenab valleys, leaves Mabel at Dharamsala with Col. & Mrs Edward Lake.

22 JUNE	leaves Holta (= Palampur) for Waru Pass, then down Ravi Valley from Bara Banghal.
12 JULY	at Chamba, meets Raja Sri Singh; about to cross Sach Pass into Chenab valley, and study trade in Himalayan rhubarb and 'asafoetida'; has completed report on timber resources of the Sutlej Valley.
1 AUGUST	at Kilar in Pangi, with J.D. Smithe, Superintendent of the Chenab Timber Agency and his assistant J.A. Murray, heading upstream towards Keylong.
10 AUGUST	promoted Surgeon Major.
11 AUGUST	near Tandi, writing note on economic plants (salep, asafoetida, madder, cumin, koot and ekulbeer) for Punjab Government.
21 AUGUST	at Keylong Mission House, then south over Rohtang Pass, down Kullu Valley, then up Kangra valley to Dharamsala.
18 SEPTEMBER	at Dharamsala making notes on plants in garden of D.F. Macleod (Financial Commissioner of Punjab), and visiting the jail (paper-making); leaves with the Rev. John Barton for Lahore (via Dalhousie and Amritsar).
19 SEPTEMBER	at Nurpur visits a red leather factory.
20 SEPTEMBER	reaches Dalhousie, and inspects Kalatope forest with E.A. Prinsep, G.G. Young, T.D. Forsyth (Commissioner of the Punjab) and the engineer Capt. Craster.
27 SEPTEMBER	at Amritsar.
1 OCTOBER	in Lahore (visits Agri-Horticultural Society garden), about to go on a 6-week trip to Murree, Hazara and Kaghan; sending seeds of *Eremurus* to Thomas Anderson in Calcutta hoping it might be introduced to England.
15 OCTOBER	at Murree with Col. Robert Maclagan and the 'Cashmere' missionary the Rev. Robert Clark; meetings with Lt. Governor of Punjab, Sir Robert Montgomery, who has asked Cleghorn to stay another year to advise on the 'newly organised' Punjab Forest department.
17 OCTOBER	with the Rev. Robert Clark sets off north from Murree on a mule.
19 OCTOBER	at Abbottabad, meets the Rev. Isidor Lowenthal who promises to help prepare a list of Pushtu and Kaghan plant names; then expedition up Kaghan valley

examining deodar forests. Travels with Dr Leonard Horner Lees.

2 NOVEMBER	at Saiful Muluk Lake (where an abundance of rhubarb).
12 NOVEMBER	at Haripur.
13 NOVEMBER	crosses Indus by bridge of boats at Attock.
16 NOVEMBER	arrived at Peshawar in a parcel van, visits museum; hears the Rev. Robert Clark deliver sermon in Pashtu; the Rev. Isidor Lowenthal is here but sick; a *hakim* (Mohammed Kasim) provides him with list of medicines from Afghanistan and Bokhara.
DECEMBER	Dietrich Brandis ordered from Burma by Lord Elgin 'on special duty', to reorganise a Forest Department under the Public Works Department.
1 DECEMBER	elected Fellow of Royal Society of Edinburgh (proposed by J.H. Balfour).
2 DECEMBER	joined by Mabel in Lahore, has just visited Peshawar Valley (Kabul river); sends seed of *Meconopsis aculeata* to RBGE; discussions on a Punjab branch of the Edinburgh Medical Missionary Society.
26 DECEMBER– 2 JANUARY	Punjab Missionary Conference in Lahore.

On Financial Board of Madras branch of Free Church of Scotland (*Madras Almanac* for 1862).

1863

2 JANUARY	appointed to committees advising missionary bodies on secular matters and on medical missionary work.
7 JANUARY– 18 APRIL	in Lahore, working on reports on Punjab forests; discussing introduction of garden plants with D.F. Mcleod.
FEBRUARY	examining more of the Rukh forests.
9 JUNE	his father Peter dies in Fife; aunts Jessie Cleghorn and Jane Campbell also died this year.
15 JUNE	at Dharamsala, proof-reading Punjab forest reports.
11 AUGUST	at Simla, suffering from 'hepatic congestion'. Torn between going home and staying on for public service; Col. Richard Strachey has 'chalked out' work for the next year.

14 AUGUST	as a result of Forest Rules drafted by Beddome for Madras writes memo with Brandis suggesting designation of Government Reserved Forests, Village Forests, and a third intermediate sort managed according to rules – what came to be called 'Protected'.
19 AUGUST	memo with Brandis on limitations of hill forests for generating revenue, and urging the development of *rukhs* in the plains for revenue (and railway fuel).
26 AUGUST	death of Rachel Brandis (*née* Marshman) in Simla.
8 OCTOBER	in Lahul again.
C. 1 NOVEMBER	in Dharamsala, consoling the dying Viceroy, Lord Elgin.
5 DECEMBER	in Lahore (via Kullu) – the end of his service with the Punjab Government (replaced as Officiating Conservator of Forests by John Lindsay Stewart).

1864

1 JANUARY	appointed with Brandis joint 'Commissioners of Forests' for India (until 1 March 1865).
4 JANUARY	week of prayer, with meetings held in the American Mission Church, Lahore; announcement of Sir John Lawrence as Viceroy gives hopes for Medical Missionary scheme.
20 JANUARY	Punjab Exhibition at Lahore; Cleghorn a member of the 'Central Committee' and exhibits woods and plant products. T.C. Jerdon (the zoologist), William Jameson (Saharunpur garden) and John Lindsay Stewart are staying with Cleghorn.
FEBRUARY	examining forests near Amritsar and Wazir.
5 MARCH	in Lahore, about to join Sir John Lawrence at Amballa and accompany him to Simla; writing catalogue of woods, and report on woods and fibres of the Punjab Exhibition.
1 APRIL	Brandis appointed Inspector-General of Forests.
19 APRIL	in Simla for the hot months, the Viceroy about to arrive.
31 MAY	though anxious to go home due to Mabel's continuing ill health, and family duties, Cleghorn and Brandis have received new forest duties, including attending the Viceroy.

14 JUNE	continuing correspondence with Balfour about sending of missionaries; the Bishop has not allowed Presbyterians to use the church in Simla, so they (including Sir John Lawrence, Sir Charles & Lady Trevelyan) have to worship in a Masonic Lodge.
JULY	Brandis goes on a six-month leave to Europe, Cleghorn left in sole charge.
AUGUST	in Lahul reading Marsh's *Man and Nature*.
19 SEPTEMBER	George Cotton (Bishop of Calcutta) to address a group in Cleghorn's Simla drawing room, on the progress of Christianity in South India.
20 OCTOBER	sets off for Calcutta via Roorkee, Saharunpur, Meerut and Delhi mainly by train, visiting schools and mission stations en route.
28 OCTOBER	at Roorkee (preface to *Forests of the Punjab* written there).
5 NOVEMBER	in Calcutta; meets Dr William Jackson Elmslie, the Punjab missionary.
	On local committee of the Medical Mission Dispensary (*Madras Almanac* for 1864). Member of General Council of University of Edinburgh for the year 1864/5.

1865	
JANUARY	Brandis returns from Europe.
10 JANUARY	the Viceroy expresses the Goverment's thanks to Cleghorn and says that 'he may be said to be the founder of Forest Conservancy in India'.
24 FEBRUARY	The Government Forests Act (no VII of 1865) receives assent of the Viceroy, to come into operation 1 May 1865.
25 FEBRUARY	with Mabel, leaves Calcutta for Madras on the steamer *Nemesis*.
14 MARCH	in Madras, packing up one set of 'glued' herbarium specimens to take home; his books already sent back to Scotland; intends visiting Lal Bagh and the Cinchona plantations before leaving for England. Visits Ooty Garden via Lal Bagh where Allan Black is the new gardener.

14 APRIL (SHORTLY THEREAFTER)	granted 6 months' leave on 'urgent private affairs', leaving open the question of whether he will return to India or not.
15 MAY	in Red Sea opposite Mount Sinai, having collected drugs in the Aden bazaar.
C. 3 JUNE	landed at Southampton.
JUNE/EARLY JULY	in London with Dietrich Brandis; meetings in India Office, in Woods & Forests Office, with E.J. Waring (compiling *Indian Pharmacopoeia*), at Kew with Thomas Thomson, and at the Linnean Society.
10 JULY	leaves London for Edinburgh and Fife with Brandis, who wants to visit the best-managed Scottish forests.
13 JULY	attends BSE meeting (John Kirk, the African explorer, and Robert Wight in the audience). Reads papers on Sutlej plants.
14–28 AUGUST	summer at Stravithie; Mabel is being treated by James Young Simpson. Negotiations for rebuilding Stravithie the following year by John Chesser.
6–13 SEPTEMBER	reads paper on deodar forests to Birmingham BAAS meeting, showing a map and photographs taken by Col. C. Hutchinson R.E.
26 SEPTEMBER	about to return to India, leaving Mabel in Britain under the care of Dr Halliday Douglas; needs to return for the 14 months required to qualify for a larger pension.
SEPTEMBER/ OCTOBER	leaves Southampton, travels through a Mediterranean ravaged by cholera, then overland via Alexandria and Cairo.
19 OCTOBER	in Red Sea near Aden, aboard the *Carnatic*, Clements Markham and a large number of 'gay dragoons' among fellow passengers.
30 OCTOBER	in Bombay; refused permission by Madras Government to accompany Markham to Ceylon.
12 NOVEMBER	in Madras, reporting on medical missionary activities to Balfour.
19 NOVEMBER	writing to the Agri-Horticultural Society of the Punjab (of which he is an honorary member) sending seed of *Convolvulus scammonia* collected in the Levant.
C. 7 DECEMBER	tour of Travancore and Madura mountains with Markham: examined coffee and cinchona in the

Peermade area, and the Travancore Government cinchona garden at Mary Ville, then to the Palni Hills via Periacolum Ghat.

1866

7 JANUARY	at Ooty.
13 APRIL	in Madras, sending seeds from the Nilgiris and Madras A-H Society Garden to Balfour.
1 MAY	arrives in Calcutta on the *Nemesis*, en route for Simla; appointed (7 May to 14 March 1867) to officiate as Inspector-General of Forests during a one-year leave of Brandis.
27 JUNE	in Simla, writing a report on fuel-wood supplies for the Punjab and Delhi railways.
2 JULY	writes a memo on a report on the forests of the Rupin and Tonse watersheds.
1 SEPTEMBER	in Simla, considering applying for the botanical chair at Trinity College, Dublin.
12 SEPTEMBER	comments on a report on increased run-off due to deforestation for coffee plantations in Coorg.
OCTOBER	excursion to the Chor Mountain (12,149 feet) a famous botanical locality; shot birds of which 64 species identified by the geologist Ferdinand Stoliczka.
4 NOVEMBER	about to leave Simla for Calcutta.
23 DECEMBER	in Calcutta 'making a clear office table' for Brandis's return; contemplating a text book on North Indian Forests (nothing came of this); Dublin application not submitted by Balfour as the Glasgow chair might become available.

1867

20 JANUARY	in Calcutta, awaiting return of Brandis on 1 March. New house at Stravithie now roofed. Sends section of a large deodar trunk to the Paris Exhibition.
30 JANUARY	writes memo on the Forest Report for Oudh.
5 FEBRUARY	writes report on the progress of the Forest Department in Bengal (mainly 'Sikhim') which had been started in

	1864 under his old friend Thomas Anderson.
5 APRIL	writes memo on Pearson's forest report for the Central Provinces
22 APRIL	on return of Brandis, Cleghorn returns to duties in Madras and tidies up preparing to leave for home; the Viceroy (still Lawrence) pays tribute to Cleghorn's 'long and successful labours in the cause of Forest Conservancy'.
1 MAY	in Madras at an Agri-Horticultural Society meeting.
28 MAY	sends a box containing 'equal proportion of Curry Paste, curry powder, Mulligatawny' for Mabel and Mrs Balfour.
5 SEPTEMBER	submits final Forest Report for the Madras Government, with the results of the first eleven years; the Government expresses appreciation for his achievements.
7 AUGUST	visits Bhavani (north of Erode) to see junction of Bhavani and Kaveri Rivers, having been asked by Government of Madras to investigate increased flooding.
5 OCTOBER	Madras Government expresses 'the high estimation in which they hold his services'.
11 OCTOBER	allowed sick leave for 20 months.
19 OCTOBER	one of his last acts in Madras is to write a letter to the Madras Government saying that the introduction of the 1865 Forest Act in Madras would have generally beneficial results.
22 NOVEMBER	meets Mabel in Malta, at Morells' Hotel, Valletta until early February. Collects information on botany and agriculture, with assistance from the Governor Sir Patrick Grant.

1868

31 JANUARY	hoping to meet up with Lord Harris who is travelling for his health.
11 FEBRUARY	to Syracuse on the postal steamer *Cariddi* for 12 days in Sicily. Up the east coast by boat, visiting botanic gardens in Syracuse and Catania, and staying overnight in Messina.
14 FEBRUARY	arrives in Palermo to stay with Col. Henry Yule; Yule translates a paper on sumach cultivation.

24 FEBRUARY	leaves Palermo on the steamer *Napoli*.
25 FEBRUARY	Mabel's birthday, in Naples they watch eruption of Vesuvius; he visits the Botanic Garden under Professor Vincenzo de Cesati, with Giuseppe Antonio Pasquale and Gaetano Licopoli; sees G. Gussone's herbarium.
2 MARCH	train from Naples to Rome, where they spend three weeks.
6 MARCH	writes to George Perkins Marsh, American Plenipotentiary in Florence, asking to meet.
9 MARCH	visit to the Colosseum. Other sights visited include Mount Pincio, the Palace of the Caesars, the Palazzo Colonnae; the gardens of the Vatican, the Quirinal Palace, the Palazzo Raspiglioni and the Villa Borghese.
21 MARCH	arrives in Florence (Hotel de Milan) for 5 or 6 days, visits the botanist Filippo Parlatore; meets Marsh who provides him with literature on Italian forestry; attends Conversazione of Naturalists at Museum of Natural History; buys cheap antiquarian books.
6 APRIL	in Marseilles by steamer from Livorno. Through Lyon to Geneva and Berne.
12 APRIL	in Basel, visits botanic garden and Dr Hans Grundert, editor of *Missions Blatt*, whom he had known in Mangalore; visits Missionary Institution under the Rev. Joseph Josenhaus; attends a service at the Eglise Consistorial Evangelique.
19 APRIL	in Nancy to visit Henri Nanquette, director of the Forest School; leaving next day for London via Paris.
20–25 APRIL	in Paris (Hôtel de Normandie); intends visiting Joseph Decaisne at Jardin des Plantes, Jules Clave at the l'Office d'Administration des Forêts, Vilmorin (seedsman) and 'M. Savi' (bookseller).
2–8 MAY	in London, still on half-pay, with duties to perform at the India Office. Meetings with Sir Stafford Northcote (Secretary of State for India) and Sir James Fergusson (Under Secretary of State for India) on forest matters; on a committee at Crystal Palace with Forbes Watson to choose gifts for the Indian Princes who had sent exhibits to the Paris Exhibition. Sees Hooker and Thomson at a Linnean Society soirée and visits Kew.
MAY/JUNE	lectures at Glasgow during Walker-Arnott's final illness, and applies to succeed him, but fails. Corresponding

	with J.D. Hooker about forestry in Malta, and proposals by Brandis for an Indian *Flora Sylvatica*.
14 MAY	at Botanical Society of Edinburgh meeting.
9 JULY	at BSE reads obituary of Walker-Arnott.
19–26 AUGUST	attends the Norwich British Association meeting, talks on the 'Distribution of the principal timber trees of India and the progress of forest conservancy'.
7 OCTOBER	elected member of the Royal and Ancient Golf Club, St Andrews.
10 DECEMBER	elected President of BSE for 1868–9.

1869

14 JANUARY	at BSE meeting, reads obituary of Martius – reads other papers this year on 11 March, 10 June, 8 July, 11 November.
25 JANUARY	attends a lecture at the Royal Geographical Society, London, given by George Bidie 'On the effects of forest destruction in Coorg'.
12 FEBRUARY	examining Forestry students on behalf of Secretary of State for India. Has decided not to return to India.
18 FEBRUARY	writes his last memorandum (other than on the training of foresters) for the Indian Forest Department – on minor forest products.
8 JULY	has visited the pine forests of Strathspey with J.L. Stewart, who has returned sick from the Punjab. Discussions over publication of Stewart's 'Forest Flora', but Stewart returned to India where he died at Dalhousie in 1873.
SEPTEMBER	Cleghorn has supervised the placing of the seven Forest Probationers chosen by Brandis in 1867, who had just completed their training in Nancy and Hanover, to work for a few weeks under foresters in Scotland before leaving for India.
17 NOVEMBER	promoted Inspector-General of Hospitals on the Madras Establishment.
29 NOVEMBER (TO C. 20 DECEMBER)	in London for 3 weeks, choosing candidates to send for training to Germany and Nancy for the Indian Forest Service
2 DECEMBER	Reads paper at the Linnean Society on *Capparis*; appears to have been visiting the Kew herbarium.

1870	Joins Royal Highland & Agricultural Society, and is one of the examiners in the Science of Forestry & Practical Management of Woods for the Society's 1st and 2nd Class Certificates in Forestry from now until 1892 (when Frederick Bailey took over).
22 SEPTEMBER	offers services to help with the training of Forest Probationers displaced from France and Germany by the Franco-Prussian War. The Secretary of State (Duke of Argyll) agrees to this and to pay Cleghorn £50 a month for supervision.
NOVEMBER	visits the ailing Robert Wight at Grazeley, perhaps the occasion on which Wight gave him his botanical drawings.
DECEMBER	delivers 20 lectures on botany at United College of St Andrews University for the displaced forestry students from Nancy – among whom is James Sykes Gamble.

1871	
JANUARY	taking active part in Edinburgh scientific life, attending BSE meetings, the Botanical Society Club, the Highland Society, and using the RBGE herbarium.
MARCH	at the India Office, London, involved in economic botany matters and urging M.E. Grant Duff to support Hooker's proposals for a *Flora of British India*. Continued discussions over 'Forest Flora', which after Stewart's death was completed by Brandis. In communication R.H. Beddome over his 'Flora Sylvatica' of southern India.
12 AUGUST	visits oil shale activities at Pitcorthie (near Anstruther) with the geologist Ramsay Traquair to look at fossil fish and plants. General and Mrs Edward Lake are staying at Stravithie, and Mr and Mrs William Carruthers (Keeper of Botany at BM) are expected; T.H. Huxley is on vacation in St Andrews.

1872	
7 MAY	sits for the first time as a Justice of the Peace at the

Quarter Sessions in Cupar; does so on a regular basis until 1893.

11 JULY	at meeting of BSE reads his obituary of Robert Wight.
6 NOVEMBER	at Masonic Lodge, George Street, delivers Presidential address to the Scottish Arboricultural Society – serves as President for two years.

1873

3 MARCH	lectures in Anstruther Town Hall on 'Plant Life'.
10 JUNE	Cleghorn's last surviving aunt, his mother's sister Helen Wyllie, dies at Teddington.
11 JULY	with Alexander Buchan, Secretary of the Scottish Meteorological Society, choses three sites at Carnwath on which to make comparative measurements of rainfall in forested and unforested areas, in response to a call by the British Association (grants of £20 given for the purpose to J.H. Balfour in 1870, 1871, 1872).
7 NOVEMBER	at RBGE, gives Presidential address to the Scottish Arboricultural Society.
13 NOVEMBER	at BSE meeting reads his obituary of John Lindsay Stewart.

1874

20 FEBRUARY	lectures on 'Forest life in India' at the Duncan Institute, Cupar.
4 NOVEMBER	at RBGE gives his Presidential address to the Scottish Arboricultural Society, and attends its annual dinner at the Albert Hotel (25 Hanover Street).

1875

JANUARY	article on 'Arboriculture' for Ninth edition of the *Encyclopaedia Britannica*.
5–8 MAY	visit to Rome, presumably to see his sister Isabella, but also sees for the last time G.P. Marsh who gives him books (by Hehn and Siemoni).
14/15 MAY	visits the Royal Forest School, Vallombrosa; staying at Florence *en route*.

1876

5 SEPTEMBER   appointed to County Licensing Committee for Fife (a member until 1892).

1877   Vice President of the Scottish Arboricultural Society for 1877/8 (also 1878/9, possibly other years).

1878

16 NOVEMBER   attends AGM of the Scottish Arboricultural Society – Cleghorn is chairman of the judges for the Society's competitive essays.

1879

8 OCTOBER   takes part in the annual excursion of the Scottish Arboricultural Society to Dalkeith.

Article on 'Forestry' for Ninth edition of the *Encyclopaedia Britannica*.

1880

8 APRIL   at BSE meeting reads paper on an exotic weed (*Aristotelia*) in the greenhouse of his father-in-law at Westerlea, Murrayfield. He was spending the spring there (probably a yearly pattern, he was there for the 1881 Census), the mansion built by Charles Cowan in 1870 as his main residence, having given up Valleyfield.

19 NOVEMBER   at a meeting at Anstruther Town Hall Cleghorn is appointed a director of the Anstruther & St Andrews Railway Company.

Active in the BSE, includes the editing of articles for its *Transactions*. On General Council of the University of St Andrews 1880/1 (probably until his death).

1881

21 JANUARY   in London, present at a meeting of Indian Section of Society of Arts at which Sir Richard Temple gave an address on 'Forest Conservancy in India'. Cleghorn invites him to give a similar talk to the Scottish Arboricultural Society in October of the same year.

SEPTEMBER	accompanies Colonel George Pearson on the tour of Scottish forests (paid for by Government of India) which he has arranged for Lucien Boppe, Eugène Reuss, Eugène Bartet and their students from L'Ecole Nationale des Eaux et Forêts, Nancy.
2–3 AUGUST	on summer excursion of Scottish Arboricultural Society to Morayshire.
5 OCTOBER	on autumn excursion of Scottish Arboricultural Society to East Lothian.

1882

8 JUNE	as Vice-President chairs meeting of BSE.
13 JULY	at BSE meeting reads obituary of William Jameson.
8–9 AUGUST	on autumn excursion of Scottish Arboricultural Society to Dumbartonshire.
4 OCTOBER	on autumn excursion of Scottish Arboricultural Society to Fife.
29 OCTOBER	at AGM of Scottish Arboricultural Society, held in RBGE classroom, gives report of the judges on competitive essays; reappointed to the committee.
9 NOVEMBER	at BSE meeting reads obituary of George Thwaites and others.

1883

13 JULY	Cleghorn and his nephew Alexander Sprot host Scottish Society of Antiquaries and Royal Physical Society to examine the ?Pictish basin cut into the cliff-top near Dunino Church.
7–8 AUGUST	on autumn excursion of Scottish Arboricultural Society to Strathearn.

1884	Takes over from the late J.H. Balfour as examiner in the Elements of Botany for forestry students of the Royal Highland & Agricultural Society (continues until 1894, from 1889 jointly with I.B. Balfour; still also examining in Forestry until 1892).
8 JULY	Opening of the International Forestry Exhibition, Edinburgh.

5 AUGUST	gives Presidential address at 31ˢᵗ AGM of Scottish Arboricultural Society (his second term, this time for three years).
6–8 AUGUST	on Scottish Arboricultural Society annual excursions to Riccarton, and Strathtay.

1885

18 JANUARY	Senatus of St Andrews University awards him degree of Doctor of Laws.
24 JULY	gives evidence before Sir John Lubbock's Committee of the House of Commons inquiring as to the advantages of establishing a School of Forestry in Britain.
4 AUGUST	delivers Presidential address to 32ⁿᵈ AGM of Scottish Arboricultural Society.
5 & 6 AUGUST	on annual excursion of Scottish Arboricultural Society to the Borders.

1886

20 JULY	attends lecture on the tropical fruits of Jamaica by Daniel Morris at the Colonial and Indian Exhibition, London; has made many visits to the exhibition.
LATE JULY	has been in Germany on 'urgent business' of an unknown nature.
3 AUGUST	delivers Presidential Address to 33ʳᵈ AGM of the Scottish Arboricultrual Society, in committee room of the Edinburgh International Exhibition of Industry, Science and Art.
4–6 AUGUST	on annual excursion of Scottish Arboricultural Society to Bute and Argyll.
11 NOVEMBER	at BSE meeting reads his obituary of William Traill. Member of a British Association committee on funding the work of W.C. McIntosh on food fish.

1887

26 JULY	chairs AGM of the Scottish Arboricultural Society.
28–9 JULY	Cleghorn chairs 10th Annual Excursion of the Scottish Arboricultural Society, to the woods of Balmoral, by permission of Queen Victoria.

28 SEPTEMBER	staying at 36 Marine Parade, Brighton.
8 DECEMBER	at BSE meeting reads his obituary of Sir Walter Elliot.
22 DECEMBER	wife Mabel dies after many years of ill-health.
	Behind the setting up of a lectureship in forestry at Edinburgh University.

1888

11–16 JUNE	in London examining students for Indian forest training, the last time after 20 years.
6 JULY	sits (probably at India Office) for portrait drawing by Theodore Blake Wirgman.
7 AUGUST	AGM of Scottish Arboricultural Society, followed by a dinner at the Waterloo Hotel, Edinburgh at which he is presented by Sir William Muir (Principal of Edinburgh University) with the portrait. Cleghorn Forest Library launched, based at the Museum of Science and Art.
8–9 AUGUST	on annual excursion of Scottish Arboricultural Society to Teviotdale.

1889

5 MARCH	at BSE meeting reads his obituary of J.T.I. Boswell Syme.
28 JUNE	attends opening (by W.C. McIntosh) of St Andrews University Botanic Garden.

1890

25 JULY	invites the Botanical Society Club to St Andrews and Stravithie.
	Member of the Caledonian United Services Club, Edinburgh, where he stays when in town.
	Until 1894 one of the Assessors on the Court of the University of St Andrews.

1891

31 JANUARY	promises (anonymously) £1,000 towards the setting up of a lectureship or chair in forestry at Edinburgh University. University did not want to commit to it,

though in 1889 it had appointed a lecturer: the money was not paid until 1895, and a chair not established until 1919.

6 APRIL donates (anonymously) £1,000 to St Andrews University towards the endowment of a lectureship, or future chair, in botany.

7 AUGUST joins Scottish Arboricultural Society annual excursion (Munches, Castle Kennedy).

1892

10 AUGUST hosts annual excursion of the Scottish Arboricultural Society at Stravithie.

1895

16 MAY at 6.25 p.m., Cleghorn dies at Stravithie, attended by his sister-in-law Margaret Cowan.

1895 Alexander Sprot donates c. 300 mainly forestry books to Edinburgh University Library.

1896 Donation of 907 volumes (and many pamphlets and botanical drawings) to what became the Cleghorn Memorial Library at the Edinburgh Museum of Science and Art (transferred to RBGE in 1940).

Index

As the Catalogue is arranged in a classified order, this rather long index provides an alphabetical list of the authors of books and papers in Cleghorn's library: their names are in capitals. Non-capitalized names are persons referred to in the Introduction, or in the listing in capacities other than authorship (including artists, publishers, booksellers, binders and previous owners of volumes). The Appendix has not been indexed.

A

B

BABINGTON, Charles Cardale, 134

BADEN-POWELL, Baden Henry, 78

BAGNERIS, Gustave, 42, 78, 83, 89

BAIKIE, Robert , 22, 108

BAILEY, Frederick, 42, 43, 89, 95

BAILEY, Jacob Whitman, 117

BAILLON, Henri Ernest, 20, 134, 152

BAKER, John Gilbert, 134, 135, 157

BAKER, John L., 97

BALFOUR, Edward Green, 78, 79, 80, 157

BALFOUR, John Hutton, 9, 18, 26, 83, 102, 103, 166, 179

Balfour, Lewis, 111

Balingall, George, 14, 175

BANFIELD, Thomas Charles, 99

BARJAVEL, Casimir François Henri, 23, 106

BARNES, George Carnac, 108

BARRON, Archibald Farquharson, 45, 103

BARTET, Eugène, 42, 94

BATCHELOR, C., 79

BATKA, Wenceslas, 135

BAUDRILLART, Jacques-Joseph, 28, 89

Bauer, Franz (Francis), 22, 49

Baumann, Dr J.M.W., 14, 67, 125

BAXTER'S *Agricultural and Horticultural Gleaner*, 43, 98

BECQUEREL, Antoine Cesar, 28, 89

BEDDOME, Richard Henry, 37, 79, 80, 119, 120, 146

'BENGAL CIVILIAN', 115

Bennet, R.H. Alexander, 113

BENNETT, John Joseph, 20, 133

BENTHAM, George, 20, 130, 131, 135

BENTLEY, John, 108

BENTLEY, Robert, 175

BÉRENGER, Adolfo di, 94

BERKELEY, Rev. Miles Joseph, 146

Berry, Andrew, 14, 176

BERWICK, Thomas, 135

BIASOLETTO, Bartolomeo, 130

BIDIE, George, 120, 158

Bielefeld, A. (Carlsruhe bookseller), 126

BIRDWOOD, George Christopher Molesworth, 43, 135, 158, 168

BLAIKIE, Francis, 27, 84

BLANCO, Manuel, 19, 131

Bloemart, Cornelis, 48

BLUME, Carl Ludwig, 135, 136, 146

BOCCONE, Paolo, 39, 130

Bogle, George, 54 n 62

BOISDUVAL, Jean Alphonse, 40, 106

BONARD, 28, 89

BONAVIA, Emanuel, 101

BONER, Charles, 84

BOOTT, Francis, 175

BOPPE, Lucien, 42, 89, 90

BOSANQUET, Edwin, 147

Botanic Garden, 24, 173

Botanical Gazette, 173

Botanical Magazine (Curtis's), 22, 24, 173

Botanical Magazine, Companion to the, 173

Botanical Register (Edwards's) , 22, 24, 173

Botany, British and Foreign, Journal of, 174

BOULGER, George Simonds, 167

BOWERBANK, James Scott, 117

BRADLEY, Richard, 24, 103

C

G

GAERTNER, Joseph, 21, 153
GAERTNER, Karl Frederick, 153
GAMBLE, James Sykes, 41, 42, 81
Garden and Forest, 174
Gardener's Magazine, 174
GARDNER, George, 115, 152
Gauci, Paul, 15
GELL, Francis, 81
GERARD, Alexander, 31, 32, 108
GERARDE, John, 177
GIBSON, Alexander, 19, 27, 81,
    121, 173
GISEKE, Paul Dietrich, 153
GLENNY, George, 45, 103
GODRON, Dominique Alexandre,
    130, 138
GORDON, Thomas, 44, 99
GORKOM, Karel Wessel van, 177
Govan, George, 32
Govindoo, 37, 119
GRAHAM, John, 14, 122
GRAHAM, Professor Robert, 11,
    49, 162
GRAHAM, Thomas, 12, 155

Grant, Colesworthy, 25
Grant-Duff, Mountstuart
    Elphinstone, 54 n 56
GRAY, Asa, 132, 139, 155
Gray, James Edward, 154
GRAY, W., 110
Great Exhibition (London, 1851),
    16, 25
GREENAWAY, Lt. Col. Thomas, 97
GREG, Robert Hyde, 98
GRÉNIER, Jean Charles Marie, 130
Greuter, Johann Friedrich, 48
GREVILLE, Robert Kaye, 11, 20,
    64, 125, 128, 147, 148
GRIFFITH, William, 19, 24, 34,
    101, 108, 109, 122, 123, 139,
    147
GRIGOR, James, 85
GRIGOR, John, 85
GRINDON, Leopold Hartley, 85
GUÉRIN-MÉNEVILLE, Félix
    Edouard, 165
GUILLEMIN, Jean Antoine, 115
GULIA, Gavinus, 38, 113

H

HAIG, T.F., 109
HAMILTON, Francis (*né*
    Buchanan), 11, 14, 21, 109, 123
HAMILTON, Thomas, 6th Earl of
    Haddington, 27, 63, 85
HANBURY, Daniel, 165, 177
HANBURY, William, 28, 85
HANCOCK, John, 177
HANCOCK, Thomas, 165
Handyside, Peter, 12
HANNAY, Simon Fraser, 161
HARKNESS, Henry, 109
Harris, George, Lord, 23, 26
HARTIG, Georg Ludwig, 36, 93
HARTIG, Theodor, 36, 93

HARVEY, William Henry, 15,
    52 n 24, 132, 133, 147, 167
HASSKARL, Justus Karl, 123, 132
Hastings, Francis Rawdon,
    Marquess of, 48
Hastings, H., 115
HAWORTH, Adrian Hardy, 139
Hay, Lord William (later 11th
    Marquess of Tweeddale), 33, 45,
    66, 88
HAYES, Samuel, 85
HEATH, Francis George, 85
HECTOR, James, 115
HEER, Oswald, 118
HEHN, Victor, 100

I

J

Q

R

S

T

V